I0730697

# AMERICAN CONCRETE INSTITUTE

## PROCEEDINGS

OF THE

## SIXTEENTH ANNUAL CONVENTION

Held at Chicago, Ill.

February 16, 17 and 18, 1920

VOLUME XVI

PUBLISHED BY THE INSTITUTE

New Telegraph Bldg., Detroit, Mich.

1920

# CONTENTS

4CONTENTS

# AMERICAN CONCRETE INSTITUTE

## OFFICERS

### *President*

HENRY C. TURNER (*Term Expires 1921 Convention*)

### *Vice-Presidents*

SANFORD E. THOMPSON
(*Term Expires 1921 Convention*)

CHARLES R. GOW
(*Term Expires 1922 Convention*)

### *Treasurer*

ROBERT W. LESLEY (*Term Expires 1921 Convention*).

### *Secretary*

HARVEY WHIPPLE, 314 New Telegraph Building, Detroit, Mich
(*Appointed by Board of Direction, Term Expires 1921 Convention*)

### *Directors*

*First District.*
EDWARD A. TUCKER (*1922*)

*Fourth District*
WILLIAM P. ANDERSON (*1921*)

*Second District*
EDWARD D. BOYER (*1922*)

*Fifth District*
WILLIAM P. KINNEY (*1921*)

*Third District*
ERNEST ASHTON (*1921*)

*Sixth District*
ARTHUR BENT (*1922*)

### *Past Presidents*

RICHARD L. HUMPHREY
LEONARD C. WASON
WILLIAM K. HATT

# TECHNICAL COMMITTEES

## AGGREGATES

SANFORD E. THOMPSON, *Chairman*, 136 Federal St., Boston, Mass.
CLOYD M. CHAPMAN, 171 Madison Ave., New York City
A. T. GOLDBECK, U. S. Bureau of Public Roads, Washington, D. C.
RUSSELL S. GREENMAN, State Engineer's Dept., Albany, N. Y.
R. L. MORRISON, 216 Clark Bldg., Birmingham, Ala.
A. N. TALBOT, 1113 W. California Ave., Urbana, Ill.
J. A. TURNER, 1713 Sansom St., Philadelphia, Pa.
R. B. YOUNG, 8 Strachan Ave., Toronto, Ont., Can.

## BARGES AND SHIPS

ROBERT W. BOYD, *Chairman*, Turner Construction Co., 244 Madison Ave., New York City
CHARLES R. GOW, 6 Beacon St., Boston, Mass.
ROBERT W. LESLEY, 611 Pennsylvania Bldg., Philadelphia, Pa.
M. M. UPSON, Raymond Concrete Pile Co., 90 West St., New York City
L. C. WASON, Aberthaw Construction Co., 27 School St., Boston, Mass.
R. J. WIG, Wig Hollister & Ferguson, Widener Bldg., Philadelphia, Pa.

## REINFORCED-CONCRETE HIGHWAY BRIDGES AND CULVERTS

A. B. COHEN, *Chairman*, D., L. & W. R. R., Hoboken, N. J.
J. H. AMES, State Bridge Engr., Ames, Iowa
C. F. BURCH, Asst. Chief Highway Engr., Springfield, Mass.
R. L. COCHRAN, Asst. State Engr., Lincoln, Neb.
A. B. FLETCHER, California State Highway Commission, Forum Building, Sacramento, Calif.
A. T. GOLDBECK, U. S. Bureau of Wisconsin, Madison, Wis.
G. A. HOOL, University of Wisconsin, Madison, Wis.
H. M. HORN, 17 Battery Pl., New York City
A. C. IRWIN, Portland Cement Assn., 111 W. Washington St., Chicago, Ill.
C. B. McCULLOUGH, Oregon Agricultural College, Corvallis, Ore.
C. T. MORRIS, Ohio State University, Columbus, Ohio
J. N. MUELLER, New Castle, Ind.
A. F. ROBINSON, Bridge Engr., Sante Fé System, Chicago, Ill.
W. J. TITUS, Bridge Engr., Ind. Highway Com., Indianapolis, Ind.
CHAS. M. UPHAM, State Highway Dept., Dover, Del.
G. G. WICKLINE, State Bridge Engr., Austin, Tex.

## CONCRETE FLOOR FINISH

N. M. LONEY, *Chairman*, 19 Wall St., New York City
W. F. BALLINGER, 17th and Arch Sts., Philadelphia, Pa.
P. M. BRUNER, 618 Frisco Bldg., St. Louis, Mo.
THOMAS A. CARR, care of Stone & Webster, Book Bldg., Detroit, Mich.
ALEX FOSTER, JR., 1600 Arch St., Philadelphia, Pa.
J. E. FREEMAN, 111 W. Washington St., Chicago, Ill.
WILLIAM F. KEARNS, 153 Milk St., Boston, Mass.
T. A. PEARSON, Fred T. Ley & Co., Inc., Springfield, Mass.
A. C. TOZZER, 178 Tremont St., Boston, Mass.
HOWARD WOOD, care of Ronald Taylor Co., 520 E. 20th St., New York City

## CONCRETE INDUSTRIAL HOUSES

EMILE G. PERROT, *Chairman*, 17th and Arch Sts., Philadelphia, Pa.
LESLIE H. ALLEN, care of Fred T. Ley, Inc., Springfield, Mass.
W. W. BOYD, JR., Unit Construction Co., St. Louis, Mo.
A. C. IRWIN, Portland Cement Assn., Chicago, Ill.
ROBT. F. HAVLIK, Mooseheart, Ill.
F. R. McMILLAN, Turner Construction Co., 244 Madison Ave., New York
C. L. WOOLDRIDGE, Conneaut Land Co., Pittsburgh, Pa.
O. H. OLMSTEAD, Portland Cement Assn., New York City
MILTON DANA MORRILL, 17 Charles St., New York City

## CONCRETE PRODUCTS

R F HAVLIK, *Chairman*, Mooseheart, Ill
JAMES B BENEDICT, 33 42d St New York City
WALTER BRASSERT, 2005 Race St , Kalamazoo Mich
A J R CURTIS, Portland Cement Association, 111 W Washington St , Chicago, Ill
J C DONALDSON, Grannette Products Co , 725 Second St , Des Moines, Iowa
J K HARRIDGE, Hydro Stone Co , Insurance Exchange Bldg , Chicago, Ill
WALLACE R HARRIS, 5235 Cornell Ave , Chicago, Ill
H A LA ROY, care of Pioneer Mfg Co Waterloo, Iowa
COLEMAN MERIWETHER, 952 Fourth St , Louisville, Ky
J L MINER, Brooklyn Crozite Brick Corporation, 140 Cedar St , New York City
S H WIGHTMAN, Builder's & Traders Exch , Penobscot Bldg , Detroit, Mich

## CONTRACTORS' PLANT

R C WILSON, *Chairman*, Turner Construction Co , 244 Madison Ave , New York City
H J BLANDERMAN, Fred T Ley Co , 19 W 44th St , New York City
W F GILCREAST, Aberthaw Constn Co , 27 School St , Boston, Mass
F I GINSBERG, R E Brooks Co , 50 Church St , New York City
A P ROBINSON, Ransome Conc Mach Co , Dunnellen, N J
ROBERT C WELLER, care of Lakewood Eng Co , Cleveland, Ohio

## FIREPROOFING

W A HULL, *Chairman*, Bureau of Standards, Washington, D C
T L CONDRON, 1433 Monadnock Bldg , Chicago, Ill
G EDWARD ESCHER, 95 Madison Ave , New York City
CHARLES L NORTON, Mass Inst of Technology Cambridge, Mass
W C ROBINSON, Underwriters' Laboratory, 207 E Ohio St , Chicago, Ill
ELWYN E SEFLYE, 101 Park Ave , New York City
W S TAIT, Hydraulic Steelcralt Co , Cleveland, Ohio
IRA H WOOLSON, 76 William St , New York City

## NOMENCLATURE

W A SLATER, *Chairman*, Bureau of Standards, Washington D C
LESLIE H ALLEN, Fred T Ley & Co , Inc , 495 Main St , Springfield, Mass
FRANK A HITCHCOCK, Bureau of Standards, Washington D C
GEORGE A HOOL, University of Wisconsin, College Hills, Madison Wis
J H LIBBERTON, Universal Portland Cement Co 210 S La Salle St Chicago, Ill
A B McDANIELS, Construction Division, Army, Washington, D C

## PLAIN AND REINFORCED-CONCRETE SEWERS

WESLEY W HORNER, *Chairman*, 306 City Hall, St Louis, Mo
ARTHUR BENT, Central Bldg , Los Angeles Calif
C F BURNTE Concrete Products of America, 805 Diamond Bank Bldg , Pittsburgh Pa
A J R CURTIS, Portland Cement Association, 111 W Washington, Chicago, Ill
ALFRED H HARTMAN 25 E North Ave , Baltimore, Md
W S LEA, 809 New Birks Bldg Phillips Square, Montreal, Que , Can
FRANK A MARSTON, care of Metcalf & Eddy, 14 Beacon St , Boston, Mass
COLEMAN MERIWETHER, 952 Fourth St Louisville, Ky
LANGDON PEARSE, 910 S Michigan Ave Chicago, Ill
JOHN L ZEIDLER, 101 Francis St St Joseph, Mo

### PUBLICATION
WILLIAM K. HATT, *Chairman*, Purdue University, Lafayette, Ind
HARVEY WHIPPLE, Editor, *Concrete*, 314 New Telegraph Bldg, Detroit, Mich
FRANK C. WIGHT, Associate Editor, *Engineering News-Record*, 10th Ave at
   36th St, New York City

### REINFORCED CONCRETE AND BUILDING LAWS
ARTHUR R. LORD, *Chairman*, 6 N. Clark St, Chicago, Ill
DUFF A. ABRAMS, Lewis Institute, Madison and Robey Sts, Chicago, Ill
WILLIAM P. ANDERSON, Ferro Concrete Construction Co, Cincinnati, Ohio
ERNEST ASHTON, Lehigh Portland Cement Co, Allentown, Pa
I. H. CISSEL, 1213 S State St, Ann Arbor, Mich
T. L. CONDRON, 1433 Monadnock Bldg, Chicago, Ill
A. W. FRENCH, 202 Russell St, Worcester, Mass
A. T. GOLDBECK, U S Bureau of Roads Washington D C
S. C. HOLLISTER, 320 Widener Bldg, Philadelphia, Pa
W. A. HULL, Bureau of Standards, Washington, D C
A. L. LINDAU, Corrugated Bar Co, Buffalo, N Y
A. W. STEPHENS, Turner Construction Co, 214 Madison Ave, New York
W. A. SLATER, Bureau of Standards, Washington, D C
SANFORD E. THOMPSON, 136 Federal St, Boston, Mass

### REINFORCED-CONCRETE CHIMNEYS
J. G. MINGLE, *Chairman*, 1600 Keenan Bldg, Pittsburgh, Pa
EDWARD D. BOYER, Atlas Portland Cement Co, 30 Broad St, New York
EDWARD GODFREY, Monongahela Bank Bldg, Pittsburgh, Pa
A. C. IRWIN, Portland Cement Association 111 W Washington St,
   Chicago, Ill
JOHN W. LOWELL, Universal Portland Cement Co, 210 S La Salle St,
   Chicago, Ill

### RESEARCH
WILLIAM K. HATT, *Chairman*, Purdue University, Lafayette Ind
DUFF A. ABRAMS, Lewis Institute, Madison and Robey Sts, Chicago, Ill
CHARLES R. GOW, 6 Beacon St, Boston Mass
S. C. HOLLISTER, 320 Widener Bldg, Philadelphia, Pa
A. E. LINDAU Corrugated Bar Co, 402 Mutual Life Bldg, Buffalo N Y
A. R. LORD, 6 N Clark St, Chicago, Ill
E. J. MOORE, Turner Construction Co 244 Madison Ave, New York City
J. C. PEARSON, Bureau of Standards, Washington, D C
W. A. SLATER Bureau of Standards, Washington, D C
A. N. TALBOT, 1113 W California Ave, Urbana, Ill
F. E. TURNEAURE, University of Wisconsin, Madison, Wis
R. B. YOUNG, 8 Strachan Ave, Toronto, Ont, Can

### ROADS AND PAVEMENTS
CLIFFORD OLDER, *Chairman*, Chief State Highway Engr, Springfield, Ill
A. N. JOHNSON, Portland Cement Assn, Chicago Ill
A. T. GOLDBECK, Bureau of Public Roads, Washington, D C
H. E. BREED, 507 Fifth Avenue, New York City
WM M. ACHESON, Division Engineer, N Y State Highway Commission,
   Syracuse, N Y
CHAS J. BENNETT, State Highway Commissioner, Hartford, Conn
H. J. KUELLING, State Highway Commissioner, Madison, Wis
WM A. McINTYRE, Atlas Portland Cement Co, 1138 Widener Bldg, Phila-
   delphia, Pa
K. H. TALBOT, Koehring Machine Co Milwaukee, Wis
W. H. THOMPSON, State Highway Engineer, Trenton, N J
W. D. UHLER Chief Engineer, Penna State Highway Commission, Harris-
   burg Pa
CHAS M. UPHAM, Chief Engineer, State Highway Dept, Dover, Del
J. T. VOSHELL, Office of Public Roads P O Building S Chicago, Ill

### STANDARDIZATION OF UNITS OF DESIGN

A B MacMILLAN, *Chairman*, Aberthaw Constn Co, 27 School St, Boston, Mass
J G AHLERS, Barney-Ahlers Construction Co, 110 40th St, New York City
H E COUSENS, care of Lockwood Greene Co, 60 Federal St, Boston, Mass
J I N HOYT, care of Albert Kahn Marquette Bldg, Detroit, Mich
N M LONEY Thompson Starrett Co, 49 Wall St, New York City
E G PERROT, 17th and Arch Sts, Philadelphia, Pa
A W STEPHENS, Turner Construction Co, 244 Madison Ave, New York City.
W S THOMSON, Corrugated Bar Co, Buffalo, N Y
J E TORREY, 652 E 26th St,, Paterson, N J
R K TURNER, Fred T Ley & Co, Inc, Springfield, Mass
A B VILLADSEN, 303 Dooly Bldg, Salt Lake City, Utah
C B WIGTON, 522 W 23d St, New York City

### STORAGE TANKS

H B ANDREWS, *Chairman*, 274 Main St, Springfield, Mass
J E FREEMAN, Portland Cement Association, 111 W Washington St, Chicago, Ill
S C HOLLISTER, 320 Widener Bldg, Philadelphia, Pa
A R LORD, 6 N Clark St, Chicago, Ill
GEORGE A SMITH, Bureau of Standards, Washington, D C
C W VAN DYKE, 30 Broad St, New York City
R E WILSON, Associated Factory Mutual Lab'y, 31 Milk St, Boston, Mass

### TREATMENT OF CONCRETE SURFACES

J. C PEARSON, *Chairman*, Bureau of Standards, Washington, D C
JOHN G AHLERS, Barney-Ahlers Construction Co, 110 40th St, New York City
EDWARD D BOYER Atlas Portland Cement Co, 30 Broad St, New York City
D K BOYD, 17th and Walnut Sts, Philadelphia, Pa
CLOYD M CHAPMAN, 171 Madison Ave, New York City
WHARTON CLAY, Associated Metal Lath Mfrs, Edison Bldg, Chicago, Ill
JOHN J EARLEY, 2131 G St, N W, Washington, D C
J E FREEMAN, Portland Cement Association, Chicago, Ill
J ARTHUR GARROD Aberthaw Construction Co, 27 School St, Boston, Mass
FRANK A HITCHCOCK Bureau of Standards Washington, D C
GEORGE E HORR, Turner Construction Co, 244 Madison Ave, New York City
JOHN B ORR, 11th St, Miami, Fla

### WASON MEDAL

SANFORD E THOMPSON, *Chairman*, 136 Federal St, Boston, Mass
W K HATT, Purdue University, Lafayette, Ind
ARTHUR R LORD, 1004 1005 Powers Bldg, Chicago, Ill
FRANK C WIGHT, *Engineering News-Record*, 10th Ave at 36th St, New York City

### REPRESENTATIVES ON THE JOINT COMMITTEE ON CONCRETE AND REINFORCED CONCRETE

S C HOLLISTER, *Chairman* 320 Widener Bldg, Philadelphia, Pa
R W LESLEY, 611 Pennsylvania Bldg, Philadelphia, Pa
A R LORD, 6 N Clark St, Chicago, Ill
E J MOORE, Turner Construction Co, 244 Madison Ave New York City
L C WASON, Aberthaw Construction Co, 27 School St, Boston 9, Mass

## ARTICLE I

### MEMBERS

SECTION 1    Any person engaged in the construction or maintenance of work in which cement is used or qualified by business relations or practical experience to co-operate in the purposes of the Institute, or engaged in the manufacture or sale of machinery or supplies for cement users, or a man who has attained eminence in the field of engineering, architecture or applied science, is eligible for membership

SEC 2    A firm or company shall be treated as a single member

SEC 3    Any member contributing annually twenty or more dollars in addition to the regular dues shall be designated and listed as a Contributing Member

SEC 4    Application for membership shall be made to the Secretary on a form prescribed by the Board of Direction    The Secretary shall submit monthly or oftener, if necessary, to each member of the Board of Direction for letter ballot a list of all applicants for membership on hand at that time with a statement of the qualifications, and a two thirds majority of the members of the Board shall be necessary to an election

Applicants for membership shall be qualified upon notification of election by the Secretary by the payment of the annual dues, and unless these dues are paid within 60 days thereafter the election shall become void An extract of the By-Laws relating to dues shall accompany the notice of election

SEC 5    Resignations from membership must be presented in writing to the Secretary on or before the close of the fiscal year and shall be acceptable provided the dues are paid for that year

## ARTICLE II

### OFFICERS

SECTION 1    The officers shall be the President, two Vice Presidents six Directors (one from each geographical district), the Secretary and the Treasurer who with the five latest living Past-Presidents, who continue to be members shall constitute the Board of Directors

SEC 2    The Board of Direction shall, from time to time, divide the territory occupied by the membership into six geographical districts, to be designated by numbers

SEC 3    There shall be a Committee of five members on Nomination of Officers elected by letter ballot of the members of the Institute, which is to be canvassed by the Board of Direction on or before September 1 of each year

The Committee on Nomination of Officers shall select by letter ballot of its members, candidates for the various offices to become vacant at the next Annual Convention and report the result to the Board of Direction who shall transmit the same to the members of the Institute at least 60 days prior to the Annual Convention  Upon petition signed by at least ten members, additional nominations may be made within 20 days thereafter  The consent of all candidates must be obtained before nomination  The complete list of candidates thus nominated shall be submitted 30 days before the Annual Convention to the members of the Institute for letter ballot, to be canvassed at 12 o'clock noon on the second day of the Convention and the result shall be announced the next day at a business session

Sec 4  The terms of office of the President Secretary and Treasurer shall be one year, of the Vice Presidents and the Directors two years  Provided, however, that at the first election after the adoption of this By Law, 1 President, one Vice President, three Directors and a Treasurer shall be elected to serve for one year only and one Vice President and three Directors for two years, provided, also, that after the first election a President, one Vice President, three Directors and a Treasurer shall be elected annually

The term of each officer shall begin at the close of the Annual Convention at which such officer is elected  and shall continue for the period above named or until a successor is duly elected

A vacancy in the office of President shall be filled by the senior Vice-President  A vacancy in the office of Vice President shall be filled by the senior Director

Seniority between persons holding similar offices shall be determined by priority of election to the office  and when these dates are the same by priority of admission to membership  and when the latter dates are identical, the selection shall be made by lot  In case of the disability or neglect in the performance of his duty, of any officer of the Institute the Board of Direction shall have power to declare the office vacant  Vacancies in any office for the unexpired term shall be filled by the Board of Direction, except as provided above

Sec 5  The Board of Direction shall have general supervision of the affairs of the Institute and at the first meeting following its election appoint a Secretary and from its own members a Finance Committee of three  it shall create such special committees as may be deemed desirable for the purpose of preparing recommended practice and standards concerning the proper use of cement for consideration by the Institute, and shall appoint a chairman for each committee  Four or more additional members on each special committee shall be appointed by the President, in consultation with the Chairman

Sec 6  It shall be the duty of the Finance Committee to prepare the annual budget and to pass on proposed expenditures before their submission to the Board of Direction  The accounts of the Secretary and Treasurer shall be audited annually

Sec 7  The Board of Direction shall appoint a Committee on Resolutions, to be announced by the President at the first regular session of the Annual Convention

Sec 8  There shall be an Executive Committee of the Board of Direction consisting of the President the Secretary, the Treasurer and two of its members, appointed by the Board of Direction

Sec 9  The Executive Committee shall manage the affairs of the Institute during the interim between the meetings of the Board of Direction

Sec. 10  The President shall perform the usual duties of the office He shall preside at the Annual Convention, at the meetings of the Board of Direction and the Executive Committee and shall be ex officio member of all committees

The Vice Presidents in order of seniority shall discharge the duties of the President in his absence

Sec 11  The Secretary shall be the general business agent of the Institute shall perform such duties and furnish such bond as may be determined by the Board of Direction

Sec 12  The Treasurer shall be the custodian of the funds of the Institute shall disburse the same in the manner prescribed and shall furnish bond in such sum as the Board of Direction may determine

Sec 13  The Secretary shall receive such salary as may be fixed by the Board of Direction

## Article III

### MEETINGS.

Section 1  The Institute shall meet annually  The time and place shall be fixed by the Board of Direction and notice of this action shall be mailed to all members at least thirty days previous to the date of the Convention

Sec 2  The Board of Direction shall meet during the Convention at which it is elected, effect organization and transact such business as may be necessary

Sec 3  The Board of Direction shall meet at least twice each year The time and place to be fixed by the Executive Committee

Sec 4  A majority of the members shall constitute a quorum for meetings of the Board of Direction and of the Executive Committee

## Article IV

### DUES

Section 1  The fiscal year shall commence on the first of July and all dues shall be payable in advance

Sec 2   The annual dues of each member shall be ten dollars ($10 00)

Sec 3   Any person elected after six months of any fiscal year shall have expired, need pay only one half of the amount of dues for that fiscal year, but he shall not be entitled to a copy of the Proceedings of that year

Sec 4   A member whose dues remain unpaid for a period of three months shall forfeit the privilege of membership and shall be officially notified to this effect by the Secretary, and if these dues are not paid within thirty days thereafter his name shall be stricken from the list of members Members may be reinstated upon the payment of all indebtedness against them upon the books of the Institute

## ARTICLE V

### RECOMMENDED PRACTICE AND SPECIFICATIONS.

Section 1   Proposed Recommended Practice and Specifications to be submitted to the Institute must be mailed to the members at least thirty days prior to the Annual Convention and as there amended and approved, passed to letter ballot, which shall be canvassed within sixty days thereafter; such Recommended Practice and Specifications shall be considered adopted unless at least 10 percent of the total membership shall vote in the negative

## ARTICLE VI

### AMENDMENT

Section 1   Amendments to these By-Laws, signed by at least fifteen members, must be presented in writing to the Board of Direction ninety days before the Annual Convention and shall be printed in the notice of the Annual Convention   These amendments may be discussed and amended at the Annual Convention and passed to letter ballot by a two thirds vote of those present   Two-thirds of the votes cast by letter ballot shall be necessary for their adoption

## SUMMARY OF THE PROCEEDINGS OF THE SIXTEENTH ANNUAL CONVENTION

Auditorium Hotel, Chicago, Ill

FIRST SESSION, MONDAY, FEBRUARY 16, 1920, 11 15 A M

The convention was called to order by W K Hatt, President of the American Concrete Institute

The report of the Committee on Nomenclature was read by its chairman W A Slater    The definitions in the report were submitted by the convention to letter ballot for adoption as standard practice.    The following papers were read and discussed

> "Examples of Application of Abrams' Water Ratio in Proportioning Concrete," by Stanton Walker
> "Wear and Strength Tests of Concrete," by R E Crepps

---

SECOND SESSION, MONDAY, FEBRUARY 16, 1920, 2 30 P M

President W K Hatt in the chair

The report of the Committee on Treatment of Concrete Surfaces was read by its chairman, J C Pearson    The Standard Recommended Practice for Portland Cement Stucco contained in that report was passed to letter ballot of the Institute

The following paper was read and discussed

> "United States Standard Sieve Series," by J C Pearson

The report of the Committee on Building Block was presented by W R Harris    Part of report which consists of resolutions, was referred to Committee on Resolutions, and part to Board of Direction

The report of the Committee on Concrete Aggregates was presented by C M Chapman    The report was received

---

THIRD SESSION, MONDAY, FEBRUARY 16, 1920, 8 P M

W K Hatt in the chair

The following paper was read and discussed

> "Flexural Strength of Concrete in Compression," by W A Slater and R R Zipprodt    The paper was presented by Mr Zipprodt

The report of the Special Committee on the Determination of Proper Value for Vertical Shear in Reinforced Concrete Design was presented by its chairman, A. R. Lord. Action on the report was deferred until a later session.

The report of the Subcommittee of the Research Committee on Recommendation for Practice in Testing Floors in Reinforced Concrete Buildings was presented by its chairman, W. A. Slater. It was received by the meeting.

---

### Fourth Session, Tuesday, February 17, 1920, 10 a.m.

W. K. Hatt in the chair.

The report of the Special Committee on Standardization of Units of Design was presented by A. W. Stephens. The report was received.

S. C. Hollister, chairman for the Institute on the Joint Committee on Concrete and Reinforced Concrete, made announcement of the organization of that Joint Committee.

The report of the Special Committee on Standardization of Specifications for Steel Bars for Concrete Reinforcement was presented by W. S. Edge. This report was changed in its wording on the floor of the convention and received as changed.

The following paper was read and discussed:

> "Pressure of Concrete Against Forms," by E. B. Smith. The paper was presented by A. T. Goldbeck.

The report of the Committee on Reinforced Concrete Barges and Ships was presented by the secretary. The report was received.

The report of the Special Committee on Contractors' Plant in Reinforced Concrete Construction was presented. The report was received.

---

### Fifth Session, Tuesday, February 17, 1920, 2.30 p.m.

W. K. Hatt in the chair.

The report of the Committee on Concrete Roads and Pavements was presented by K. H. Talbot. Changes in Standard Specifications for Concrete Roads were received to be printed in the current Proceedings as information. Changes in Recommended Practice as printed in Proceedings, A. C. I., 1919, p. 413, were sent to letter ballot of the Institute as standard specifications.

The report of the Special Committee on Contractors' Plant was discussed.

The report of the Committee on Reinforced Concrete Highway Bridges and Culverts was presented by the chairman in abstract.

The report of the Committee on Sidewalks and Floors was presented by the chairman, J. E. Freeman, and received by the meeting

The report of the Committee on Concrete Storage Tanks was presented by Chairman H. B. Andrews. Recommendations governing the construction of reinforced concrete fuel oil tanks were received and ordered printed in the Proceedings. Resolutions offering the suggestion that the Institute join with the National Fire Protection Association in the preparation of standard specifications were referred to the Board of Direction

The report of the Special Committee on Different Types of Concrete Floor Finish was presented in abstract and discussed

---

SIXTH SESSION, WEDNESDAY, FEBRUARY 18, 1920, 10.30 A. M

L. C. Wason in the chair
The following paper was read and discussed

"Recent Ideals on Vocational Training Applied to Concrete Workers" by W. K. Hatt

W. K. Hatt in the chair
The report of the Committee on Plain and Reinforced Concrete Sewers was presented by Chairman W. W. Horner. The Specifications prepared by this Committee were passed by the meeting to letter ballot of the Institute

### Business Session

The secretary read the report of the Board of Direction
The secretary read the report of the treasurer
The secretary reported that the letter ballot had resulted in the election of the following officers for the ensuing year

*President,* Henry C. Turner
*Vice-President,* Charles R. Gow
*Treasurer,* Robert W. Lesley
*Directors, First District,* Edward D. Boyer
   *Second District,* Edward A. Tucker
   *Sixth District,* Arthur Bent

The report of the Committee on Reinforced Concrete and Building Laws was presented by A. L. Lindau. The Building Regulations prepared by this Committee, with amendments on the floor, were adopted to be sent to letter ballot of the Institute.

The report of the Special Committee on Determination of Proper Value for Vertical Shear in Reinforced Concrete Design was brought up again and the report was received to be printed as information in the Proceedings

The following paper was read and discussed

"Fire Tests of Concrete Columns" by W. A. Hull

The report of the Committee on Fireproofing was presented by W. A. Hull, its chairman and received by the meeting

———

Seventh Session Wednesday February 18 1920 2 30 p. m.

Joint session with the National Conference on Concrete Housing Construction

The report of the Committee on Concrete Industrial Houses was presented by K. H. Talbot, its chairman

The following paper was read and discussed
"New Developments in Surface Treated Concrete and Stucco." by J. C. Pearson and J. J. Earley

# THE WASON MEDAL



## Awarded 1919 to

W. A. SLATER for his paper, "Structural Laboratory Investigations in
Reinforced Concrete Made by Concrete Ship Section
Emergency Fleet Corporation"

## PREVIOUS AWARDS

1916—A. B. McDANIEL, 'Influence of Temperature on the Strength of
Concrete"

1917—CHARLES R. GOW, 'History and Present Status of the Concrete Pile
Industry"

1918—DUFF A. ABRAMS, 'Effect of Time of Mixing on the Strength and
Wear of Concrete"

Papers Read Before the 16th Annual
Convention of the American
Concrete Institute

# FIRE TESTS OF CONCRETE COLUMNS *

By W. A. HULL †

Progress reports covering a large part of the fire tests of concrete columns which have been conducted at the Pittsburgh laboratories of the Bureau of Standards were published in the proceedings of the American Concrete Institute for 1918 and 1919. The tests already reported may be outlined as follows

1. A comparison of the fire resistance of four types of columns from the same aggregate

2. A comparison of the fire resistance of columns from six types of aggregates

3. Methods for safeguarding columns made from gravels high in quartz or granite

    *a* By plastering on the completed column

    *b.* By substituting several types of plaster for protective concrete

    *c* By casting columns in gypsum forms which take the place of protective concrete

In addition to the work already reported tests have been made of columns from one additional type of aggregate, and of columns protected by additional types of plaster, other columns protected by gypsum forms have been tested, another method for safeguarding columns made from gravels high in quartz has been investigated. This method consists of providing light metallic reinforcement in the outer concrete to prevent spalling and the consequent loss of the covering. It is the purpose of this, the third report to present a condensed statement of the results of the entire investigation

## TYPES OF COLUMNS

In the first part of the investigation a comparison was made of four types of columns viz

1. Vertically and spirally reinforced cylindrical columns

2. Vertically reinforced cylindrical columns

3. Plain cylindrical columns

4. Vertically reinforced square columns

---

* By Permission of the Director, Bureau of Standards   For full details regarding these tests see forthcoming paper by Bureau of Standards
† U S Bureau of Standards, Washington, D C

Columns representing the cylindrical types were made 18 in diameter and 12 in diameter. Square columns were 16 × 16 in. All columns were 8 ft 9 in in length. Details as to reinforcement are given in the tables.

### AGGREGATES

From information obtained from an earlier investigation[1] it was anticipated that widely different results would be obtained from columns made from different aggregates, that gravels of high quartz content would give the poorest results and limestone aggregates the best. Columns representing the three most important types were accordingly made from Pittsburgh gravel and from limestone from West Winfield, Butler County, Pa. The limestone was furnished by T K Morris, of Pittsburgh. Following the testing of columns representing the four types above enumerated tests were made for the comparison of additional aggregates, including trap rock, blast furnace slag and three additional types of gravel. It was found, from the tests made in the first part of the investigation that the typical tendencies of different aggregates were shown more clearly in those cylindrical columns which had spiral reinforcement and in the square columns than in cylindrical columns without spiral. Consequently, only a few columns of this last type were included in tests for the comparison of aggregates

### MIXING AND CONSISTENCY

One proportion, 1 2 4, was used in all columns

Concrete was mixed and placed by hand. Throughout the greater part of the investigation, the consistency maintained was that resulting from the use of a weight of water approximating 8 percent of the total weight of the dry batch. It might properly be called a quaking consistency, when first mixed, it would stand in a slightly flattened mound without spreading out over the floor. The concrete required considerable puding in placing but was of good workable consistency. There was not much tendency for water to separate and rise to the top, when the form was filled to overflowing, the overflow was mortar for the most part, rather than separated water. Test cylinders made of material taken from the top of the form at the finish of the casting of columns failed to show any consistent difference in strength from test cylinders made from the concrete before placing. The columns did not show a tendency to give top failures. In the latter part of the investigation, columns were made with expanded metal in the space between the reinforcement and the form. For these columns and others made at about the same time, a somewhat more fluid consistency was adopted. It is obvious, however, that with hand mixing excessively high proportions of water could not be used

---

[1] A Comparison of the Heat Insulating Properties of Some of the Materials Used in Fire Resisting Construction. Bureau of Standards Tech Paper 130

### TEST APPARATUS

The test apparatus used consists essentially of a gas fired furnace which is provided with a loading equipment so that a load can be kept on the column during test and that the column can be tested for strength, while still hot, if desired   The furnace is fired with natural gas, using twelve burners of a blast type, compressed air being used to secure a quick and thorough mixture of gas and air which burns with a short flame   Fires were kept oxidizing   Baffles are so arranged in front of the burners that the flames spread out over the walls of the furnace to some extent on entering the furnace chamber, giving fairly uniform distribution of the heat throughout the furnace and avoiding any localized impingement on the column

The load equipment consists of a hydraulic jack with separate hand pump, the jack being supported above the center of the furnace by two pairs of I beams which are held by tension rods passing through the ends of a reinforced-concrete girder which extends under the furnace support ing the foundation for the column   The capacity of the jack is 500 tons   The capacity of the steel structure is rated at 600,000 lb   With the 500-ton jack and hand test pump, the 600,000 lb load can be applied without difficulty   The jack and test pump with gage, were calibrated in one of the testing machines in the engineering testing laboratory of the bureau, and this calibration was used in the determination of the loads on the columns.

Temperatures were measured, both in the furnace and in the interior of the column, by means of non-constant and thermocouples and a Leeds and Northrup potentiometer indicator   The couples in the column were placed before the column was cast, a special device being used to hold the couples in position during the placing of the concrete

In all tests, the working load of the column was kept on the column during the fire test.   The load was increased, at the finish of the fire test, up to the ultimate strength of the column or to the capacity of the test apparatus   If the column withstood the 600,000 lb load, it was permitted to cool, transferred to the 10 000 000 lb machine and tested in that

The firing of the furnace was regulated, as closely as possible. to conformance with the standard time-temperature curve which has been adopted for general use in the control of fire tests [2]

### POSITION OF STEEL—ASSUMPTIONS AS TO EFFECTIVE AREAS

In all columns having reinforcement, the latter was placed so as to leave a thickness of $1\frac{1}{2}$ in of concrete outside the steel   The effective diameter in spirally reinforced columns was taken as the horizontal distance between centers of the spiral steel   Vertical rods in columns

---

[2] Proc A S T M 1917 Report of Committee on Fireproofing, p 296

having only vertical reinforcement were placed at the same distance from the outside of the column as the vertical rods in spirally reinforced columns, the effective diameter being assumed to be the same as that for spirally reinforced columns of the same size   In the square columns, the vertical rods were placed at the same distance from the surface of the concrete as in the round ones and the effective area was taken as that portion within a square with its sides located 5/32 in  beyond the outside of the rods to correspond with the criterion followed in calculating the effective area of spirally reinforced round columns

### TEST DATA OF TABLE I—18 IN  SPIRALLY REINFORCED COLUMNS

The outstanding feature of the data given in this table is the great contrast between the columns made from gravels of high quartz or high granite content and those from limestone aggregates  including the Elgin gravel, of which dolomitic limestone pebbles constituted approximately 90 percent.  The Pittsburgh gravel is a mixed gravel containing a small percentage of pure quartz pebbles and a much larger proportion of pebbles of sandstone and of other, harder rock, all appearing to be high in quartz  The "Pure quartz gravel" in columns 42 and 43 was from Long Island, it was made up almost entirely of smooth nearly white pebbles fairly well graded as to size   The so-called "Cow Bay Gravel" was comprised mainly of three kinds of pebbles   There was a large proportion of large pebbles of coarse-grained granite and a considerable proportion of large pebbles of gneiss   Most of the other pebbles were of quartz   The Elgin gravel was composed of approximately 90 percent of pebbles of dolomitic limestone, together with a mixture of pebbles of other types of rock   It will be noted that six of the eight fire tested columns from the first three types of gravel failed under the working load before the end of the four-hour fire test, of the remaining two columns made from the Pittsburgh gravel, one, No 2, failed under the working load after the fire test had gone four hours and fifteen minutes and the other, No 3, tested by increasing the load at the end of the four hour fire test, failed at a load approximately 40 percent higher than its working load  but at a load of only approximately 20 percent of that withstood by Nos 5 and 75, which were tested without fire test

On the other hand, all the fire tested columns made from high limestone aggregates, including the dolomitic gravel and the high calcium crushed limestone  were capable of withstanding, while hot, at the end of the four-hour fire test, the maximum load of the furnace loading equipment, 3480 lb per sq  in  of effective area   Columns from these two limestone aggregates when tested cold after the four-hour fire test and the load test in the furnace, showed an ultimate strength approximately 90 percent as high as similar columns tested without fire test   The columns made from blast furnace slag and from trap rock showed an ultimate

TABLE I

18 in cylindrical columns
Thickness of concrete outside the steel, 1½ in
Reinforcement 2 per cent vertical, 8 round rods, ⅞ in diam
    1 per cent spiral 5/16 in diam 2 in pitch 2 spacers
Effective area of concrete 168 7 sq in
Area of vertical steel, 3 53 sq in
Effective area of column, 172 sq in
Working load, 822 lb per sq in

| Aggregate | Column Number | Age at Time of Test | | Stress at Maximum Load, lb per sq in | | | Maximum Temperature at End of Fire Test deg C | | |
|---|---|---|---|---|---|---|---|---|---|
| | | Mo | Days | Without Fire Test | At End of 1-hr Fire Test | Tested Cold after 1-hr Fire Test | At Depth of Vertical Rods | Midway between Steel and Center | At Center of Column |
| Pittsburgh gravel Pittsburgh sand | 1 | 6 | 4 | | * | | 950 | 110 | 240 |
| | 2 | 6 | 7 | | * | | 1 050 | 460 | 290 |
| | 3 | 7 | 9 | | 1 115 | | 945 | 355 | 210 |
| | 5 | 6 | 24 | 6,310 | | | | | |
| | 73 | 4 | 0 | | * | | 980 | | |
| | 74 | 4 | 0 | | * | | 780 | | |
| | 75 | 4 | 4 | 4,880 | | | | | |
| | *77 | 4 | 3 | | 1 993 | | 660 | | |
| | *78 | 4 | 0 | | 2,120 | | 605 | | |
| Pure quartz gravel Long Island sand | 12 | 4 | 10 | | * | | 990 | | |
| | 13 | 4 | 7 | | * | | 990 | 350 | 100 |
| Cow Bay gravel Cow Bay sand | 46 | 4 | 3 | | * | | 985 | 275 | 100 |
| | 47 | 4 | 5 | | * | | 1,000 | 250 | 105 |
| Elgin (Ill) gravel Elgin (Ill) sand | 85 | 4 | 1 | | | 1 440 | 180 | | |
| | 86 | 4 | 1 | | | 5 210 | 520 | | |
| | 87 | 4 | 4 | 5,620 | | | | | |
| West Winfield (Pa) limestone Pittsburgh sand | 17 | 7 | 1 | | | 4 770 | 520 | 240 | 120 |
| | 18 | 8 | 17 | | | 5 320 | 560 | 180 | 100 |
| | 20 | 7 | 4 | 6 890 | | | | | |
| Blast furnace slag Pittsburgh sand | 18 | 1 | 0 | | 2 700 | | 180 | 85 | 85 |
| | 19 | 1 | 7 | 4 870 | | | | | |
| | 50 | 1 | 21 | | 2 260 | | 165 | 110 | 100 |
| New Jersey trap rock Pittsburgh sand | 54 | 1 | 7 | | 2 420 | | 610 | 190 | 100 |
| | 55 | 1 | 16 | | 3 000 | | 560 | 230 | 110 |

Column No 1 failed under working load at end of 3 hr 45 min
Column No 2 failed under working load at end of 4 hr 15 min
Column No 73 failed under working load at end of 3 hr 50 min
Column No 74 failed under working load at end of 3 hr 20 min
Columns Nos 77 and 78 had expanded metal in the protective concrete
Column No 12 failed under working load at end of 3 hr 32 min
Column No 43 failed under working load at end of 3 hr
Column No 46 failed under working load at end of 3 hr 37 min
Column No 47 failed under working load at end of 3 hr 40 min

strength while hot, at the end of the four-hour fire test, approximately 50 percent as great as columns of the same general type that were not fire tested.

### CAUSE OF POOR SHOWING OF THREE TYPES OF GRAVEL.

The most obvious cause of the unsatisfactory results obtained from the first three gravels was the spalling of the outer concrete. It was characteristic of the columns made from these aggregates that the outer concrete would begin to show evidence of destructive stresses within approximately thirty minutes after the beginning of the fire test. Cracks would appear, giving the column the appearance of a column that was failing under compression. Cracks would continue to appear and to

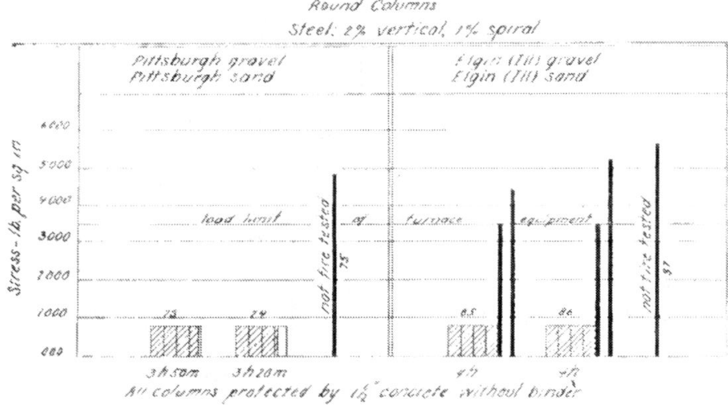


FIG. 1.—COLUMNS PROTECTED WITH CONCRETE.

lengthen rapidly until they intersected other cracks, thus dividing the outer concrete into large slabs which gradually separated from the rest of the column so that after approximately one hour of firing, slabs would begin to fall, exposing the spiral reinforcement and the load bearing portion of the concrete to the direct heat of the furnace. It is obvious that a column, stripped of its protection within the first hour of a four-hour fire test, could not be expected to compare favorably with columns which retained the protective concrete. The high temperatures attained in the steel and in the interior of columns affected in this way, by the spalling of the outer concrete, is consistent with their comparatively rapid loss of strength in the fire test.

In the fire tests of columns made from the other aggregates included in the investigation there was no spalling and no cracking of importance.

It will be noted that the results from columns 77 and 78 are distinctly better than those from the other columns made from the Pittsburgh gravel. This was due to the fact that a light grade of expanded metal was imbedded in the outer concrete of these columns to prevent its spalling and falling off. When these columns were exposed to the fire test, the same tendency to spall was observed as in similar columns without the expanded metal. Slabs separated from each other and to some extent from the rest of the column, but very little material actually fell away. The column received a large part of the protection which it would have received had there been no spalling, as is shown by comparing the temperatures attained in the steel of these columns with those attained in the other columns given in this table.

TEST DATA OF TABLE II—18-IN. COLUMNS WITHOUT SPIRAL REINFORCEMENT

In the fire tests of the gravel columns included in this table there was much less spalling than in tests of hooped columns from the same aggregates. The behavior of the cylindrical columns without spiral reinforcement indicates that concrete of a type which has a tendency to spall will spall much worse in columns with spiral reinforcement than in columns of the same form without the spiral. In columns without spiral steel the breaking up of the outer concrete was a much more gradual process than in spirally reinforced columns from the same aggregate and the proportion of protective concrete that actually fell away from the column was relatively small. The explanation which naturally suggests itself to account for this fact is that the spiral reinforcement makes a more definite separation between the column proper and the protective concrete than is made by the vertical reinforcement and its ties without the spiral. It should be taken into consideration however, that the working load carried by the columns without spiral reinforcement was much lower than that carried by columns which had it and that the lower working load may have been a contributing factor to the reduction in spalling. It will be observed that the temperatures attained in the gravel concrete columns in Table II, while higher than those in the limestone columns, are lower than in those made from the same types of gravel in Table I. This was obviously due in large measure to the fact that a comparatively small part of the protective value of the outer concrete was lost in the columns without spiral steel in Table II, whereas the hooped columns in Table I went through a large part of the fire test without any protection whatever. Likewise, while the differences between the temperatures attained in the gravel concrete columns in Table II and the corresponding limestone columns is attributable mainly to the fact that these gravel columns lost some portions of the outer concrete whereas the limestone columns lost none whatever, yet this should not be regarded as a true measure of the amount of protective concrete lost by the gravel concrete columns during the fire test. The temperatures attained in the gravel columns would be somewhat higher than those attained in limestone columns, even though all the protective material remained in place in both cases  This statement is based on a study of the data of this investigation and also on the findings of an earlier investigation of thermal properties of building materials [3]

Column No  41 was made by placing tar paper around the outside of the reinforcement and pouring gravel concrete inside the tar paper, at the

### Table II

18-in  cylindrical columns
Thickness of concrete outside the steel  1½ in
Reinforcement  2 per cent vertical, 8 round rods, ⅞ in  diam   Ties ½ in  diam , 12 in  centers
Effective area of concrete  168 7 sq  in
Area of steel, 3 53 sq  in
Effective area of column  172 sq  in
Working load  99 750 lb  = 580 lb  per sq  in

| Aggregate | Column Number | Age at Time of Test | | Stress at Maximum load, lb per sq in | | Maximum Temperature at End of Fire Test, deg C | | |
| | | Mo | Days | Without Fire Test | At End of 4-hr Fire Test | At Depth of Vertical Rods | Midway between Steel and Center | At Center of Column |
| --- | --- | --- | --- | --- | --- | --- | --- | --- |
| Pittsburgh gravel | 7 | 7 | 1 | | * | 1,010 | 310 | 210 |
| Pittsburgh sand | 8 | 7 | 19 | | 1 305 | 630 | 270 | 130 |
| | 9 | 9 | 11 | | 1 320 | 700 | 310 | 180 |
| | 10 | 6 | 29 | 4,600 | | | | |
| Cow Bay gravel | 37 | 8 | 7 | | 1 336 | | 280 | 130 |
| Long Island sand | 38 | 5 | 22 | | 872 | | 320 | 160 |
| West Winfield (Pa ) limestone | 21 | 7 | 7 | | 2 150 | 580 | 240 | 100 |
| | 22 | 7 | 2 | | 2,180 | 580 | 230 | 100 |
| | 24 | 7 | 3 | 4,290 | | | | |
| Pittsburgh gravel in load bearing portion   Bituminous cinders in protective concrete   Pittsburgh sand throughout | 41 | 5 | 20 | | 1,900 | 530 | 200 | 110 |

* Column No 7, after five-hour fire test, was loaded to failure   Maximum stress 1075 lb per sq in

same time filling the space between the paper and the form with cinder concrete from bituminous cinders   In the fire test, the cinder concrete shell cracked extensively but stayed in place   The temperatures attained show that the protection afforded the column was good, compared with that obtained with other kinds of concrete as shown in Tables I and II   Difficulty was experienced in making this column and it does not seem probable that such a type is likely to come into use

[3] A Comparison of the Heat Insulating Properties of Some of the Materials Used in Fire Resistive Construction   Bureau of Standards Technologic Paper 130

### TEST DATA OF TABLE III—18 IN. PLAIN COLUMNS

Plain columns were not made from any other aggregate than the Pittsburgh gravel  In the fire tests the spalling tendency of concrete from this gravel was in evidence, the action being less rapid and less extensive than in spirally reinforced columns from the same aggregate, but somewhat faster and more extensive than in corresponding columns with vertical reinforcement but no spiral  It is noteworthy that these plain columns made a better average showing than spirally reinforced columns from the same aggregate  The working load was of course much lower, and this appears to have been more than sufficient to compensate for the value of the steel in spirally reinforced columns at the high temperatures which were attained

### TABLE III

18-in cylindrical columns
Thickness of concrete considered as protective material 1½ in
Reinforcement, none
Effective area 180 sq in
Working load 81,000 lb = 450 lb per sq in

| Aggregate | Column Number | Age at Time of Test | | Stress at Maximum Load, lb per sq in | | Maximum Temperature at End of Fire Test, deg C | | |
|---|---|---|---|---|---|---|---|---|
| | | Mo | Days | Without Fire Test | At End of 4-hr Fire Test | At 2¼ in from Surface | At 5¾ in from Surface | At Center of Column. |
| Pittsburgh gravel | 12 | 7 | 10 | | 835 | 1 070 | 450 | 205 |
| Pittsburgh sand | 14 | 9 | 23 | | * | 950 | 240 | 120 |
| | 15 | 7 | 10 | 3,650 | | | | |

* Column No 14 failed under working load at end of 3 hr 45 min

### TEST DATA OF TABLE IV—16 IN. SQUARE COLUMNS

In the data of this table, the effect of the spalling tendency of the concrete from two types of gravel is exceedingly plain.  Spalling took place more rapidly and extensively in the square columns than in round ones having vertical reinforcement without spiral, but was not as destructive as in spirally reinforced columns  In the fire tests of the square columns made from gravel aggregates  there was a strong tendency for that portion of the corners of the column outside of the vertical rods to split off or split loose and in course of time to fall away from the column  In the latter part of the test deep cracks approximately vertical, opened in the sides of the columns  While the spalling action was more rapid and more destructive in the square gravel columns than in the round ones without spiral, the fact that these square columns gave somewhat better results than corresponding spirally reinforced columns should not be lost sight of, the fact should be emphasized, in addition, that in the fire tests of the square columns from trap rock, limestone and blast furnace slag there was no spalling at all. The results of these tests do not indicate that there is any advantage in point of fire resistance, in round columns over square columns, except in the case of aggregates which show a tendency to spall.

## Table IV

16-in square columns
Thickness of concrete outside the steel 1½ in
Reinforcement 2 per cent vertical 4 rods 1 in diam
Ties ½ in diam, 12 in centers
Effective area of concrete 156 sq in
Area of steel, 314 sq in
Effective area of column, 159 sq in
Working load 92 000 lb = 578 lb per sq in

| Aggregate | Column Number | Age at Time of Test | | Stress at Maximum Load lb per sq in | | Maximum Temperature at End of Fire Test deg C | |
| --- | --- | --- | --- | --- | --- | --- | --- |
| | | Mo | Days | Without Fire Test | At End of 4-hr Fire Test | At Depth of Vertical Rods | At Center of Column |
| Pittsburgh gravel | 25 | 7 | 24 | | 1 005 | 775 | 160 |
| Pittsburgh sand | 26 | 8 | 4 | | 830 | 905 | 165 |
| | 28 | 7 | 1 | 5 030 | | | |
| Pure quartz gravel | 11 | 4 | 8 | | 680 | 1,000 | 250 |
| Long Island sand | 15 | 4 | 24 | | 868 | 1 000 | 280 |
| West Winfield (Pa ) limestone | 29 | 8 | 14 | | 2,360 | 660 | 100 |
| Pittsburgh sand | 30 | 8 | 27 | | 2,420 | 630 | 100 |
| | 32 | 7 | 25 | 5 090 | | | |
| Blast furnace slag | 51 | 4 | 5 | | 2 278 | 690 | 100 |
| Pittsburgh sand | 52 | 4 | 26 | 4 700 | | 770 | |
| | 53 | 4 | 12 | | 1 905 | | |
| New Jersey trap rock | 56 | 4 | 5 | | 1 855 | 690 | |
| Pittsburgh sand | 57 | 4 | 12 | 4 480 | | | |

### Test Data of Table V—12-in Spirally Reinforced Columns

The fire tests of the 12 in hooped columns made from Pittsburgh gravel showed the same spalling tendency as the 18-in hooped columns from the same aggregate In the case of column 33, the outer concrete broke up gradually and it was not until near the finish of the four hour fire test that the first slab fell away from the column At the end of the fire test only a small percentage of the column proper was exposed In the fire test of column 35, the spalling was more rapid, a large portion of the surface of the column proper, including the spiral reinforcement, was exposed within approximately one hour after the beginning of the test The early failure of such a small column, after being stripped of its protection, is not difficult to understand

### CAUSE OF SPALLING OF CONCRETE

The effect of spalling has been shown by the foregoing data and discussion. Good results have been obtained consistently, from certain aggregates and comparatively poor results from others. In most cases, a large part of the difference in behavior between columns from different aggregates may reasonably be attributed to the loss of protection and the correspondingly rapid heat penetration. Observations made in fire tests during the process of spalling give the impression that the spalling is due to destructive stresses in the outer concrete. The spalling action looks like local failure due to excessive stress. Expansion stresses unquestionably exist in the outer concrete of columns from all types of aggre-

### TABLE V.

12-in cylindrical columns
Thickness of concrete outside the steel, $1\frac{1}{2}$ in
Reinforcement  2 per cent vertical 4 round rods $\frac{5}{8}$ in diam
         1 per cent spiral, $\frac{1}{4}$ in diam , $2\frac{1}{4}$ in pitch, 2 spacers
Effective area of concrete, 60 87 sq in
Area of vertical steel, 1 23 sq in
Effective area of column  62 sq in
Working load, 820 lb per sq in

| Aggregate | Column Number | Age at Time of Test | | Stress at Maximum Load, lb per sq in | | Maximum Temperature at End of Fire Test deg C | | |
|---|---|---|---|---|---|---|---|---|
| | | Mo | Days | Without Fire Test | At End of 4-hr Fire Test | At Depth of Vertical Rods | Midway between Steel and Center | At Center of Column |
| Pittsburgh gravel { Pittsburgh sand { | 33<br>35<br>36 | 7<br>10<br>7 | 4<br>5<br>6 | <br><br>4,840 | 1,145<br>* | 690 | 560 | 480<br><br>* |

* Columbus No. 35 failed under working load at end of 2 hrs

gates, when under fire. Why should these cause spalling in certain types of concrete and not in others? In the case of crushed limestone vs gravels made up of smooth pebbles, it may be suspected that the crushed limestone concrete resists the expansion stresses better than the smooth gravel concrete because of better bond. This hypothesis loses probability, however, in the light of the fact that there was but little difference in the strength of the concrete from these two aggregates when tested cold, either in the form of test cylinders or of full-size columns. Furthermore, concrete from gravel composed largely of limestone pebbles, columns 85 and 86, Table I, gave results which clearly class it with limestone aggregates rather than with the other three types of gravel included in the investigation. There was no spalling in the columns from this limestone gravel and the strength at the end of the four-hour fire test was higher than that of columns from crushed trap rock and those from blast furnace slag   Rounded pebbles of one mineralogic type showed superiority over crushed rock of another

The foregoing evidence indicates that the tendency of some types of concrete to spall and of other types not to spall is not due to differences in their ability to resist expansion stresses   We must, therefore, consider the magnitude of the expansion stresses in the different types of concrete, and this introduces the question of the relative expansion behaviors of different mineralogic types of aggregates at high temperatures   Attention has been called, in an earlier report [4] to the peculiarities of the expansion of quartz and of granite

As pointed out by Woolson [5] the cubical expansion of quartz, at ordinary temperatures, is about twice that of feldspar which is one of the predominant minerals in trap rock   Furthermore, the expansion in the direction of the major axis of the quartz crystal is only about half that in the direction of the axis perpendicular to the major axis   Recent investigation of the volume changes of minerals at high temperatures [6] has brought out the fact that when quartz is heated to high temperatures, a sudden expansion of relatively great magnitude takes place when the temperature reaches 575° C, at which point the inversion from Alpha to Beta quartz takes place   Beyond the inversion point, a slight contraction is reported   Granites also showed sudden expansion of great magnitude at 575° C   It is also stated that "About 575° C granite undergoes a permanent dilation caused by the shattering effect due to the different expansion co efficients of its minerals and to the escape of gases"

An expansion curve given for Sudbury diabase, which is similar to the Palisade diabase, commonly called trap rock, shows a gradual increase of volume with temperature the magnitude of which is less up to 1000° C than that shown for quartz and for one of the granites up to 600° C   No data were given applying to other minerals entering into concrete aggregates

The sudden expansion of great magnitude occurring in quartz and granites at 575° C seems sufficient to explain the spalling of concrete made from aggregates in which these minerals predominate   Stresses due to the sudden expansion of the outer concrete before the inner concrete reaches the temperature at which this sudden expansion takes place would be of an entirely different order of magnitude from those occurring in concrete from an aggregate composed mainly of minerals which do not have this peculiar expansion property

In case the temperature of the outer portion of the load bearing concrete of a column were to reach the temperature of 575° C the stress on this portion would suddenly be increased, in concrete made from the

<hr>

[4] A Comparison of the Heat Insulating Properties of Some of the Materials Used in Fire Resistive Construction   Bureau of Standards Technologic Paper No 130 p 33

[5] Investigation of the Thermal Conductivity of Concrete and the Effect of Heat Upon Its Strength and Elastic Properties, by Prof Ira H Woolson   A S T M 5 1905 and 6 1906

[6] The Determination of Mineral and Rock Densities at High Temperatures by Day, Sosman and Hostetter, Am Jour, Sci, 37, p 1, 1914

unfavorable aggregates Such stresses caused by the unequal expansion of the concrete in different portions of the column proper, may be regarded as a factor contributing to the relatively poor records made by columns from these aggregates in cases like columns 8 and 9, where the strength was low at the end of the fire test, although no considerable portion of the protective concrete had been lost by spalling It must be taken into account, in this connection, that when these columns were fire tested, the expansion of the column as a whole was not permitted to increase the load on the column At the beginning of the test, the working load of the column was applied by means of a hydraulic jack operated by a hand test pump As the fire test proceeded and the column expanded, oil was let out of the jack by cracking a valve at the pump to prevent the load from increasing on account of the increasing length of the column This valve was cracked at intervals, the frequency of which depended on the rate at which the column expanded

It is conceivable that in a fire in a building, the stress due to the increased length of a column might become excessive It is true that if all the columns on each story of a building were heated at the same rate, during a fire, so that all increased in length at the same rate, this would not be the case It is not likely, however, that such a condition ever exists in an actual fire Fire is reasonably sure to find better fuel or better draft conditions or both, in some parts of any story than in others and to burn fiercely where fuel and draft permit The columns in such portions, becoming heated in advance of columns in other parts of that story would exert the pressure necessary to raise a portion of the floors above In order to accomplish this, these columns would have to bend the floor structures of the upper floor The restraint of the floors could account for the failure of columns, especially of those made from aggregates of high quartz or granite content, even in fires which would otherwise not seem severe enough to cause such failure The very fact that the fire was especially severe in but one portion of any floor might cause the failure of columns and of contiguous floor structures in that portion Such a condition may account for failures in fires which do not seem, on the whole to have been unusually severe

### PREVENTION OF SPALLING

The obvious method for the prevention of spalling and of related effects of excessive expansion is the elimination of aggregates having high quartz or granite content and the use of aggregates which produce concrete which does not show a tendency to spall While this can be done economically, in many localities, there are other localities in which the only materials available at moderate cost for concrete aggregates are in the spalling class and it is therefore of importance to devise means whereby the safety of concrete structures in which such aggregates are used can be enhanced Of the various expedients which suggest themselves in this connection, three methods have been tried in this investigation·

1   Addition of other protective material, over the concrete, to retard the passage of heat

2   Substitution of other insulating material for the protective concrete

3   The use of light reinforcement in the protective concrete

TABLE VI

Cylindrical columns
Diameter increased from 18 to 20 in by plastering
Thickness of protective material 2½ in
Reinforcement  2 per cent vertical 8 round rods, ⅞ in diam
               1 per cent spiral, 5/16 in diam, 2 in pitch 2 spacers
Effective area of concrete, 168 7 sq in
Area of vertical steel 3 53 sq in
Effective area of column, 172 sq in
Working load, 822 lb per sq in

| Aggregate | Column Number | Age at Time of Test | | Stress at Maximum Load, lb per sq in | | Maximum Temperature at End of Fire Test, deg C | | |
|---|---|---|---|---|---|---|---|---|
| | | Mo. | Days | At End of 4-hr Fire Test | Tested Cold after 4-hr Fire Test | At Depth of Vertical Rods | Midway between Steel and Center | At Center of Column |
| Pittsburgh gravel | *4 | 12 | 2 | * | 5 970 | 375 | 155 | 90 |
| Pittsburgh sand | 6 | 5 | 10 | | 5 615 | 410 | 160 | 110 |
| | 76 | 6 | 25 | 3,270 | | 460 | | |
| West Winfield (Pa ) limestone Pittsburgh sand | 19 | 10 | 23 | | 6,050 | 410 | 135 | 90 |

* Columns Nos 4, 6 and 19 were given the additional protection of 1 in of plaster composed of portland cement and sand with a small percentage of lime hydrate   The plaster covering was reinforced with light expanded metal

Column No 76 was plastered with a mixture of portland cement and crushed bituminouscinders, increasing the thickness of protective material from 1½ to 2½ in   No metallic binder provided for the plaster

## DATA OF TABLE VI—PLASTER OVER PROTECTIVE CONCRETE

The test data of columns 4 and 6 show the effectiveness of additional insulating material over the concrete of columns which would otherwise have a strong tendency to spall under fire   As shown in Table I, all the spirally reinforced columns of ordinary construction from Pittsburgh gravel spalled in the fire test and gave results that were extremely poor compared with columns from made non-spalling aggregates   To columns 4 and 6 was added 1 in of plaster from portland cement and sand with a small percentage of lime hydrate   Before plastering, the column was covered with a light grade of expanded metal, furred out about ½ in   In the fire test, cracking occurred in both the plaster and the outer concrete, but all the material stayed in place   Both columns withstood the maximum furnace load, while hot, at the end of the four hour fire test, and showed ultimate strength, when tested cold, after the fire test but slightly lower than similar columns that had not been fire tested   Column 19 was pro tected in the same way   This being a limestone column and one of a group in which no spalling took place and from which good results were obtained without additional protection the improvement was not great

Column 76 was plastered with 1 in  of plaster made from a mixture of portland cement and bituminous cinders crushed fine enough to take the place of sand   No metallic reinforcement was used to hold this plaster in place and a large part of it came off in the course of the fire test   The same kind of plaster was tried on column 69 a, Table VII, where it made a better showing

### Test Data of Table VII—Substitution of Plaster for Protective Concrete

While the addition of plaster with reinforcement to hold it in place has been shown to be extremely effective in improving the behavior of columns of a type which spalls under fire test conditions, this expedient obviously adds to the cost of the column   Plaster substituted for protective concrete would not increase the cost so much and the expense would be still further reduced if the reinforcement could be omitted from the plaster   A number of columns were accordingly made for the purpose of trying this expedient with different kinds of plaster   Some of the columns were made in the usual way except that smaller forms were used  making columns 16 in  in diameter instead of 18 in , to be increased to 18 in  by plastering, others were made by wrapping ordinary, diamond mesh metal lath around the reinforcing steel over the spiral, wiring it in place and using that as the form   No serious difficulty was experienced in making columns in this way without the usual form  the pressure of the mass of concrete was exerted mainly against the spiral reinforcement, the metal lath merely retaining the material which came through the spiral   With a consistency as wet as could reasonably be attained in hand mixing  the quantity of wet mortar which escaped through the metal lath was not important   Considerable poling was required to make the concrete fill out reasonably well against the lath

All columns were plastered by the trowel method, those not cast in metal lath were hacked and the surfaces of all columns were made wet before plastering   A thin coat of very rich mortar was applied to the concrete and followed immediately by the scratch coat   Columns cast in metal lath did not require hacking and did not receive the bonding coat of rich mortar.

Columns 63, 66  71 and 72 were plastered with a mixture of 1 part portland cement  1/10 part lime hydrate and 2½ parts sand  by volume In the fire test, the outer coat of plaster invariably showed cracks in the first few minutes   Cracks extended rapidly and bulging of the outer plaster was usually observed   The outer plaster of the columns of this group or a large part of it fell off in the course of the fire test   This took place more rapidly in some tests than in the others  but the process was similar in all and appeared to be caused by expansion of the plaster itself rather than by pressure from steam or other gas from within, although one or more unimportant cases were observed in which small

Table VII

18-in cylindrical columns
Protective material applied by plastering
Reinforcement 2 per cent vertical 8 round rods ⅜ in diam
         1 per cent spiral ⅜ 16 in diam , 2 in pitch 2 spacers
Effective area of concrete 168 7 sq in
Area of vertical steel, 3 53 sq in
Effective area of column, 172 sq in
Working load 822 lb per sq in

| Aggregate | Column Number | Age at Time of Test | | Stress at Maximum load lb per sq in | | Maximum Temperature at End of Fire Test, deg C | | |
|---|---|---|---|---|---|---|---|---|
| | | Mo | Days | At End of 1-hr Fire Test | Tested Cold after 4-hr Fire Test | At Depth of Vertical Rods | Midway between Steel and Center | At Center of Column |
| Pittsburgh gravel Pittsburgh sand | *63 | 9 | 17 | 1.770 | | 590 | 185 | 90 |
| | 65 | 4 | 26 | * | 4,915 | 440 | 220 | 100 |
| | 66 | 4 | 4 | 1,290 | | 765 | 335 | 150 |
| | 67 | 4 | 22 | * | 5,315 | 185 | 95 | 90 |
| | 71 | 4 | 0 | 2 455 | | 570 | 250 | 110 |
| | 72 | 4 | 0 | 1,280 | | 780 | | |
| | 88 | 1 | 1 | 3,120 | | 510 | | |
| | 89 | 4 | 1 | 1,885 | | 685 | | |
| | 90 | 5 | 14 | 2,000 | | 670 | | |
| | 69-a | * | | 3,200 | | 520 | 215 | 175 |

* Column No 63 was made 16 in in diameter and plastered with a mixture of portland cement lime hydrate and sand increasing its diameter to 18 in

Column No 65 was made 16 in in diameter and plastered with a special plaster, containing portland cement, asbestos and sand, increasing its diameter to 18 in This column did not fail at the end of the four-hour fire test under the maximum furnace load, 3480 lb per sq in

Column No 66 was cast in a form made by covering the spiral reinforcement with metal lath and plastering on the metal lath with cement plaster

Column No 67 was made by pouring concrete in a form made of metal wrapped around the reinforcing steel Column then plastered with a mixture of gypsum, lime and kieselguhr Poultry netting used for binder in plaster Total thickness of protective material, 1½ in thickness of plaster, approximately 1 in This column did not fail at the end of the four-hour fire test under the maximum load of the furnace loading equipment, 3480 lb per sq in

Column No 71 was made 16 in in diameter and plastered with a mixture of cement, lime hydrate and sand, increasing its diameter to 18 in

Column No 72 was cast in a form made by covering the spiral reinforcement with metal lath Protective material added by plastering with a mixture of portland cement, lime hydrate and sand

Column No 88 was a duplicate of No 65

Columns No 89 and 90 were cast in a form made by covering the spiral reinforcement with metal lath Protective material added by plastering with a mixture of lime hydrate gypsum and sand

Total thickness of protective material 1½ in Thickness of plaster approximately 1 in No metallic binder in plaster

Column No 69-a was originally cast in a gypsum form (see Table VIII) Column was subjected to four-hour fire test in the gypsum form At the end of four-hour fire test, did not fail under the maximum furnace load, 3480 lb per sq in After fire test gypsum form removed and protective material added by plastering on concrete with a mixture of portland cement and crushed bituminous cinders

portions appeared to be blown off by steam In these four columns, the scratch coat remained in place throughout the fire test It will be observed that the strength of columns 63 and 71 which were made 16 in in diameter, in a steel form and afterward plastered was distinctly better than that of Nos 66 and 72, which were cast in metal lath and afterward plastered  It will be noted, also, that the temperature attained in the steel in the four hour fire test was considerably higher in the latter columns than in the former ones  These differences in results were probably due at least in large part, to the fact that the 16 in concrete column, with its scratch coat maintained a greater thickness of protective material over the steel, after the outer plaster had fallen off, than was afforded by the scratch coat of plaster on the columns cast in metal lath over the spiral

Columns 65 and 88 were made and protected by the same method as Nos 64 and 71 by plastering on 16 in columns excepting that the plaster, in this case, was made from a special mixture which is used commercially, as a roofing material  It is composed of portland cement sand and Nalecode compound  The Nalecode compound used in the tests was furnished by Paul Mende, of New York City  While some cracking took place in the plaster on these columns in the course of the fire test the plaster remained in place and afforded the column reasonably good protection, as may be seen from the test data

Column 67 was plastered with a mixture consisting of 56 percent neat gypsum plaster, 24 percent hydrated lime and 20 percent kieselguhr. by weight  The kieselguhr used was a grade known as Sil O Cel and was furnished by the Celite Products Co through E J Deckman, of Pittsburgh  The column had been cast in metal lath covering the steel  The plaster was put on in three coats, followed by a thin finish coat of gypsum and hydrated lime  After the second plaster coat was applied, the column was covered with light, 2 in mesh, poultry netting, drawn fairly tight The third coat of plaster concealed the poultry netting, which was intended to prevent the plaster from coming off in the fire test  In the fire test, the finish coat came off in the first fifteen minutes  Cracks were observed to form in the third coat, which contained the poultry netting but this coat and those beneath it stayed in place throughout the fire test  This plaster mixture was one that was selected after considerable experimental work, not yet published  had been done in an attempt to find a practical mixture of ordinary commercial materials of moderate cost which would possess insulating qualities superior to the kinds of plaster now in use The temperature data for this column indicate that this mixture does possess such qualities  Considering the extremely good protection afforded. the cost of such plaster can hardly be regarded as excessive  It is not probable that it would stay in place satisfactorily, through a fire test, without the poultry netting or other binding material  Another disadvantage is that such a plaster might be more easily damaged by rough usage than plasters commonly in use

Columns 89 and 90, cast in metal lath, were plastered with a mixture of neat gypsum plaster, hydrated lime and sand in the proportion 50 20 30 by weight  The mixture was selected as being the most promising one of a number that had been tried, in this investigation just referred to, in an attempt to find a mixture of these three materials in which neither shrinkage nor expansion would be great under fire and which would give good protection to a column without requiring any special binding material to hold the plaster in place. The difficulty with such an undertaking is that in those mixtures in which the expansion of the sand is most nearly balanced by the shrinkage of the other ingredients, expansion is shown by the plaster in the first few minutes of firing followed by shrinkage after that time. The plaster on these columns cracked and fell off in a manner similar to that described for plaster from the mixture of portland cement, lime hydrate and sand used on columns 63, 66, 71 and 72. It is probable that the protection afforded by the plaster used on columns 89 and 90 would have been fairly satisfactory if metal binding material had been provided, to keep the plaster in place as in the case of column 67.

Column 69 A had originally been No. 69, which, as shown in Table VIII, was cast in a gypsum form. Since this column withstood the maximum load of the furnace equipment at the end of the four-hour fire test and since it was indicated by the temperature attained that the column was still in good condition it was decided to use it for the testing of one of the plaster mixtures. The column was accordingly stripped of the gypsum covering which was, of course, damaged by the fire test, and plastered with a mixture of portland cement and crushed bituminous cinders. This plaster showed cracks in the fire test but stayed in place and gave fairly good protection, as shown by the test data. It should be noted that plaster from cement and crushed cinders did not do so well in the case of column 76, Table VI.

## Columns Cast in Gypsum Forms —Table VIII

As shown by the description, Table VIII these columns had protective covering 2 19/32 in. thick, of which 2 5/32 in. was the thickness of the gypsum forms in which the columns were cast. These forms were made in hollow cylindrical sections like sewer pipe without sockets. The ends were so formed as to be self-centering and the sections were set one on another to the required height. The forms were made in the laboratory from "Structolite," which was furnished by the United States Gypsum Co. Other columns not given in this table made in gypsum forms $2\frac{1}{2}$ in. thick, had demonstrated that such forms would give good protection for approximately two hours and would then fall off, due to dehydration accompanied by shrinkage and loss of strength. In the fire test of column No. 60, the form fell away from the column after the test had gone approximately $1\frac{1}{4}$ hours, the shorter time being attributable to the difference in thickness. Holes 7/16 in. in diameter were bored through the sections for the form of column No. 61 before the form was set up and looped wires were placed in these holes with their ends extending inward so as to gain an anchorage in the concrete. This is not to be regarded as a practical expedient but was done to make use of forms that had been made before column No 60 was tested  This anchored form remained in place during approximately three hours and forty-five minutes of fire test

It had been demonstrated that the best results could not be expected from gypsum covering, in long fire tests, unless some anchorage or binding material were provided  In making the forms for columns Nos 68, 69 and 70 metallic binding material was included  Light weight, 2-in mesh poultry netting was imbedded in part of the sections and a light grade of expanded metal in the others  In some sections the binding material was placed close to the inner surface of the form and in others it was placed near the middle of the shell, in some places it was near the outer surface

### TABLE VIII

Columns cast in gypsum forms
Thickness of form 2 5/32 in    Total thickness of protective material  2 19 33 in
Reinforcement  2 per cent vertical, 8 round rods ⅜ in diam
             1 per cent spiral, 5/16 in diam , 2 in pitch, 2 spacers
Effective area of concrete, 168 7 sq in
Area of vertical steel 3 53 sq in
Effective area of column  172 sq in
Working load 822 lb per sq in

| Aggregate | Column Number | Age at Time of Test | | Stress at Maximum Load lb per sq in | | | Maximum Temperature at End of Fire Test, deg C | | |
|---|---|---|---|---|---|---|---|---|---|
| | | Mo | Days | Without Fire Test | At End of 4-hr Fire Test | Tested Cold after 4-hr Fire Test | At Depth of Vertical Rods | Midway between Steel and Center | At Center of Column |
| Pittsburgh gravel Pittsburgh sand | *60 | 2 | 0 | | 1 205 | | 810 | 260 | 90 |
| | 61 | 4 | 7 | | 2,800 | | 185 | 150 | 110 |
| | 68 | 4 | 0 | | | 5,420 | 305 | 95 | 85 |
| | 69 | 4 | 2 | | * | | 190 | 90 | 90 |
| | 70 | 4 | 3 | 6,480 | | | | | |

* No anchorage was provided for the gypsum form on column No 60
Form was anchored to concrete of column No 61 by means of wires
In the forms for Columns Nos 68, 69 70 light metal reinforcing material  poultry netting or expanded metal was used

The light reinforcement was effective in all sections, the poultry netting apparently serving the purpose as well as the expanded metal  Observations indicated that it would not be best to have large portions of such binding material placed within less than ¼ in of the outer surface of the form

There is an apparent discrepancy in the results from columns 61, 68 and 69 in that No 61 failed at a lower load than the temperatures attained would indicate it should be capable of carrying  Column 68, on the other hand, gave good load test results with a higher temperature in the vertical steel  Some allowance should be made for the fact that the temperatures were measured in the vertical steel and not in the spiral and that a few minutes were required to make the load test, after the fire test was completed Since the gypsum covering fell off in the test of No 61 fifteen minutes before the end of the test the spiral steel on this column was undoubtedly at a much higher temperature when the load test was finished than that indicated in the vertical steel at the end of the fire test

The protection afforded to columns 68 and 69 was good, as shown by the results of the load tests Column 69 has already been referred to under the number 69-A Table VII where it was shown to have made a fairly good record in a second fire test after the gypsum form had been removed and the column plastered with a mixture of portland cement and crushed cinders

TABLE IX

20-in cylindrical columns
Thickness of protective concrete 2½ in
Reinforcement 2 per cent vertical 8 round rods, ⅞ in diam
1 per cent spiral, 5/16 in diam , 2 in pitch, 2 spacers
Effective area of concrete, 168 7 sq in
Area of vertical steel 3 53 sq in
Effective area of column 172 sq in
Working load 822 lb per sq in

| Aggregates | Column Number | Age at Time of Test | | Stress at Maximum Load lb per sq in | | | Maximum Temperature at End of Fire Test deg C |
|---|---|---|---|---|---|---|---|
| | | Mo | Days | Without Fire Test | At End of 4 hr Fire Test | Tested Cold after 4-hr Fire Test | At Depth of Vertical Rods |
| Pittsburgh gravel Pittsburgh sand | *79 | 1 | 8 | | 1,495 | | 1 000 |
| | 80 | 4 | 1 | | 1,640 | | 960 |
| | 81 | 4 | 23 | 5,590 | | | |
| | 82 | 1 | 5 | | | 5 115 | 410 |
| | 83 | 4 | 0 | | | 4 950 | 530 |
| | 84 | 1 | 11 | 5,155 | | | |

* Columns Nos 79, 80 and 81 had no metallic binder or reinforcement in the protective concrete
Columns 82, 83 and 84 had a light grade of expanded metal in the protective concrete

## COLUMNS WITH 2½ IN OF PROTECTIVE CONCRETE —TABLE IX

On account of the unsatisfactory results obtained from columns made from gravels high in quartz content, with 1½ in of protective concrete, a series of columns was made with 2½ in of concrete over the steel In three of these, expanded metal was placed in the outer concrete to prevent its coming off by spalling

As in the case of other spirally reinforced columns from similar aggregates, evidence of spalling was visible after approximately thirty minutes in the fire tests of columns 79 to 80 There was this important difference, however in the spirally reinforced columns with 1½ in of protection the outer concrete broke up into slabs which were bounded on the inside by the hooping itself and left it exposed when they fell off whereas in these columns with 2½ in protection, the first slabs to separate were comparatively thin, so that when they fell a considerable thickness of concrete still remained over the steel. The spalling proceeded somewhat less rapidly in these columns than in those with only 1½ in. of protective concrete, but it continued throughout the test. A second series of slabs proceeded to separate after the falling of the first set had exposed new areas of concrete and, after approximately two hours of firing, the spiral began to be exposed. It may be judged from the temperatures attained in the steel that the superiority of the record made by these columns, in the strength test, over those made by similar columns with 1½-in. protection, is attributable to lower temperatures in the interior concrete. These columns were not exposed so early in the burn nor so completely.

FIG. 2. — COLUMNS PROTECTED WITH VARIOUS PLASTERS.

Columns 82 and 83, in which the 2½-in. covering of protective concrete was tied together with a light grade of expanded metal, were observed to develop cracks after approximately thirty minutes of firing. Cracks continued to form and to widen throughout the fire test, but practically all the material stayed on the column throughout the test. The low final temperatures and high ultimate stresses testify to the effectiveness of the protection.

The expanded metal used was a grade known as "Floorbinder," which was furnished by the Consolidated Expanded Metal Co. Specifications for this material are as follows: Thickness, 16-gage (U. S. Std.), 0.0625 in., weight, per sheet 5 ft. by 8 ft. 8 in., 8 lb. In building these columns in the laboratory the reinforcement was set up first and the expanded metal placed around it before the form was set up. The expanded metal occupied approximately the middle of the space between the spiral and the form. It did not interfere with the placing of concrete.

## Summary.

The results obtained in this investigation indicate that concretes may properly be divided, with respect to their fire-resistive properties, into two general classes, those which show a tendency to spall when exposed to fire and those which do not. The tendency to spall depends on the nature of the aggregate. Concrete made from three types of gravel showed this tendency strongly. One of these was a mixed gravel containing a large proportion of sandstone pebbles; another was composed almost entirely of smooth, nearly white, quartz pebbles; the third contained a large proportion of granite and gneiss pebbles with a small proportion of quartz pebbles. In the first two of these gravels the predominating mineral was

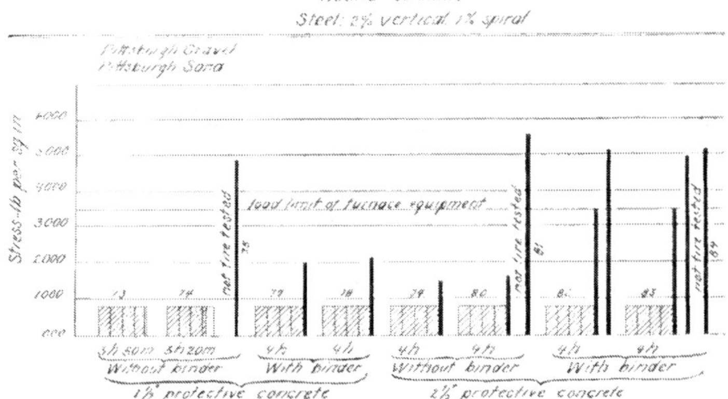



FIG. 5.—COMPARISON OF PROTECTION WITH AND WITHOUT BINDER.

quartz. In the third, granite predominated. Attention has been called to the peculiar expansion behavior of quartz and granite at high temperatures, including a sudden increase in volume of 575° C., which would have a strong tendency to produce exceedingly high stresses in large masses of concrete when heated rapidly. The fact that spalling did not take place in the fire tests of columns from trap rock, blast furnace slag, limestone and a type of gravel containing approximately 90 percent of limestone pebbles is attributed to the smaller and more regular rate of expansion of the mineral constituents of these aggregates.

Some spalling was observed in columns of all types made from the three gravels which are classed as spalling aggregates, but was more rapid and more destructive in columns with spiral reinforcement than in other types. Spirally reinforced columns with 1½ in. of protective concrete lost a large part of the concrete covering so early in the test that most of these columns failed under the working load, before the end of the four hour fire test. Square columns without spiral made from these aggregates spalled badly. Cylindrical columns without spiral spalled less than corresponding columns with spiral reinforcement. Columns made from the other aggregates enumerated above including a limestone gravel did not spall in columns of any type included in the investigation.

The loss of strength in the four-hour fire test of columns made from non-spalling aggregates, as determined by comparing the ultimate strength of the column, tested hot at the end of the fire test with that of a similar column not fire tested, was approximately 50 percent in most cases but less than 50 percent in spirally reinforced columns made from limestone aggregate. The strength records are better for columns from the limestone aggregates, including the limestone gravel, than from the other aggregates. The poorest records made by columns of non-spalling concrete show an ultimate strength nearly three times as high as the working load of the column, in a considerable number the ultimate strength at the end of the fire test was more than four times the working load.

Pittsburgh gravel concrete, which spalled badly in spirally reinforced columns without special protection, made excellent records in similar columns covered with 1 in of portland cement plaster held in place by imbedded expanded metal.

Hooped columns made from Pittsburgh gravel protected by 1½ in of material in which plaster was substituted for the outer inch of concrete made widely varying records. Plasters included the following combinations. Portland cement lime hydrate and sand, portland cement and crushed cinders, gypsum, lime and sand, and Nalecode roof mixture. Part of the columns so protected were made by casting the concrete in the basket formed by the column reinforcement covered with ordinary diamond mesh metal lath. In all cases the scratch coat of plaster remained in place throughout the four hour fire test. The outer coats of plaster from cement and sand and from gypsum lime and sand came off, starting in the early part of the test. The plaster from cement and crushed cinders stayed in place and made a comparatively good record, but failed to do so on a column in another series. The Nalecode roofing mixture remained in place on both columns and made good records.

A number of columns were cast in forms built up of hollow cylindrical gypsum sections the total thickness of protective material being 2 19/32 in. Gypsum forms without metallic ties of any kind, did not stay in place satisfactorily in the fire test, forms with either expanded metal or poultry netting imbedded in the gypsum to hold it in place gave excellent protection to columns made from Pittsburgh gravel concrete.

In spirally reinforced columns from Pittsburgh gravel 2½ in of protective concrete was found to give better protection than 1½ in. Spalling took place but the material did not come off as rapidly or as completely as from similar columns with 1½ in of protective concrete.

The results were not as good as from columns from non-spalling concrete with 1½ in protection

Expanded metal embedded in the outer concrete of columns from Pittsburgh gravel to prevent loss of protective concrete by spalling gave fairly good results in columns with 1½ in of protective concrete and made excellent records in columns from the same aggregate with 2½ in of protective concrete

One spirally reinforced column made from Pittsburgh gravel concrete on which the outer inch of the 1½ in of protective material was applied in the form of plaster made from a mixture of neat gypsum plaster lime hydrate and kieselguhr (Sil-O-Cel) gave excellent results as to both heat insulation and strength. Poultry netting was imbedded in the plaster to hold it in place

## CONCLUSIONS

One of the primary functions of an investigation of this sort is to supply engineering data from which it is possible to determine the best methods of providing, economically, for a reasonable factor of safety, in respect to fire, in buildings of fire-resistive construction. A full discussion of the application of the data supplied by this investigation to questions involved in the fire protection of columns would necessarily be long, it may be proper however to call attention to the more important points

It may be assumed that the factors of safety employed in design are only such as are regarded as necessary to amply provide for the various uncertainties such as are involved in engineering calculations in the quality of materials and in methods and workmanship in the construction of buildings. The factors of safety provided by allowable working stresses for concrete columns especially where governed by municipal building codes, are intended to safeguard buildings against a number of uncertainties which have been eliminated in part by the improvement in the art of concrete construction and by the entrance of a considerable number of responsible and reliable contracting firms into this field. The resulting factors of safety are so ample that the possibility that a column would fail, under actual loading conditions due to a 50 percent reduction in strength is somewhat remote. Fire tests showed that columns of three important types made from concrete which did not spall under fire suffered a reduction of strength not exceeding approximately 50 percent of the original strength. Therefore it may be judged that columns made from concrete which does not spall under fire and provided with 1½ in of protective concrete uniformly over the reinforcement would be capable of withstanding in all but very exceptional cases, an extremely severe fire of four hours' duration. Considering the fact that reinforcement is not likely to be centered in the forms with the same accuracy in the field as in the laboratory, the adoption of a 2 in rather than a 1½ in standard for this thickness would seem to be justified for construction

in which it is considered necessary to provide protection against severe
fire conditions of such extremely long duration

It may be concluded, from the results of the tests in which spalling
took place, that the provision of a 2 in. thickness of protective concrete
over the steel is not a suitable method for the protection of columns made
from concrete which is likely to spall. The practice of providing and
depending on a coating which is likely to come off under severe fire conditions is not justifiable. The use of a light grade of metal reinforcement
in the outer concrete has been shown to be effective in reducing the loss of
material from columns in which spalling takes place. While the results
from such columns with $1\frac{1}{2}$ in. of reinforced protective concrete were
not as good as those from columns made from non-spalling concrete, with
the same thickness of protective concrete, the results shown by columns
made from concrete having a tendency to spall, with $2\frac{1}{2}$ in. of outer
concrete, with the reinforcement indicate that 2 in. of reinforced protective
concrete should provide sufficient protection even against a fire of four
hours' duration.

Results indicate that the addition of 1 in. of portland cement plaster,
with light reinforcement to hold it in place would be a satisfactory safeguard in the case of columns already made from concrete with a tendency
to spall and protected in the usual way. There is no evidence that other
kinds of plaster would not serve the same purpose if used with the reinforcement.

The problems involved in the possible use of gypsum forms for the
making and fire protection of the columns have not received sufficient consideration, as yet, to justify recommendations in regard to such a method.
This statement applies equally to the possible use of metal lath over the
reinforcement to provide a form for columns which are to be plastered.

While no recommendations as to the use of plaster to take the place
of protective concrete seem to be justified as yet, it seems probable that
this method may be found economical for columns made from concrete
which has a tendency to spall. The more general use of the cement gun
may be expected to favor the adoption of this method after a more thorough knowledge of the fire resistive properties of different kinds of plaster
has been gained. The evidence so far secured indicates that the most
important consideration in respect to a plaster is whether it can be
depended on to stay in place under fire conditions. Differences in heat
insulating properties are probably of secondary consideration but some
attention should be given to the fact that good results can be obtained
with small thicknesses of plasters which have superior heat insulating
properties.

Progress is steadily being made in the development of the art of concrete construction. Sources of uncertainty as to strength in concrete
structures are being at least partially eliminated and the logical result
will be the use of higher unit stresses in design with a corresponding
reduction in the size of columns for a given load requirement and an

increase, in many cases, in the importance of providing against loss of strength in the steel  The tendency of this progress is to make the problems of safeguarding concrete columns against fire more nearly like those of protecting steel columns  and the importance of adequacy and reliability of heat insulating covering to keep the temperatures low in the steel and the load bearing concrete will be increased  In the interest of economy, careful study will need to be devoted to the protection required by columns and other members of concrete structures in buildings of different classes  The fact has been established beyond reasonable doubt that there are few classes of occupancy in which fire approximating in severity the conditions represented by the standard fire test can be maintained in any one portion of a building of fire resistive construction for four hours  For most classes of buildings the four hour fire test carries with it a factor of safety, in itself which may be justified in the present state of our knowledge  but which may properly be reduced as this knowledge becomes more definite and comprehensive

## DISCUSSION

MR. MONTGOMERY It seems to me that time is an important element in such tests as these During the past month or so I have had occasion to heat up small samples of neat cement 1-in square and perhaps ½ in thick for as long as 50 hours ranging from a temperature of 200° up to 1050° C or about 1900° F Over that entire range I have had loss, which means that something is decomposing, in this case it would be chiefly water with a small amount of carbon dioxide If we have only a four-hour fire test it means that we have only gotten to the exterior layer of that concrete, and the longer the fire test the further in you will drive off this water and carbon dioxide when this concrete is exposed to moisture the moisture will react with the concrete and loosen it up My reason for stating this is that the samples, after they were heated up for 50 hours, were then placed in desiccators over water That meant that we had a moisture-saturated an practically carbon dioxide free, because the desiccators were small and what carbon dioxide was in the air was negligible The samples were left in this desiccator for one week At the end of that week one of these samples, I believe the one made from a cement which contains aluminum in place of iron, had doubled in size, and was full of cracks The slag cement had increased slightly in size and was not so full of cracks So it seems to me that the time factor is very important

MR. E. G. PERROT—In reference to the time of fire test, I had some experience back in 1906 on a test on a floor system with columns that failed during the test due to several causes one of which was the fact that the concrete was too green having been poured in the winter time and not having had the proper environment to cure properly I took a piece of the concrete which had failed under the fire, which was very brittle, so brittle that it could be crumbled easily in the hand and set that on the window sill of my office for about six months, and it got very hard I do not just recall the length of time the sample was in the fire, but it was at least $2\frac{1}{2}$ or 3 hours It was a traprock concrete of standard mixture, and I have always felt that concrete that has been in the fire will absorb moisture from the air or if water is applied in some manner afterwards, sufficient to regain a certain amount of strength Just what the strength will be we had no way of determining One of our buildings did go through a very severe trial and one column was subjected to very severe heat action from the adjoining frame building which burned to the ground The contents of the building a glue factory, burned out, there were a lot of glue racks in it, and the glue and the racks burned entirely up, and this particular column which was subjected to the greatest heat, spalled on the edges It was a square column The building did not suffer very much from the fire and the remedy to repair the damage was simply to wrap the column with a mesh of wire and put up forms and pour a fireproof jacket about 2 in thick around the column.  The column is still there, and that was done about eight years ago

Regarding the laboratory tests just mentioned, I do not think we can make comparison between laboratory tests and actual field practice where the buildings have been subjected to an ordinary fire  I have in mind another building of ours which went through a fire  The top story contained japanning ovens of a very inflammable nature  The contents were in the oven  The contents burned out without doing any damage at all to the concrete structure

Mr S H Ingberg —I have no comment to make on the general subject of the paper  I think that both from building fires and from tests concrete with properly selected aggregate has shown a high degree of fire resistance  There is one point I would like to call attention to, I think it was suggested in the paper that building columns as now designed, have perhaps an over ample factor of safety  and while I do not discount the possibility of improvement in the manufacture and placing of concrete I doubt that the present experimental data give ground for any decided increase in unit stresses as applied to columns  In the first place, I doubt that our testing methods, by which we test concrete today  bring out the actual quality of the material as used in the structures  and laboratory tests may be very defective in that respect  Until we have developed tests that more nearly do so the grounds for increase in stress are necessarily not very valid

Mr Frank Ginsburg —I may say, in a general way  that water effects in relation to concrete not only apply to columns  but to wall structures  that the water will carry away the portions damaged during the fire, that if you have little fire damage you have little water damage so that from the results of fire tests you can form a very good idea what a given aggregate will do

Mr Perrot —I understand, from previous tests on columns, that the best reinforcement for a column was cement  in other words, the richer the concrete the stronger the column  Does that apply in a fire?  In other words, does a rich mixture behave better in a fire than a leaner mixture?  If you have a 1  1  2 mixture for a hooded column  will it behave better than a 1  2  4 mixture?

Mr W A Hull —We have kept the same relation throughout the column test  but in a previous investigation where a cylinder 8 in in diameter and 16 in long was tested  we had two mixtures  a 1  2  4 and a 1  2  6  and there was not a great deal of difference in the apparent effect of the fire, although the leaner mixture made a somewhat poorer showing in the gravel concrete specimen than the richer mixture

Mr W A Hull *(by letter)*  While Mr Montgomery is entirely correct as to the importance of the time factor in connection with fire resistance, it may be regarded as a safe assumption that very few structural members are likely to be subjected to a severe fire exposure of more than four hours' duration, and that the vital question is what takes place in the first four hours or less

In regard to Mr Perrot's statement as to the comparisons between laboratory tests and fires occurring in buildings there is no question that there are a good many things to be taken into consideration in making such comparisons  On the other hand it would not appear that there is necessarily any discrepancy between the facts which he submits on the performance of concrete structures on which he has made observations after fires had occurred in them and the performance of the columns in our fire tests  The fact that we can break a column with a hydraulic jack while the column is still hot, at the end of a four hour fire test, does not mean that that column would not have gone through a severe fire in a building without failure, but when we know how much it takes to break it, in this condition, and how much it takes to break a corresponding column that has not been in the fire, it gives us information as to how much weaker a column is while it is hot than it was before it was subjected to fire

What we want to guard against are failures, and the failures are more likely to come during the fire than before or after  We want to know how much a given column has to go and come on—how much of a factor of safety it has—at the time when its strength is at the minimum  It is not possible to tell much about that by field observations after a fire is over, and it is not possible to go in and estimate loads and measure deflections while a fire is going on  Field observations are of great value, but they raise questions which can best be answered in the laboratory

While agreeing with Mr Ingberg that these columns, made in the laboratory, under carefully controlled conditions and with approximately the right amount of water for maximum strength of concrete, should not be used as a criterion for increasing allowable stresses in design, the writer does believe that there is and is going to be a tendency toward better control in the field  Things are moving rapidly and investigations of this sort take time, it seems important, therefore, to look ahead at the probable trend of our fire-resistance problems so that our conclusions will have a tendency to increase in usefulness as time goes on rather than to go quickly out of date

SPECIFICATIONS FOR THE U S STANDARD SIEVE SERIES

By J C Pearson.*

It has been recognized for many years that a standardized series of
testing sieves based upon some definite and logical succession of sieve
openings is needed in the testing of materials and for many industrial
purposes  The W S Tyler Co, Cleveland, Ohio, was the first manufacturer
to undertake the production of a series of testing sieves of this kind, and
the development of the now well-known Tyler Screen Scale Sieves has been
a most important factor in facilitating the study of the properties of finely
divided materials  The Tyler Scale † is based on a series of openings which
form a geometric series starting with 0 0029 in , the opening of the present
standard 200-mesh sieve and having the square root of 2, or 1.414, as the
ratio  The point to which attention is called  however, is that neither the
Tyler series nor any other complete series of testing sieves has been manu
factured under published specifications which include definite tolerances,
or allowable variations from the nominal openings and wire diameters

There is always a demand for certification of sieves of sizes other than
those included in the present standards, and the Bureau of Standards has
received in the past many communications urging that something be done
to establish standards for a complete series of testing sieves  In conse
quence the Bureau has devoted a considerable amount of study to the
requirements of various industries using sieves, and has consulted the
manufacturers of wire cloth as to the desirability of different screen scales
and the practicability of their manufacture

To consider the adoption of a standard series of testing sieves, a con
ference was called at the Bureau of Standards April 20 1916, of representatives of various committees of the American Society for Testing Materials,
American Society of Civil Engineers, American Institute of Mining Engineers, American Foundrymen s Association  Mining and Metallurgical Soci
ety of America, American Water Works Association  American Institute of
Metals and the American Spice Trade Association, also representatives of
the Committee of Revision of the U S Pharmacopœia, the U S Geological
Survey, the U S Bureau of Mines, the U S Office of Public Roads and
Rural Engineering, the U S Office of Grain Standardization and the U S
Bureau of Standards, also representatives of a number of private firms
engaged in industries in which sieves are used such as the glass, the drug
milling, the abrasive, the asphalt  the mining, the spice, the chemical, and
the graphite industries, also representatives of the firms in this country
manufacturing wire cloth and sieves  At this conference three different

---

* U S  Bureau of Standards, Washington, D C

† See paper by G A  Dısbro  "Screen Scale Sieves Made to a Fixed Ratio"
Proc A S T M , 1913

series of testing sieves were proposed, one of which was the existing Tyler Screen Scale Series   The others were suggested by the Bureau, one being based on the inch opening, the other on the millimeter opening   In all of these the openings varied by the fixed ratio of the square root of 2, or the fourth root of 2   After a full discussion of the merits and defects of these three series, the conference voted for the adoption of the metric series, subject to certain revisions which would more nearly include the sieves then in use in the testing of road materials   These revisions were subsequently made, and the series was adopted by letter ballot

Before any move was made toward the production of sieves according to the proposed specifications, a deluge of war work came upon the Bureau, and it was impossible to give the matter any continuous attention until early in 1919   In the meantime however, some study had been given to the new specifications and it was found that in the endeavor to include existing sieves and to adhere to the use of stock sizes of wire and wire cloth, very considerable deviations from the series of openings originally planned had been introduced and that in order to maintain the mesh in the approximate multiple of ten numbers per lineal inch, the wire diameters were in many cases poorly selected   To discover what improvement might be brought about in the relation of wire diameters to openings a graphical method was very conveniently employed   Since a sieve is completely defined by the size of opening and the size of wire, a diagram was made by plotting sieve openings horizontally and wire diameters vertically   Any given sieve is represented on such a diagram by a single point, and a series of sieves by a series of points, which show at a glance the regularity of the ratios of wire diameters to openings   Thus, not only the proposed series of sieves but all the sieves in actual use in the laboratory were first plotted in this manner and those points corresponding to sieves which were known from experience to have either undesirably heavy or undesirably light wires were marked off   A smooth curve was then drawn through the average positions of the remaining points and from this curve were taken off new wire diameters corresponding to existing sieve openings   From subsequent conferences with manufacturers it was learned that these revised wire diameters were more suitable for weaving the several grades of cloth than those commonly employed and that the use of them would tend to improve the uniformity of cloth   It was learned further that any desired size of wire was as easily produced in the wire drawing process as the stock sizes, and that a special reed was as easily constructed as any other reed of similar fineness   In short there were no real obstacles to the manufacture of wire cloth based on the original, mathematically exact, series of openings, woven with wire that was most suitable for the purpose

In view of the foregoing information it was the consensus of opinion among the several sections of the Bureau of Standards concerned with the use of testing sieves that the 1916 specifications should be so revised as to make the proposed series of testing sieves as nearly ideal as practical limitations would permit   It was also suggested that the term "mesh" be abandoned in connection with the proposed sieves as superfluous and misleading, and that some simpler designation than the decimal size of the openings be selected for the individual sieves that would indicate their position in the series and be readily carried in mind   This latter suggestion was very easily met by giving each sieve an arbitrary number which was approximately that of the number of meshes per lineal inch and, therefore familiar to all users of sieves

The abandonment of all direct reference to "mesh" in both specifications and tolerances was unquestionably a step in the right direction, since it was thus possible to allow considerable latitude in the choice of wire and still retain the desired openings   Revised and simplified specifications embodying the proposed changes were then submitted to the manufacturers for approval   There were found to be no objections from a manufacturing standpoint, and thereafter the revised specifications were resubmitted to the participants in the original conference, and to others who were known or believed to be interested in the subject   The approval of the revised specifications was nearly unanimous, but pending the action of a number of committees of the American Society for Testing Materials, the new series of sieves, which will probably be referred to as the U S Standard Sieve Series, has not yet been formally adopted

The specifications for the new sieves are as follows

SPECIFICATIONS FOR SIEVES OF THE U S STANDARD SIEVE SERIES

*Paragraph 1*—Wire cloth for standard sieves shall be woven (not twilled except that the cloth of the No 230 ( 062 mm ), the No 270 ( 053 mm ) and the No 325 ( 044 mm ) sieves may be twilled until further notice) from brass bronze, or other suitable wire and mounted on the frames without distortion   To prevent the material which is being sieved from catching in the joint between the cloth and the frame the joint shall be smoothly filled with solder, or so made that the material will not catch

*Paragraph 2*—The opening of any given sieve should be that given in Column 2 of the attached table, and shall not differ from this amount by more than the 'Tolerance in average opening" given in Column 6

The diameter of the wires of the cloth of any given sieve should be that given in Column 4 of the attached table, and the average diameter of the wires shall not differ from this amount by more than "Tolerance in wire diameter" given in Column 7.

No opening between adjacent parallel wires shall be greater than the nominal width of opening for that sieve by more than the "Tolerance in maximum opening" given in Column 8 of the attached table

*Paragraph 3*—The Bureau of Standards also reserves the right to reject sieves for obvious imperfections in the sieve cloth or its mounting as, for example, punctured loose or wavy cloth, imperfections in soldering etc

With reference to the accompanying Table 1 it will be noted that the complete series contains 31 sieves, the openings having the fixed ratio of the fourth root of 2, or 1 189  The reason for having so many sieves is to make the series applicable to all requirements, and it is not expected that any one industry will require all the sieves  There has been no attempt to carry the series beyond the No  2½ sieve, for the actual sizes of openings

TABLE 1 —U S STANDARD SIEVE SERIES

| Sieve No | Sieve Opening (mm ) | Sieve Opening (in ) | Wire Diameter (mm ) | Wire Diameter (in ) | Tolerance in Average Opening (per cent) | Tolerance in Wire Diameter (per cent) | Tolerance in Maximum Opening (per cent) | Mesh per cm | Mesh per in |
|---|---|---|---|---|---|---|---|---|---|
| 2½ | 8 00 | 0 31ɔ | 1 85 | 0 073 | 1 | 5 | 10 | 1 | 2 6 |
| 3 | 6 72 | 0 265 | 1 65 | 0 065 | 1 | 5 | 10 | 1 2 | 3 0 |
| 3½ | 5 66 | 0 223 | 1 45 | 0 057 | 1 | 5 | 10 | 1 1 | 3 6 |
| 4 | 4 76 | 0 187 | 1 27 | 0 050 | 1 | 5 | 10 | 1 7 | 4 2 |
| 5 | 4 00 | 0 157 | 1 12 | 0 044 | 1 | 5 | 10 | 2 | 5 0 |
| 6 | 3 36 | 0 132 | 1 02 | 0 040 | 1 | 5 | 10 | 2 3 | 5 8 |
| 7 | 2 83 | 0 111 | 0 92 | 0 036 | 1 | 5 | 10 | 2 7 | 6 8 |
| 8 | 2 38 | 0 094 | 0 84 | 0 033 | 2 | 5 | 10 | 3 | 7 9 |
| 10 | 2 00 | 0 079 | 0 76 | 0 030 | 2 | 5 | 10 | 3 5 | 9 2 |
| 12 | 1 68 | 0 066 | 0 69 | 0 027 | 2 | 5 | 10 | 4 | 10 8 |
| 11 | 1 41 | 0 0557 | 0 61 | 0 024 | 2 | 5 | 10 | 5 | 12 5 |
| 16 | 1 19 | 0 0468 | 0 54 | 0 021 | 2 | 5 | 10 | 6 | 11 7 |
| 18 | 1 00 | 0 0394 | 0 48 | 0 0187 | 2 | 5 | 10 | 7 | 17 2 |
| 20 | 0 84 | 0 0331 | 0 42 | 0 0165 | 3 | 5 | 25 | 8 | 20 2 |
| 25 | 0 71 | 0 0278 | 0 37 | 0 0146 | 3 | 5 | 25 | 9 | 23 6 |
| 30 | 0 59 | 0 0234 | 0 33 | 0 0129 | 3 | 5 | 25 | 11 | 27 5 |
| 35 | 0 50 | 0 0197 | 0 29 | 0 0113 | 3 | 5 | 25 | 13 | 32 3 |
| 40 | 0 42 | 0 0166 | 0 25 | 0 0098 | 3 | 5 | 25 | 15 | 37 9 |
| 45 | 0 35 | 0 0139 | 0 22 | 0 0085 | 3 | 5 | 25 | 18 | 44 7 |
| 50 | 0 30 | 0 0117 | 0 188 | 0 0074 | 4 | 10 | 40 | 20 | 52 4 |
| 60 | 0 25 | 0 0098 | 0 162 | 0 0061 | 4 | 10 | 40 | 24 | 61 7 |
| 70 | 0 21 | 0 0083 | 0 140 | 0 0055 | 4 | 10 | 40 | 29 | 72 5 |
| 80 | 0 177 | 0 0070 | 0 119 | 0 0047 | 4 | 10 | 40 | 31 | 85 5 |
| 100 | 0 149 | 0 0059 | 0 102 | 0 0040 | 4 | 10 | 40 | 40 | 101 |
| 120 | 0 125 | 0 0049 | 0 086 | 0 0034 | 4 | 10 | 40 | 47 | 120 |
| 140 | 0 105 | 0 0041 | 0 071 | 0 0029 | 5 | 15 | 60 | 56 | 143 |
| 170 | 0 088 | 0 0035 | 0 063 | 0 0025 | 5 | 15 | 60 | 66 | 167 |
| 200 | 0 074 | 0 0029 | 0 053 | 0 0021 | 5 | 15 | 60 | 79 | 200 |
| 230 | 0 062 | 0 0025 | 0 046 | 0 0018 | 5 | 15 | 60 | 93 | 233 |
| 270 | 0 053 | 0 0021 | 0 041 | 0 0016 | 5 | 15 | 60 | 106 | 270 |
| 325 | 0 041 | 0 0017 | 0 036 | 0 0014 | 5 | 15 | 60 | 125 | 323 |

NOTE —In order to utilize cloth now on the market it will be permissible until notice is given to the contrary  to use wire whose diameter is within a tolerance of 10 per cent for the first three groups and 20 per cent for the last two groups

of coarser sieves than this can readily be determined by the user  The arbitrary designation numbers were selected to suggest approximately the number of meshes per linear inch, as previously explained  The sieves fall naturally into five groups, seven in the first group and six in each of the others  In any one group the tolerances are the same, and it will be noted that the designation numbers can readily be carried in mind in relation to these groups  The numbers in the first group are necessarily irregular, but run up to No. 7, which is the number of sieves in that group  The second group contains the successive even numbers from 8 to 18, the third multiples of 5 from 20 to 45, and the fourth and fifth multiples of 10, which are easily remembered

While the sieves are based on the millimeter opening and for convenience will be certified in metric units, it need make little difference to the manufacturer or user whether he prefers to employ the metric or English dimensions  For ordinary purposes the user will need to select only every other sieve or every fourth sieve in the series, and it is a peculiarity of the series that every fourth sieve beginning with the first will give even multiples or even fractions of a millimeter, while every fourth sieve beginning with the second will give approximately even fractions of an inch   Thus the No 3 sieve has an opening very nearly ¼ in , the No 6 sieve an opening very nearly ⅛ in  and so on

It is another peculiarity of the series that the subdivision of the millimeter happened to land on the opening of the present standard 200 mesh sieve, although it may be pointed out that the specified tolerance in opening for this sieve is somewhat different from that in the existing specifications   In fact the tolerances in the new specifications may have to be modified somewhat as experience with the new sieves accumulates   As stated in the note accompanying the table, a larger tolerance in wire diameter will be permitted until it has been established that this is no longer necessary

The accompanying diagram contains a plot of the new sieve series, together with the existing standard sieves, and also the sieves of the Tyler Screen Scale   The data for these sieves are given in Tables II, III, and IV   As previously explained the wire diameters are plotted vertically and sieve openings horizontally   Since the tolerances in wire diameters and sieve openings are definite for the new standard series these tolerances are represented on the diagram by dotted rectangles   Any point falling outside these rectangles represents a sieve which would not meet the specifications for the new sieves but it is to be noted that the tolerance rectangles are based on the data given in the table and not on the larger tolerances for wire diameter as given in the footnote   The diagram shows very clearly the irregularities in the wire diameters of the existing standards and also in the Tyler sieves

On the other hand, the diagram shows that the great majority of the sieves here plotted come within the tolerances for opening, and would, therefore, be usable sieves of the standard series, but not all of these could be certified as conforming to these standards   It may be remarked that, at the present time, little is known of the effect of the size of wire on the sieving performance of sieves having the same size openings, except that sieves with too coarse wire become badly clogged in use, and those having too light wire are more easily damaged   It is hoped that tests of the new sieves in comparison with existing sieves will give definite information on this point

In conclusion attention may be called to the fact that the majority of the Tyler Screen Scale sieves nominally conform to the new specifications

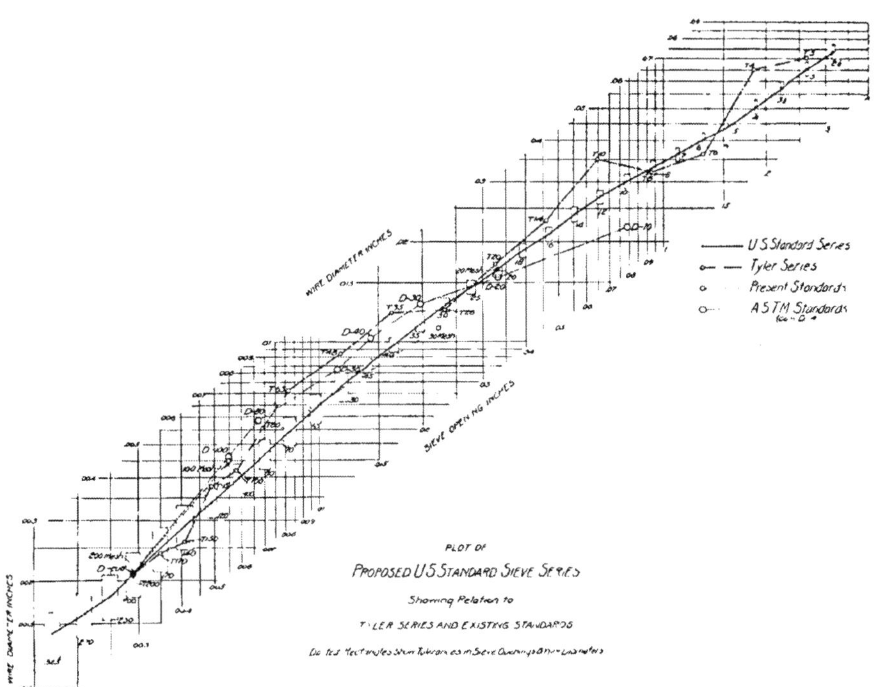

WIRE DIAMETER INCHES
SIEVE OPENING INCHES
WIRE DIAMETER INCHES
U S Standard Series
Tyler Series
Present Standards
A S T M Standards
PLOT OF
PROPOSED U S STANDARD SIEVE SERIES
Showing Relation to
TYLER SERIES AND EXISTING STANDARDS
Dotted Rectangles Show Tolerances in Sieve Openings and Wire Diameters

Since the Tyler openings are based on the present standard 200 sieve opening, and the latter is included in the new series, the sieve openings in the two series must run together, and this is clearly shown in the diagram Some of the wire diameters in the Tyler sieves differ considerably from those of the new standards, enough to throw out four or five, under the present tolerances  The Newark Wire Cloth Co, Newark, N J, which

#### Table II—Standard Sand and Cement Sieves

| Sieve No | Sieve Opening (in ) | Wire Diameter (in ) | Tolerance in Wire Diameter |
|---|---|---|---|
| 20 | 0 0335 | 0 0165 | ±0 0005 |
| 30 | 0 0223 | 0 0110 | ±0 0005 |
| 100 | 0 0055 | 0 0045 | ±0 0003 |
| 200 | 0 0029 | 0 0021 | ±0 0002 |

Taken from Bureau of Standards Circular 39 )

#### Table III—A S T M Standard Sieves

| Mesh Designation | Unit of Measure | Actual Mesh | Opening | Wire Diameter | Permissible Variations | |
|---|---|---|---|---|---|---|
| | | | | | Mesh | Diameter |
| 10 | cm | 3 9 | 0 200 | 0 056 | ±0 04 | ±0 005 |
| | in | 9 9 | 0 079 | 0 022 | ±0 1 | ±0 002 |
| 20 | cm | 8 | 0 085 | 0 040 | ±0 2 | ±0 0015 |
| | in | 20 3 | 0 0335 | 0 0157 | ±0 5 | ±0 0006 |
| 30 | cm | 12 0 | 0 050 | 0 033 | ±0 1 | ±0 0012 |
| | in | 30 5 | 0 0197 | 0 0130 | ±1 0 | ±0 0005 |
| 40 | cm | 16 | 0 036 | 0 026 | ±0 6 | ±0 0010 |
| | in | 40 6 | 0 0142 | 0 0102 | ±1 5 | ±0 0004 |
| 50 | cm | 20 | 0 029 | 0 021 | ±0 8 | ±0 0010 |
| | in | 50 8 | 0 0111 | 0 0083 | ±2 | ±0 0004 |
| 80 | cm | 31 | 0 017 | 0 015 | ±1 | ±0 0008 |
| | in | 78 7 | 0 0067 | 0 0059 | ±3 | ±0 0003 |
| 100 | cm | 39 | 0 014 | 0 0116 | ±1 | ±0 0008 |
| | in | 99 1 | 0 0055 | 0 0046 | ±3 | ±0 0003 |
| 200 | cm | 79 | 0 0074 | 0 0053 | ±3 | ±0 0005 |
| | in | 200 7 | 0 0029 | 0 0021 | ±8 | ±0 0002 |

Taken from 1918 A S T M Standards p 663 )

made a very commendable and successful effort to produce the finer mesh cloth when the European supplies were cut off by the war, has undertaken the manufacture of the new sieves, and some of them are already available  Before the end of the year the sieves of this series necessary for all ordinary testing purposes should be on the market  Other manufacturers have signified their willingness to produce the new sieves, and in the course of the next few months it is hoped that the majority will be in a position to furnish sieves under these specifications

## TABLE IV —TYLER SCREEN SCALE SIEVES

| Sieve No. or Mesh | Sieve Opening (mm.) | Sieve Opening (in.) | Wire Diameter (in.) |
|---|---|---|---|
| 3 | 6 680 | 0 263 | 0 070 |
| 4 | 4 699 | 0 185 | 0 065 |
| 6 | 3.327 | 0 131 | 0 036 |
| 8 | 2 362 | 0 093 | 0 032 |
| 10 | 1 651 | 0 065 | 0 035 |
| 14 | 1 168 | 0 046 | 0 025 |
| 20 | 0 833 | 0 0328 | 0 0172 |
| 28 | 0 589 | 0 0232 | 0 0125 |
| 35 | 0 417 | 0 0164 | 0 0122 |
| 48 | 0 295 | 0 0116 | 0 0092 |
| 65 | 0 208 | 0 0082 | 0.0072 |
| 80 | 0 175 | 0 0069 | 0 0056 |
| 100 | 0 147 | 0 0058 | 0 0042 |
| 115 | 0 124 | 0 0049 | 0 0038 |
| 150 | 0 104 | 0 0041 | 0 0026 |
| 170 | 0 088 | 0 0035 | 0 0024 |
| 200 | 0 074 | 0 0029 | 0 0021 |

(Taken from Tyler Catalogue 36 )

# PRESSURE OF CONCRETE AGAINST FORMS

## By Carl B. Smith*

The cost of forms for concrete work constitutes in many cases a rather large percentage of the total cost of the finished structure and this cost can only be kept low by rationally studied design methods. In so many cases the form is not designed but is merely laid out by guess and constructed by the carpenter with the result that an unwarranted amount of lumber has been used to prevent failure or spreading. The dimensions and the spacing of the supports and braces should have careful attention to secure sufficient stiffness and ample strength. The sheathing and bracing should be so proportioned as to secure ample stiffness against springing and misalignment. Mere strength without ample stiffness and rigidity is not sufficient for good work.

The proper design of forms cannot be concluded without knowing the lateral and vertical pressures of plastic concrete against the forms. To secure this information the U S Bureau of Public Roads has made a few tests which seem to accord in general with the results obtained by others†, but which go further in indicating the values of some of the factors influencing the results. At the present time sufficient data have not been obtained to make any final statement as to the law of pressure of concrete and the effect on each factor but rather than hold these data longer with the expectation of making them more complete at some future date, they are now offered with the desire that they may serve to make a little more definite the usual practice in the design of concrete forms, also that they may suggest a needed field of investigation for other experimenters.

The series of tests presented in this paper were carried out by W E Rosengarten in the laboratory of the research section of the Bureau of Public Roads, located at the Arlington Experimental Farm near Washington. The field tests were made during the construction of the walls and columns of a reinforced concrete building.

The apparatus used to measure the concrete pressures were cells and gages similar to those described in the 'Proceedings of the American Society for Testing Materials 1917 page 641, and used for the past few years by this laboratory in measuring earth pressures behind retaining walls and under fills. Details of the instrument are shown in Fig 1. It consists essentially of an air tight metal cell having a circular weighing face 10 sq in in area. The concrete pressures against the face of the cell are balanced by admitting compressed air to the inside of the cell. When

---

* Senior Assistant Testing Engineer, U S Bureau of Public Roads

† Design of Concrete Forms R A Sherwin Eng Record Feb 26 6 278, Pressure of Concrete on Forms F R Shunk, Eng News Sept 9 1909, p 289, Pressure of Wet Concrete on the Sides of Column Forms, A B McDaniel and N B Grover, Eng News, May 18, 1916, p 933

the pressures are balanced an electrical contact is broken which extinguishes a light and indicates that the pressure shown on the gage connected with the air pipes is equal to the pressure of the concrete. Tests on these cells show them to be accurate considerably beyond that necessary for these tests, and that the movement of the face is less than one ten thousandth of an inch to break contact, thus making the cell admirably suited for tests on pressures exerted by granular materials, soils, mud and concrete.

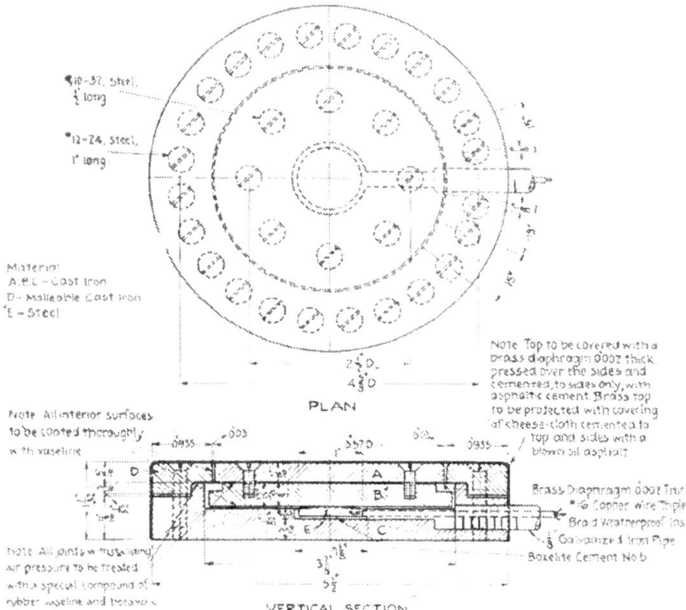


FIG. 1.—DIAPHRAGM CELL FOR DETERMINING SOIL PRESSURE.

Several other experimenters have attempted to obtain such data, but some have been greatly handicapped by not having a suitable apparatus for determining the concrete pressures. Any scheme for determining the pressure values that depends upon a movement of the concrete at the time of making the readings is evidently not reliable. The values desired are the static pressures of concrete against an immovable surface, and not the pressures necessary to stop a moving mass of concrete, nor to start a movement of the mass. And any scheme requiring first the disturbance or movement of the mass before making the pressure readings is also undesirable.

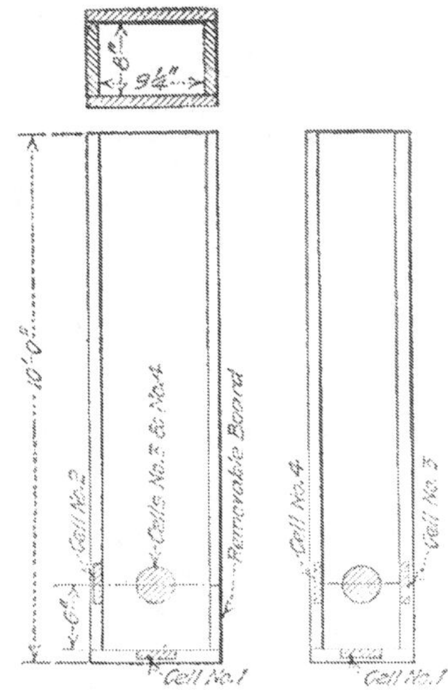


FIG. 2.—FORM USED IN TESTS OF PRESSURE OF CONCRETE.

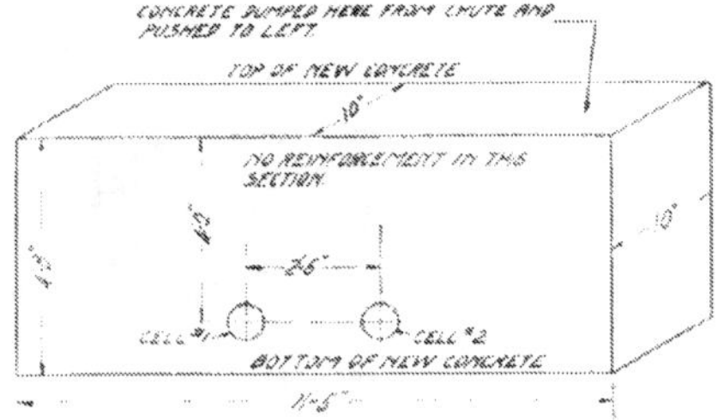


FIG. 3.—LOCATION OF PRESSURE CELLS NO. 1 AND 2 DURING LABORATORY CONSTRUCTION

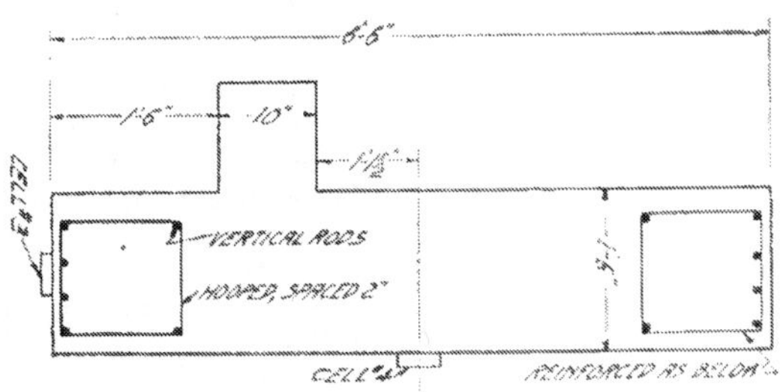

The arrangement of the pressure cells and the concrete form used during the laboratory tests is shown in Fig. 2 and photographs. The form was built of 2 in. planks giving an inside horizontal cross-section of 7.8 x 9.1 in., and a height of 10 ft. Four cells were placed in the form, with the weighing face flush with the inside of the forms. Cell No. 1 was placed in

### TABLE I.—LABORATORY TESTS OF PRESSURES OF CONCRETE AGAINST FORMS.

| Mix. | Aggregate. | Consistency. | Temperature, deg. C. | | Rate of Pouring, (ft. per hr.) | Maximum Pressure. | | Head at Maximum Pressure. | | Time of Maximum Pressure, Min. | | Curve in Fig. |
|---|---|---|---|---|---|---|---|---|---|---|---|---|
| | | | Air | Water | | Vert. | Lat. | Vert. | Lat. | Vert. | Lat. | |
| 1:3:3½ | | | 23 | | 1.5 | 1.15 | 68 | 2.5 | 2.9 | 90 | 90 | |
| 1:2½:3½ | | | 26 | | 2.7 | 1.45 | 90 | 3.7 | 3.5 | 78 | 61 | No. 9 |
| 1:2½:3½ | | | | | 3.3 | 1.65 | 73 | 3.3 | 2.5 | 49 | 44 | |
| 1:3:6 | Cem. 13820 | Quaky | 19 | 21 | 1.63 | 15.5 | .52 | 2.77 | 1.70 | 79 | 61 | |
| 1:3:6 | | " (forms) | 15 | 18 | 3.32 | 1.65 | .43 | 4.15 | 2.53 | 70 | 50 | |
| 1:3:6 | | " (Dry) | 19 | 20 | 6.72 | 1.07 | .21 | 6.56 | 3.80 | 57 | 37 | |
| 1:3:6 | | " | 17 | 19 | 11.26 | 1.35 | .41 | 10.00 | 5.12 | 48 | 29 | |
| 1:3:6 | | " | 17 | 21 | 9 ft. in 1 batch | .86 | .35 | 9.28 | 8.78 | 10 | 10 | |
| 1:3:6 | Grav. 13822 | Quaky | 21 | 19 | 1.78 | .98 | 90 | 1.71 | 2.08 | 36 | 66 | |
| 1:3:6 | New lot cem. | " 1st test (forms wet) | 18 | 20 | 3.46 | 2.02 | .85 | 3.72 | 3.22 | 37 | 37 | |
| 1:3:6 | " | " | 16 | 19 | 7.08 | 2.53 | 1.40 | 5.50 | 5.00 | 49 | 49 | No. 10 |
| 1:2:4 | Grav. 13822 | Quaky 14 in. dia. | 19 | 18 | 1.75 | 2.27 | 1.50 | 3.46 | 2.65 | 96 | 86 | |
| 1:2:4 | New cells | " 13 in. " | 24 | 18 | 3.60 | 2.35 | 1.16 | 4.50 | 3.16 | 66 | 56 | No. 8 |
| 1:2:4 | " | " 13 in. " | 23 | 23 | 7.32 | 1.78 | 1.21 | 4.55 | 4.05 | 37 | 37 | |
| 1:1½:3 | Grav. 13822 | Quaky | 21 | 24 | 1.88 | 2.73 | 1.89 | 3.99 | 3.45 | 106 | 106 | |
| 1:1½:3 | | " 12 in. diam. | 20 | 17 | 3.84 | 3.19 | 2.40 | 4.79 | 4.29 | 66 | 66 | No. 7 |
| 1:1½:3 | " | " 13 in. diam | 17 | 17 | 7.50 | 4.60 | 3.16 | 7.10 | 6.60 | 60 | 60 | |
| 1:2:4 | Fine gravel No. 14192 | Quaky (Dry) 10½ in. di. 9½ in. Sl. | 25 | 18 | 1.78 | 1.75 | .98 | 2.09 | 1.87 | 45 | 56 | |
| 1:2:4 | " | 11½ in. di. 9½ in. Sl. | 27 | 18 | 7.35 | 2.41 | 1.95 | 3.35 | 2.85 | 28 | 28 | No. 8 |
| 1:1½:3 | Grav. 13822 | Sloppy 12½ in. dia. 3 in. Sl. | 16 | 15 | 1.84 | 2.37 | 1.17 | 3.05 | 2.85 | 75 | 75 | |
| 1:1½:3 | This test and all previous er. grav. 13822 | Sloppy 14 in. dia. 8½ in. Sl. | 17 | 15 | 7.60 | 3.31 | 2.05 | 4.80 | 4.30 | 38 | 38 | No. 7 |
| 1:2:4 | 1st test fine grav. 14192 | Sloppy 17 in. dia. 9½ in. Sl. | 18 | 17 | 1.86 | 2.75 | 1.63 | 3.38 | 2.85 | 85 | 85 | |
| 1:2:4 | " | Sloppy 16 in. dia. 9½ in. Sl. | 19 | 17 | 7.44 | 1.97 | 1.19 | 3.33 | 2.83 | 27 | 27 | No. 8 |

the center of the base and indicated the vertical pressure. Cell No. 2 was set in the center of the rear wall of the form. Cells Nos. 3 and 4 were placed in the center of the right and left side walls of the forms respectively. The centers of these cells for obtaining the lateral pressure were all 6 in. above the base. Air control pipes leading from all cells were arranged in order, with connections and nipples conveniently located for taking the readings on the four cells very quickly.

The materials for the concrete used in the tests were carefully weighed and mixed by hand. Immediately upon completing the mixing the concrete was shoveled into buckets and dumped into the top of the forms. The mixing floor and the wood forms were well wetted before the test was begun. The concrete was tamped on top by the use of a long

FIG. 5.—PRESSURE GAGES APPLIED TO      FIG. 6.—TEST FORM IN LABORATORY.
COLUMN FORM IN BUILDING.

stick having a 2 x 6 in. foot on the lower end. The outside of the forms were also vibrated by striking with a heavy hammer. The height to which the concrete stood in the column form was then measured, and the pressures on the bottom and three side cells were immediately read and recorded. The batches were varied in size so that when a new batch was added each 10 minutes the head of concrete in the form would increase at the rate desired. Readings were taken on the pressure cells immediately after placing the concrete, and again about 5 minutes later or shortly before placing the next batch of concrete

The air and the mixing water temperatures were recorded each day tests were run. Slump tests of the concrete were made to determine the consistency used in each test, and are recorded as inches slump or where very wet as inches diameter of the mass. Fresh batches of concrete were added every 10 minutes until after the pressures on the cells had passed a maximum and indicated a decided decrease in pressure. The tabulated data and results of these laboratory tests are shown in Table I also plotted in Figs 7-10, inclusive

Several field tests were run in addition to the laboratory tests described above during the construction of a reinforced concrete building at the Arlington Farm. The pressure cells were inserted in the wall and

Table II.—Field Test of Pressure of Concrete Against Forms

| Mix | Consistency | Temperature, deg C | | Rate of Pouring ft per hr | Distance Cell to Opposite Side of Form | Maximum Pressure Lateral | Head at Maximum Pressure Lateral | Time at Maximum Pressure Mins Lateral |
|---|---|---|---|---|---|---|---|---|
| | | Air | Water | | | | | |
| 1 2 4 | Sloppy | 13 | 13 | 12 0 | 8 in | 1 9, | 3 25 | 17 |
| | | | | 12 0 | 8 in | 2 45 | 3 25 | 17 |
| 1 2 4 | Sloppy | 14 | 15 | 20 0 | 3 in to reinf | 2 45 stopped | 4 62 | 23 |
| | | | | 20 0 | 18 in | 3 90 pour | 4 62 | 23 |
| 1 2 4 | Sloppy | 23 | 23 | 9 0 | 18x28 in hole | 2 2 | 3 0 | 20 |
| 1 2 4 | | 23 | 23 | 12 5 | $9\frac{1}{2}$ in | 1 85 | 2 3 | 11 |
| 1 2 4 | | 23 | 23 | 10 6 | $9\frac{1}{4}$ in | 1 15 | 2 3 | 13 |

column forms, as shown in Figs 3-5, and pressure readings taken at the time the concrete was being poured. The concrete was machine mixed raised in an elevator and directed into the forms through a system of chutes. It was then spaded or tamped with a stick having a small blade on the end. The concrete was a 1 2 4 mix river gravel being used for the coarse aggregate, and the consistency rather sloppy flowing readily around steel reinforcing. The results from these field tests conform favorably with those obtained from the laboratory and are shown in Table II and Fig 11

The results shown by these experiments indicate that the fundamental pressure of concrete against the form is about 1 lb per sq in for the first 1 ft of head. However, this is by no means all that should be said. A study of the results reported by others and those obtained from this series of tests show that the following factors have an influence upon the pressure, namely: (1) Rate of filling the forms, (2) cross-sectional area of the forms, (3) consistency of the concrete, (4) amount of cement in the concrete, (5) temperature of the concrete and the time of set of the cement, and (6) character of the fine and the coarse aggregate

Sufficient data are not yet available to make final statements as to the law by which each of these factors influence the pressure of the concrete against the form. The results do show that the initial pressure under small heads is equal to the hydrostatic pressure of a liquid having the approximate density or weight of the concrete, that is, approximately 1 lb.

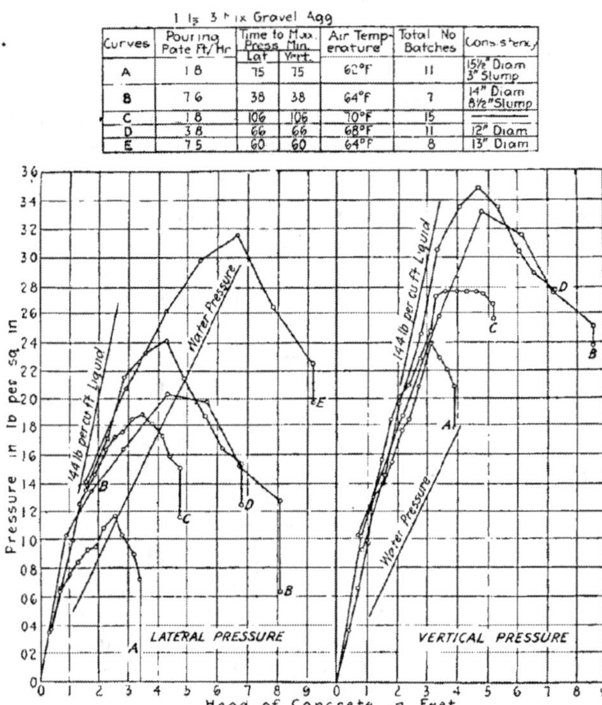



| Curves | Pouring Rate Ft/Hr | Time to Max. Press. Min. | | Air Temperature | Total No Batches | Consistency |
|---|---|---|---|---|---|---|
| | | Lat. | Vert. | | | |
| A | 1 8 | 75 | 75 | 62°F | 11 | 15½" Diam 3" Slump |
| B | 7 6 | 38 | 38 | 64°F | 7 | 14" Diam 8½" Slump |
| C | 1 8 | 106 | 106 | 70°F | 15 | |
| D | 3 8 | 66 | 66 | 68°F | 11 | 12" Diam |
| E | 7 5 | 60 | 60 | 64°F | 8 | 13" Diam |



FIG 7.—CURVES OF PRESSURE OF $1.1\frac{1}{2}.3$ CONCRETE IN LABORATORY TESTS.

per sq. in., or 144 lb per sq ft for the first foot head. As pouring is continued this pressure, however, soon falls below the straight line hydrostatic pressure and the amount of this deviation depends upon one or more of the factors mentioned above.

It is important to notice that the results prove that if filling is continued indefinitely the lateral pressures near the base of the form finally reach a maximum value and then decrease gradually to zero, regardless of the fact that fresh concrete is continually added above. The vertical pressures are in all cases greater than the lateral pressures—they decrease in value after a maximum has been attained, but not to zero. The total weight of the concrete mass in ordinary construction is not supported entirely upon the bottom of the form, but because of the roughness and

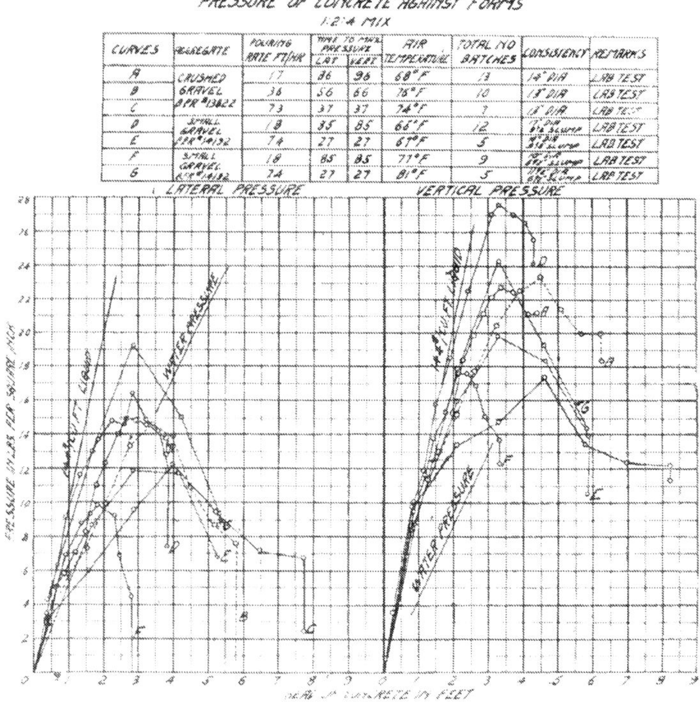


FIG. 8.—CURVES OF PRESSURE OF 1:2:4 CONCRETE IN LABORATORY TESTS.

friction against the sides the planking takes part of the weight or vertical pressure. Of course, for wide and shallow masses of concrete, such as floor slabs, the vertical pressure is equal to the weight of the concrete.

## SUMMARY.

A summary of the data at hand seems to lead to the following conclusions regarding the effect of the various influencing factors.

(1) The maximum pressure exerted upon the forms increases as the rate of filling increases. At a slow rate of about 1 ft. per hour the press-

me is approximately 1 lb per sq in but as the rate increases beyond this value the pressure increases approximately as the 0.3 power of the rate

(2) Field tests, which were made in places where the distance between the form walls differed indicate that the maximum pressures obtained increase slightly with the mass of the concrete when the consistency is wet and sloppy This conclusion probably does not hold in the case of dry mixes Reinforcing just inside the form tends to slightly decrease the pressures, but probably this effect would be neglected in determining the final pressures for use in design

| Curves | Pouring Rate, Ft/Hr | Time to Max Press Min | | Air Temperature | Total No Batches |
|---|---|---|---|---|---|
| | | Lat | vert | | |
| A | 15 | 90 | 90 | 74°F | 9 |
| B | 27 | 61 | 78 | 80°F | 10 |
| C | 33 | 44 | 49 | | 14 |

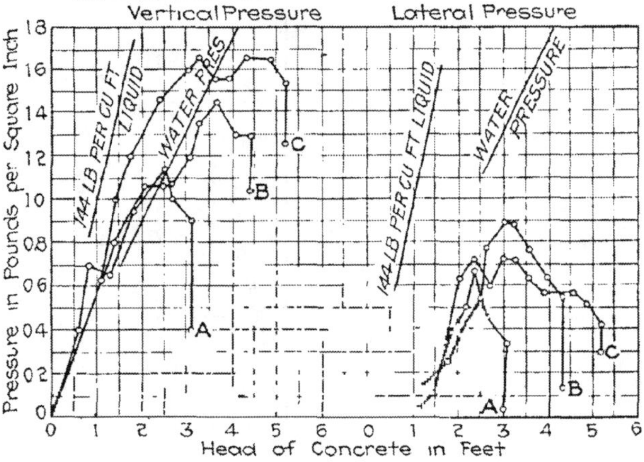

FIG 9 CURVES OF 1 2¼ 3¾ CONCRETE IN LABORATORY TESTS

(3) The results show in general that the maximum pressure was increased as the consistency of the concrete was made drier within the limit of workability This is probably different from what might be expected but the tests show it to be the case It is probably due to the fact that under the usual conditions of placing dry concrete it requires more tamping which, because of its dryness, seems to develop a permanent wedging action between the particles In the case of wet or sloppy concrete this wedging action does not exist as we have approximately a static fluid pressure For low heads the dry concrete (when tamped as usual) will give the greater lateral pressure, but for heads of 4 ft or

more and within the time when initial set becomes an influencing factor the sloppy mixtures give the greater pressure. The average increase of pressure due to the effect of dry mixtures seems to be 0.3 lb. per sq. in. for each inch decrease in the standard slump test less than a 5-in. slump.

(4) The richness of the mix also affects the maximum pressures obtained. The richer the mix the greater the maximum pressure, the average increase being 0.12 lb. per sq. in. for each percent increase in the ratio of the cement to the aggregate beyond 12 percent.

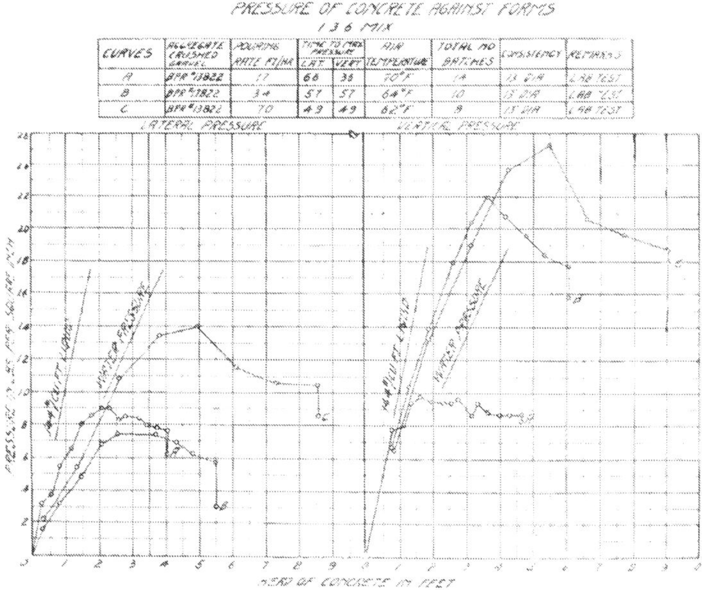


FIG. 10.—CURVES OF 1:3:6 CONCRETE IN LABORATORY TESTS.

(5) A decrease in the temperature of the concrete retards the set of the cement, and it is natural to suppose that this is the limiting factor in the maximum pressure obtained, since the pressure increases with the head until the cement takes a sufficient set to begin to support the overlying concrete. Therefore, as the temperature is reduced and the time of the set of the cement is increased the height of fill may be increased and thus produce or make possible a higher total pressure. Since the cement begins to set and stiffen in about 30 minutes, the maximum pressure is attained under whatever head of concrete may exist at this time. The

value for $H$, the head of concrete, to be used in the formula given below should not be greater than one-half the rate of fill; except where agitation

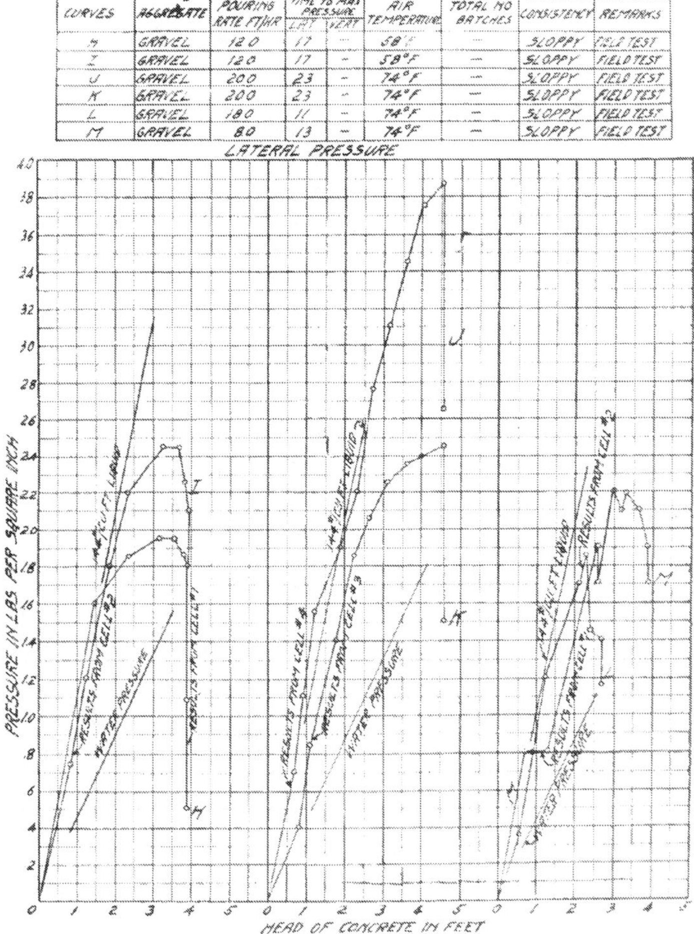



| CURVES | AGGREGATE | POURING RATE FT/HR | TIME TO MAX PRESSURE LAT | VERT | AIR TEMPERATURE | TOTAL NO BATCHES | CONSISTENCY | REMARKS |
|---|---|---|---|---|---|---|---|---|
| H | GRAVEL | 120 | 17 | — | 58°F | — | SLOPPY | FIELD TEST |
| I | GRAVEL | 120 | 17 | — | 58°F | — | SLOPPY | FIELD TEST |
| J | GRAVEL | 200 | 23 | — | 74°F | — | SLOPPY | FIELD TEST |
| K | GRAVEL | 200 | 23 | — | 74°F | — | SLOPPY | FIELD TEST |
| L | GRAVEL | 180 | 11 | — | 74°F | — | SLOPPY | FIELD TEST |
| M | GRAVEL | 80 | 13 | — | 74°F | — | SLOPPY | FIELD TEST |

FIG. 11. CURVES OF 1:2:4 CONCRETE IN FIELD TESTS.

is vigorous and continuous in a sloppy mix, then this ratio may be taken up to three-fourths.

An empirical formula, giving the lateral pressures required for use in the design for the investigation of the strength of concrete forms, and taking into account the above numerical factors, is

$$P = H^{0.2}R^{0.8} + 0.12C - 0.38$$

$P$ being the resultant lateral pressure in pounds per sq in., $R$, the rate of fill in feet per hour $H$, the head of concrete fill, $C$ the percent by volume of cement to the combined fine and coarse aggregate  and $S$, the consistency in inches of slump

The vertical pressure is obtained by adding $0.25H$ to the value of $P$ as found above  Except when the inside distance between the vertical sides of the form is greater than one half the depth of fill  then the value should be taken as equal to the weight of the concrete

In the practical application of this formula  as with all formulas there is abundant opportunity for the exercise of common sense and good judgment  The formula will give pressures somewhat higher than exact values  It shows the effect of continuous and vigorous agitation of the concrete mass only as this is introduced through good judgment in select ing the value for the head of concrete, $H$  For usual conditions $H$ may be taken as not greater than one half of $R$  For ordinary cement in cold weather, or when continuously and well agitated $H$ may be three fourths of $R$, when the filling is continuous beyond one hour  A second pouring on top of concrete that has been in place for 15 minutes or more does not add to the pressures already existing at the bottom of the fill

The values for $C$ may be taken as the next higher whole number in the percent of cement by volume as the required accuracy does not justify fractional percents  Values for $S$ may also be taken as whole numbers since the slump test is not accurate closer than 1 in.

The value of $P$ obtained by the formula is the lateral pressure against the form at the lowest point of the fill  Since the pressures are not uni form from top to bottom, but vary approximately as the ordinates of a parabola  the center of pressure or point of resultant pressure may be taken at 0.6 of the height of fill $H$, from the top

### EXAMPLES OF COMPUTING PRESSURE

The following examples may serve to show the use of the above formula

*Example I*   For reinforced mass concrete  Mix to be 1:3:5, con sistency rather sloppy, or 9 in. slump  the rate of fill $R$ to be 8 ft per hour  The total height of concrete filled within one hour, 7 ft  Since this concrete is placed from a chute in a large form  and men are continually walking around in it, the value to be chosen for $H$ is 6  or three-fourths of $R$  Then, substituting in the formula

$$P = 6^{0.2}8^{0.8} + (0.12 \times 13) - (0.3 \times 9)$$
$$P = 1.53 \text{ lb per sq in.}$$
$$\textit{The vertical pressure} = 7 \text{ lb per sq in.}$$

*Example II* For reinforced concrete column  Mix to be 1 2 4, consistency 8 in slump, rate of fill to be 24 ft per hour  Total height of column and final fill, 11 ft  made in one pouring  since this is done in less than 30 minutes the value for $H$ is 11  Substituting in the formula

$$P = 11^{0.2} 24^{0.3} + (0.12 \times 17) - (0.3 \times 8)$$
$$P = 3.83 \ lb \ per \ sq \ in$$
$$Vertical \ pressure = P + 0.25H = 6.58 \ lb \ per \ sq \ in$$

*Example III* For thin curtain walls and reinforced bulkheads  Mortar mix 1 5, consistency 8 in slump  rate of fill 20 ft per hour  Total height of fill in one pouring 14 ft  the value to be selected for $H$ should be 10  since that is the height of fill at 30 minutes when the effect of stiffening and set begins  Substituting we have

$$P = 10^{0.2} 20^{0.3} + (0.12 \times 20) - (0.3 \times 8)$$
$$P = 3.89 \ lb \ per \ sq \ in$$
$$Vertical \ pressure = P + 25H = 6.39 \ lb \ per \ sq \ in$$

*Example IV* For dry mix mass concrete  Mix to be 1 3 6, consistency, 3 in slump, rate of fill 6 ft per hour  distance between sides of form, 3 ft  total height of fill within 30 minutes 4 ft  Then,

$$P = 4^{0.2} 6^{0.3} + (0.12 \times 11) - (0.3 \times 3)$$
$$P = 2.68 \ lb \ per \ sq \ in$$
$$Vertical \ pressure = 4 \ lb \ per \ sq \ in$$

# NEW DEVELOPMENTS IN SURFACE TREATED CONCRETE AND STUCCO.

By J. C. Pearson* and J. J. Earley.†

The joint authorship of this paper requires a word of explanation. The writers have been closely associated by their membership on the Advisory Committee of the Bureau of Standards' Stucco Investigation,

FIG. 1.—SIXTEENTH ST. ENTRANCE TO MERIDIAN HILL PARK, WASHINGTON, D. C.
Architectural detail well executed in concrete.

and on the Committee on Treatment of Concrete Surfaces of this Institute. Both residing in Washington, they have had an unusual opportunity to study and discuss together the results obtained from the experimental work of the Bureau in concrete and stucco, as well as those from Mr. Earley's work in connection with his contracting business. These dis-

* U. S. Bureau of Standards, Washington, D. C.
† Architectural Sculptor, Washington, D. C.

cussions often led to the consideration of possibilities somewhat beyond the range of established practice, and, in fact, beyond the limitations of established theories relating to the gradation and proportioning of the ingredients of mortar and concrete. It was therefore natural that ideas were conceived which were too visionary to be of use to any committee, but nevertheless deemed worthy of further investigation on the writers' own account. If these ideas proved to have no value, no one would be the loser; if they did amount to anything, the results would be a contribution to our knowledge of stucco and concrete.

Hence it is a matter of some gratification to the authors to be able to describe these new developments in the treatment of concrete surfaces,

FIG. 2.— UPPER LEVEL OF MAIN ENTRANCE TO MERIDIAN HILL PARK.
Precast concrete tile balustrades, seats and planting boxes.

the success of which is due largely to scientific studies of the behavior of combinations of various sized particles, and the development of a technique adequate for the molding of these combinations of particles in any desired form and place.

Studies of the experimental stucco panels at the Bureau of Standards led to the general conclusion that by adherence to well-established practice, structurally sound and durable stucco could be secured, but that a great deal could be, or ought to be, done to improve its appearance. Crazing and map cracking are common to most stuccos, and are especially objectionable on surfaces of fine texture; the monotony of the cold grey cement color is objectionable, and is only partially relieved by the use of white cement and mortar colors; and finally the muddy appearance (due to

cement, or cement and pigment, being too much in evidence) is objectionable from an artistic standpoint. Consideration of these matters suggested at once the use of less cement, and it became evident that by
efforts in this direction improvement in appearance might be obtained.
The apparently insurmountable obstacle to this departure from usual
practice was, of course, the lack of plasticity in the leaner mixtures.
Various methods of overcoming this difficulty were considered, and some
experiments were made which indicated that a real improvement might

FIG. 32.—DETAIL OF ENTRANCE TO MERIDIAN HILL PARK.

Three textures are shown. Fine on the reveal of the arch, left; medium on the panel
of the wing wall, right; coarse on the rusticated blocks, center. The blocks are
precast and set, the wing wall is monolithic, poured in place, and the color is
uniform throughout.

be obtained by substituting fine inert material for a portion of the cement.
The easiest way to accomplish this result seemed to be by using blended
cements, that is, normal cements ground with a certain percentage of
sand, stone-screenings, or other suitable materials. These experiments
were never carried very far, however, for it did not seem possible that any
method which might be devised for retaining plasticity could bring about
the desired result, viz., the elimination of all the objectionable features
mentioned above.

Serious as was this lack of plasticity in the lean stucco mixtures,
it was, after all, something that could be overcome by *work*. This was

demonstrated by the fact that mixtures as lean as one part cement to six parts of stone-screenings were applied on some of the Bureau of Standards' panels, with excellent results. But the improvement in these panels as compared with some of the easier working combinations did not

FIG. 4.—GATE POSTS AT U. S. NAVAL HOSPITAL RESERVATION, WASHINGTON, D. C.

seem great enough to justify the increased cost of application. The question finally arose whether by careful attention to gradation of the aggregates this improvement in appearance might not be so enhanced that the cost would be a secondary consideration.

This idea came from the fact that Mr. Earley had succeeded in making complicated casts of concrete from specially graded aggregates in such manner that a very large percentage of the area of the treated surface (first wire brushed and then washed) was aggregate, and a very small percentage cement. Possibly due in part to the higher reflecting power of the surfaces of the exposed aggregates, the color of the concrete surfaces thus produced was determined almost wholly by the color of the aggregates, and only very slightly affected by the cement itself. A most convincing demonstration of this fact was obtained by constructing two con-

FIG. 5.—ENTRANCE TO AN ESTATE NEAR WASHINGTON.

crete slabs containing exactly the same proportions of specially graded aggregate, the one being mixed with grey cement, the other with white cement. After the surface treatment of brushing and washing had been applied, only an expert could have determined which slab contained the grey cement and which the white.

To digress still further for a moment, this method of obtaining permanent and very pleasing colors in concrete surfaces is such an important item in the development of the processes here described, that it is worthy of fuller explanation. Before color in concrete surfaces can be under artistic control, a technique must be developed which has for its medium the elements of the concrete itself. Although in problems involving appearance aggregate is by reason of its greater bulk the major element, and cement the minor, it is, nevertheless, the color of the cement which is the natural color of normal concrete. The reason for this is that the

FIG. 6. DETAIL OF ENTRANCE SHOWN IN FIG. 5.
Note the sharpness of the arrises of the moldings

cement is finely ground and deposits itself, paint-like, over the surfaces of the aggregates and colors the whole mass.

If, therefore, concrete is to receive its color from the cement paste, variation must be obtained by the addition of pigments to the cement following the well-established practice of mixing paints; but if the aggregate is to be the source of color, the concrete must be so designed and manipulated as to deposit in the surface the greatest possible amount of aggregate. Any great degree of success can hardly be expected in coloring concrete through the cement. The choice of colors is restricted by chemical reaction with the cement, which causes them to fade or change; depth of color is restricted by strength requirements of the concrete which limits very closely the amount of pigment which may be added to the cement. Therefore, with the choice of color limited by one requirement and the depth of color by another, the cement itself must remain dominant.

On the other hand, in coloring concrete through the aggregate all such restrictions are removed, and colors may be obtained from white to black through all the range of possible aggregates. An examination of

FIG. 7.—CONCRETE FLOWER POT.
Note the delicacy of form as compared with
the massive construction elsewhere illustrated.

drawings done in hard pastelles and of paintings of the impressionist school suggests a technique in coloring which is peculiarly adaptable to the coloring of concrete by means of the aggregate. In the pastelles tones are produced by hatching and cross-hatching with lines of pure color without blending on the surface of the drawing, in the paintings by spotting with pure colors one beside the other, and without blending. In both cases the tones are effected by the blending of the light rays reflected from the picture to the observer. Wonderful depth and clarity of tone are characteristics of this school of coloring, and in it are to be found a great deal of exact knowledge and valuable precedent. When this knowledge is translated in terms of concrete aggregates, it is obvious that if the aggregates are carefully selected and carefully placed, all the elements are present for the successful coloring of concrete surfaces. The results obtained in practice bear out the theory given above, and there is every reason to believe that the aggregate is the proper source of color for concrete.

Hence it was a most important conception that a similar result might be obtained with stucco. The success of this depended, first, upon securing

FIG. 8.—SOUTH PORTICO OF FIELD HOUSE IN EAST POTOMAC PARK, WASHINGTON, D. C.

The portico is of precast concrete. The building is of stucco on terra cotta tile. Both concrete and stucco are of the exposed aggregate type and are of the same color and texture.

a suitable gradation of the stucco aggregate, and, second, upon being able to apply such a mixture, once it were satisfactorily compounded. It was known at the onset that these mixtures would be harsh, therefore plasticity no longer played any part in the calculations.

The laboratory program was fairly simple. The plan consisted simply in working first with concrete mixes in miniature, in which the sizes of cement particles, sand particles and coarse aggregate particles were reduced from the normal sizes in the ratio of about 1:10, this being taken as the approximate ratio of the size of particles passing a No. 8 sieve to pebbles

FIG. 9.—DETAIL OF POTOMAC PARK FIELD HOUSE SHOWING EXCELLENCE OF TECHNIQUE IN THE BUILDING UP OF THE CORNER QUOINS.

1 in. in diameter. It was assumed that the density of such mixes would depend mainly on relative sizes of the component particles, with due allowance for the water content. If these mixes appeared to be satisfactory for

the purpose, it was assumed that any reduction within the 1:10 ratio would also be satisfactory, and the actual reduction to be employed in compounding any given stucco mixture of this type would be as slight as the requirements of texture and the difficulties of application would permit. To make a long story short these experiments in the laboratory with the

FIG. 10.—DETAIL OF SECONDARY PORCH, POTOMAC PARK FIELD HOUSE.

Cornice, columns and balustrade of precast concrete; base of monolithic concrete poured in place; walls of stucco on terra cotta tile; all surfaces of the same color and texture.

miniature concretes were very successful. Not the least important part of the laboratory work was the microscopic examination of the structures of these little concretes, which yielded many valuable suggestions for the gradation in size of particles, and for the proper proportions of the various sizes, to yield the desired effects in the treated surfaces.

The first attempt to apply the new product to a vertical wall was not wholly discouraging. Small areas were treated successfully, and eventually a terra-cotta tile pent house on one of the new laboratories of the Bureau of Standards was coated with the exposed aggregate stucco. This example was the forerunner of the work illustrated in this paper, and while it is not as free from imperfections as the more recent work, it has attracted most favorable notice. Fortunately, the mechanics who were selected for this work developed a real interest in the new type of finish, and subsequently a pride in the results of their work, which made for very rapid progress in the development of the methods of application and treatment. New requirements in thoroughness of mixing, consistency, and

FIG. 11.— DETAIL OF EXPOSED AGGREGATE STUCCO, POTOMAC PARK FIELD HOUSE.

control of the absorption of the undercoats were met, and other improvements in the general process were gradually introduced as essential parts of the routine. Not all of the problems have been solved, but there has been very gratifying progress in the comparatively short time that the new stucco has been applied commercially.

The illustrations accompanying this paper have been selected as typical of Mr. Earley's work in the vicinity of Washington, D. C. They are arranged in nearly chronological order and show the gradual improvement that is being made as experience accumulates.

Figs. 1, 2 and 3 are views of the concrete work at Meridian Hill Park, Washington, D. C. Fig. 1 is a general view of one of the main

entrances, the construction of which was described in the Proceedings of
this Institute in 1918. Fig. 2 is a view of the upper level of the entrance
shown in Fig. 1. The balustrade, seat and planting box are of precast
concrete containing Potomac River gravel as coarse aggregate, the concrete tile are fabricated from black trap rock. The detail of the entrance
shown in Fig. 3 illustrates the use of different textures for architectural

FIG. 12.—CENTER GATE, FORT LINCOLN
CEMETERY, PRECAST CONCRETE.

scale, but with no variation in color. The aggregate is Potomac River
gravel without additions or modification of any sort.

Fig. 4 is a view of the gate posts at the entrance to the grounds of
the U. S. Naval Hospital. The aggregate is Potomac River gravel, but
slightly modified to obtain a color harmonizing with that of the buildings
in the background.

Fig 5 and 6 are views of an entrance to a private estate. The aggregate used in these gate posts is crushed quartz of light buff, the color being heightened by occasional spots of red and green.

Fig. 7 is included to show the adaptability of surface-treated concrete to fine ornamental work. Attention is called to the delicacy of the beads, the depth of which is less than the dimensions of the crushed gravel aggregate. The pot is specially reinforced to withstand the pressure of roots.

Figs. 8, 9, 10 and 11 are views of the Potomac Park Field House. Fig. 8 shows a portion of the south wing of the structure, of which the

FIG. 12.— GATE LODGE AT FORT LINCOLN CEMETERY.
Exposed aggregate stucco on terra cotta tile. The uniformity in color and texture of the stucco surface is excellent.

stucco walls match the precast columns in color and texture. Fig. 9 shows a corner of the north wing upon which the quoins are well done in stucco. Fig. 10 is a detail which shows an interesting combination of precast work, monolithic concrete (poured in place), and stucco, all of the same color and texture. The capitals are interesting in that they are cast in one piece with all details complete. The surface treatment is applied to the undercuts as well as to the more exposed portions. Fig. 11 is a close view of the stucco surface. Attention is called to the close disposition of the larger pieces of aggregate and the evenness of the texture.

Figs. 12, 13 and 14 are views of the concrete work at Fort Lincoln Cemetery, as yet uncompleted. In Fig. 12 attention is called to the cap which is cast in one piece above the neck molding. In spite of difficult form work the moldings and arrises are sharp and well defined even in the deep recess. The color of the aggregate is such that from a moderate distance the structure resembles cut granite, but it is in no sense an imitation of granite. Fig. 13 shows a typical stucco treatment of the exposed aggregate type. The uniformity of texture and color is probably

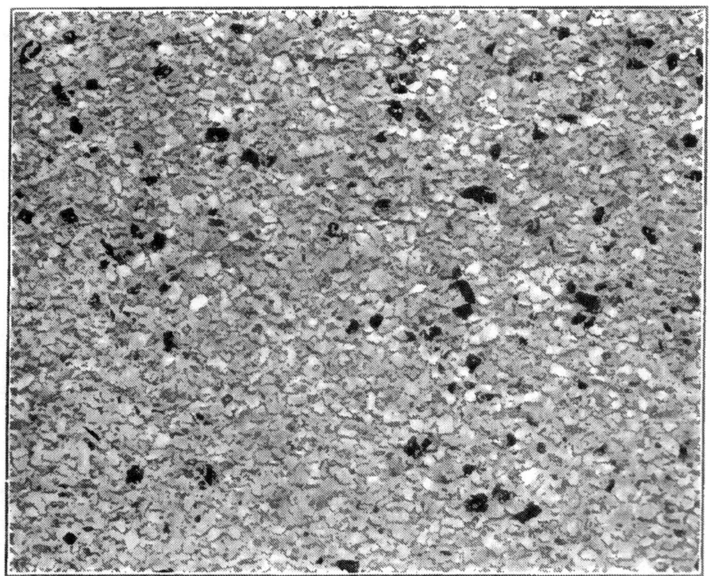

FIG. 14.—DETAIL OF EXPOSED AGGREGATE STUCCO, FORT LINCOLN CEMETERY.
Note the close proximity of the coarse aggregate which is the source of the remarkably clear color in this type of stucco finish.

superior to that obtainable with any other finish. Fig. 14 is interesting in showing the remarkable proximity of the stucco aggregate. In comparison with Fig. 11, this detail shows improvement in control and workmanship.

Fig. 15 is a good example of overcoating. An old brick front, similar to the one on the right in the illustration, has been renovated with exposed aggregate stucco, and compares favorably in appearance with the limestone front on the left. It was the first case in which exposed aggregate stucco moldings were made in place.

Figs. 16 and 17 are detail views of the vestibule of a private residence. This has recently been completed, and is a very interesting combination of precast work, monolithic concrete, and stucco. The color is nearly white

FIG. 15.—OLD BRICK HOUSE OVERCOATED WITH EXPOSED
AGGREGATE STUCCO, WASHINGTON, D. C.

with an occasional spot of brown, the texture is characteristic of concrete and not of stone, and both color and texture are uniform throughout.

The writers believe that the work here described shows progress in the development of concrete and stucco as materials worthy of a place in the highest type of buildings or structures. It is to be noted especially that none of this work is an imitation of stone. Close inspection shows at a glance that it is concrete, with textures that vary widely, but always characteristic of concrete. Furthermore, the material may be cast in any form the architect may desire, with all details complete; no cutting, tooling, or dressing is required other than the prescribed treatment of cleanly exposing the aggregate. Finally, the material provides a medium for the expression of color in infinitely greater variety than that which obtains in the natural building stones.

FIG. 16.—VESTIBULE, PRIVATE RESIDENCE, WASHINGTON, D. C.
Console and cluster of fruit of precast concrete set in place. Moldings of monolithic concrete (poured in place), remainder of exposed aggregate stucco. Color and texture are uniform throughout.

In conclusion, the writers would add a word about stucco. The new type of exposed aggregate finish cannot fail to arouse new interest in stucco, as a product, regardless of the nature and treatment of the finishing coat. The product should be more widely used, and the reason it is not more widely used is that it has too often been applied by contractors or mechanics who consider it only as an outside plaster. This paper has attempted to convey the impression that cement stucco is more like concrete than plaster, and that plasticity is not essential. The point the writers wish to emphasize is that the art of applying durable stucco is very different from the art of plastering, and, in their opinion, stucco will take the place it deserves among building products only when this fact is generally recognized.

FIG. 17.—ENTRANCE TO VESTIBULE SHOWN IN FIG. 16.

An excellent example of the adaptability of exposed aggregate stucco and precast concrete of the same color and texture to extreme architectural requirements.

# EXAMPLES OF THE APPLICATION OF ABRAMS' WATER-RATIO TO PROPORTIONING CONCRETE

By Stanton Walker[*]

The question often arises as to which of two sands to choose for use in concrete. A coarse, well graded sand may be available at a considerable expense. Perhaps a finer sand, satisfactory in every respect except its grading, may be obtained at a nominal cost. In the vast majority of cases concrete of equal strength and durability can be made from either sand. The question of which to use is one of economy, and can easily be answered if one is able to calculate the proportions which will give the same strength for both sands.

It is with such problems in mind that this paper is written. It is our purpose to point out the methods to be used so that the engineer can apply them to specific cases rather than to attempt to tabulate the great diversity of combinations of size and grading of aggregates met with in practice.

This study is based on results of tests made at the Structural Materials Research Laboratory, Lewis Institute, Chicago. Many fundamental relations concerning the strength of concrete have been discovered as a result of the researches carried out through the cooperation of Lewis Institute and the Portland Cement Association. Some of the more important of these relations are given in Bulletin 1, "Design of Concrete Mixtures," by Duff A. Abrams, professor in charge of the laboratory.

## THEORY OF CONCRETE MIXTURES

It is common knowledge that the quantity of cement (the mix), the plastic condition of the concrete and the size and grading of the aggregate, each exert an important influence on the strength of the concrete. However, the role of each of these factors was not clearly understood until it was established by Professor Abrams that, for given materials and conditions, the strength of the concrete is determined by the quantity of mixing water, so long as the concrete is plastic and the aggregate is not too coarse for the quantity of cement used. This has become known as the water ratio theory. The water ratio is defined as the ratio of volume of water to volume of cement in the batch, assuming one cubic foot of cement to weigh 94 pounds.

[*] Associate Engineer, Structural Materials Research Laboratory, Lewis Institute, Chicago, Ill.

Several thousand tests made at this laboratory have shown that the
relation between the water content and the strength of the concrete may
be expressed by an equation of the form

$$S = \frac{1}{B^x} \tag{1}$$

Where $S$ = compressive strength of concrete
$x$ = water ratio (an exponent)
$1$ and $B$ = constants whose values depend on the quality of the
cement and other conditions of test

For average conditions for tests made in this laboratory equation (1)
becomes

$$S = \frac{14000}{7^x} \tag{2}$$

Where $S$ = compressive strength of concrete expressed as lb per
sq in, after 28 days' storage in a damp place

From the above equation it will be seen that the compressive strength
increases as the water ratio decreases. It should be borne in mind that
these constants were determined for definite conditions of test. It would
not be expected that the same constants would be found for tests made in
other laboratories although the form of the equation should be the same

It will be seen that the water ratio of a batch of concrete may be
reduced by

(1) Increasing the quantity of cement
(2) Using an aggregate of coarser size or grading
(3) Making the concrete drier

Therefore, in accordance with the water ratio theory, the strength of
concrete is increased by

(1) Increasing the cement content
(2) Using coarser aggregates (so long as they are not too coarse
for the quantity of cement used)
(3) Using less water (so long as sufficient water is used to pro
duce a plastic mix)


## EXPLANATION OF TERMS

The term concrete is used to include what are generally referred to
as mortar mixtures. The distinction between mortar and concrete is
purely arbitrary and depends only on the size of the aggregate. The
proportions of cement and aggregate in concrete are most conveniently
expressed as the ratio of the volume of cement to the volume of mixed
aggregate with cement expressed as unity. In all of the recent studies
made at this laboratory the mixtures have been expressed in this way,

since the proportions expressed in the usual way (volumes of cement fine aggregate and coarse aggregate) introduce a second variable—the grading of the aggregate.

We have therefore designated as the *Nominal Mix* the quantities as they are usually expressed in practice 1 2 3 1 2 4, etc and as the *Real Mix* the quantities as they are expressed in the new way 1 4, 1 5 etc For example the *Nominal Mix* 1 2 3 expressed as a *Real Mix* would be about 1 4 3 in other words, two volumes of fine and three volumes of coarse aggregate shrink about 15% when mixed The method of calculating the reduction in volume will be made clear below.

The size and grading of the aggregate have long been recognized as exerting an important influence on the strength of concrete Various attempts have been made to designate this function in a quantitative manner generally using the sieve analysis of the aggregate.

Careful studies made at this laboratory have shown that the sieve analysis is the proper basis for proportioning aggregate in concrete Professor Abrams has developed a function known as *Fineness Modulus* which gives a numerical measure of the size and grading of the aggregate and properly interprets its relation to the water content of the concrete.

The *Fineness Modulus* is the sum of the percentages in the sieve analysis divided by 100 if the sieve analysis is expressed as per cents coarser than the following sieves

| Sieve No | 100 | 48 | 28 | 14 | 8 | 4 | ⅜ | ¾ | 1½ |
|---|---|---|---|---|---|---|---|---|---|
| Size of square opening in | 0 0058 | 0 0116 | 0 023 | 0 046 | 0 093 | 0 186 | 0 37 | 0 75 | 1 5 |

The sieves are of square-mesh wire cloth manufactured by The W S Tyler Co, Cleveland. Ohio The size of the wire is such that each sieve has square openings double those of the preceding sieve.

A close approximation of the fineness modulus may be obtained from a sieve analysis made on alternate sieves No 48 14 4 and ⅜-in, etc The percentages for the omitted sieves may be determined by interpolation from an analysis curve This forms a very convenient set of sieves for field use.

A few trial calculations will show that the fineness modulus becomes greater as the aggregate becomes coarser and that the same fineness modulus may be obtained from an infinite number of sieve analyses Our tests have shown that aggregates having the same fineness modulus will produce concrete of the same strength no matter what the path of the sieve analysis curve *so long as other conditions are equal, and the aggregate is not too coarse for the quantity of cement used* (See Table 1 )

The fineness modulus of a mixture of two or more aggregates and also the proportions in which to mix them to make a given fineness modulus may be calculated from the fineness moduli of the individual materials

TABLE 1

MAXIMUM PERMISSIBLE VALUES OF FINENESS MODULUS OF
AGGREGATES

For *mixes* other than those given in the table, use the values for the next leaner mix

For *maximum sizes* of aggregate other than those given in the table, use the values for the next smaller size

*Fine aggregate* includes all material finer than No 4 sieve, *coarse aggregate* includes all material coarser than the No 4 sieve

This table is based on the requirements for *sand and-pebble* or *gravel* aggregate composed of approximately spherical particles in ordinary uses of concrete in reinforced concrete structures For other materials and in other classes of work the maximum permissible values of fineness modulus for an aggregate of a given size is subject to the following corrections

(1) If *crushed stone* or *slag* is used as coarse aggregate *reduce* values in table by 0 25 For crushed material consisting of unusually flat or elongated particles, *reduce* values by 0 40

(2) For *pebbles* consisting of *flat particles, reduce* values by 0 25

(3) If *stone screenings* are used as fine aggregate, *reduce* values by 0 25

(4) For the top course in *concrete roads reduce* the values by 0 25 If finishing is done by *mechanical means*, this reduction need not be made

(5) In work of *massive proportions*, such that the smallest dimension is larger than 10 times the maximum size of the coarse aggregate, *additions may be made* to the values in the table as follows For ¾ in aggregate 0 10, for 1½ in 0 20, for 3 in 0 30, for 6 in 0 40

*Sand* with fineness modulus lower than 1 50 is undesirable as a fine aggregate in ordinary concrete mixes Natural sands of such fineness are seldom found

*Sand or screenings* used for fine aggregate in concrete must not have a higher fineness modulus than that permitted for mortars of the same mix Mortar mixes are covered by the table and by (3) above

*Crushed stone* mixed with both finer sand and coarser pebbles requires no reduction in fineness modulus provided the quantity of crushed stone is less than 30% of the total volume of the aggregate

| Mix Cement-Aggregate | Size of Aggregate | | | | | | | | | | | | | |
|---|---|---|---|---|---|---|---|---|---|---|---|---|---|---|
| | 0 to No 28 | 0 to No 14 | 0 to No 8 | 0 to No 4 | 0 to No 3* | 0 to ⅜ in | 0 to ½ in* | 0 to ¾ in | 0 to 1 in* | 0 to 1½ in | 0 to 2 in* | 0 to 3 in | 0 to 4½ in* | 0 to 6 in |
| 1 12 | 1 20 | 1 80 | 2 40 | 2 95 | 3 35 | 3 80 | 4 20 | 4 60 | 5 00 | 5 35 | 5 75 | 6 20 | 6 60 | 7 00 |
| 1 9 | 1 30 | 1 85 | 2 45 | 3 05 | 3 15 | 3 85 | 4 25 | 4 65 | 5 00 | 5 40 | 5 80 | 6 25 | 6 65 | 7 05 |
| 1 7 | 1 40 | 1 95 | 2 55 | 3 20 | 3 55 | 3 95 | 4 35 | 4 75 | 5 15 | 5 55 | 5 95 | 6 40 | 6 80 | 7 20 |
| 1 6 | 1 50 | 2 05 | 2 65 | 3 30 | 3 65 | 4 05 | 4 45 | 4 85 | 5 25 | 5 65 | 6 05 | 6 50 | 6 90 | 7 30 |
| 1 5 | 1 60 | 2 15 | 2 75 | 3 45 | 3 80 | 4 20 | 4 60 | 5 00 | 5 40 | 5 80 | 6 20 | 6 60 | 7 00 | 7 45 |
| 1 4 | 1 70 | 2 30 | 2 90 | 3 60 | 4 00 | 4 40 | 4 80 | 5 20 | 5 60 | 6 00 | 6 40 | 6 85 | 7 25 | 7 65 |
| 1 3 | 1 85 | 2 50 | 3 10 | 3 90 | 4 30 | 4 70 | 5 10 | 5 50 | 5 90 | 6 30 | 6 70 | 7 15 | 7 55 | 8 00 |
| 1 2 | 2 00 | 2 70 | 3 40 | 4 20 | 4 60 | 5 05 | 5 45 | 5 90 | 6 30 | 6 70 | 7 10 | 7 55 | 7 95 | 8 40 |
| 1 1 | 2 25 | 3 00 | 3 80 | 4 75 | 5 25 | 5 60 | 6 05 | 6 50 | 6 90 | 7 35 | 7 75 | 8 20 | 8 65 | 9 10 |

* Considered as 'half size' sieves not used in computing fineness modulus

The fineness modulus of a mixture of two or more aggregates may be calculated from the following formula

$$m = r_1 m_1 + r_2 m_2 + \ldots + r_n m_n \qquad (3)$$

Where $m$ = fineness modulus of the mixed aggregate.

$m_1, m_2 \ldots m_n$ are the fineness moduli of the individual aggregates

$r_1, r_2, \ldots r_n$ are the volumes of the individual aggregates expressed as ratios to the sum of the separate volumes of the total aggregate

To determine the proportions in which to mix two aggregates of known fineness moduli to obtain a given fineness modulus, use the following formula

$$r = \frac{m_c - m}{m_c - m_f} \qquad (4)$$

Where $r$ = ratio of volume of fine aggregate to sum of separate volumes of fine and coarse aggregate,

$m_c$ = fineness modulus of coarse aggregate,

$m_f$ = fineness modulus of fine aggregate,

$m$ = fineness modulus of mixed aggregate.

To determine the proportions in which to mix three or more materials to obtain a given fineness modulus the solution must be made in steps involving only two aggregates at a time. The method to be followed is illustrated in Problem 5. It will be noted from the above equations that the fineness modulus of a mixed aggregate is directly proportional to the fineness moduli of the individual aggregates and the proportions in which they occur.

It was pointed out above that the aggregate must not be too coarse for the mix used. Table 1 gives the maximum value of fineness modulus which it is permissible to use with a given aggregate for different quantities of cement. This table was compiled as a result of observations on several thousand tests in which the size and grading of the aggregate were varied over a wide range.

The plastic condition of the concrete is designated in this paper by the term *relative consistency*. A concrete of normal consistency (relative consistency = 1.00) is of such plasticity that a 6 x 12 in. cylinder of concrete will slump ½ to 1 in. upon removal of the metal form by a steady upward pull immediately after molding the specimen. Concrete of a relative consistency of 1.10 will slump 5 to 6 in., or 1.25 will slump 8 to 9 in. If the slump specimen is molded in a 4 x 8 in. truncated cone 12 in. long, the slumps for the above consistencies will be about ¼ to ¾, 3 to 4, and 6 to 7 in., respectively.

Concrete of a relative consistency of 1.00 is somewhat dry for most work, but can be used where tamping is practicable. A relative consistency

of 1 10 represents concrete that can be used in road construction where
finishing is done by hand  a somewhat drier consistency may be used where
the finishing is done by machine  A relative consistency of 1 25 is about
the wettest that need be used in reinforced concrete construction

The term *relative consistency* should not be confused with the *water-
ratio*  The relative consistency refers to the *plastic condition* of the concrete without reference to the actual quantity of water in the batch, while
the water ratio refers to the actual quantity of water (as compared with
the cement), and takes no account of the plasticity of the concrete

The dependency of the water-ratio on the mix, size and grading of the
aggregate, and relative consistency of the concrete was pointed out above
It is therefore important to be able to express this relation in mathematical
terms  The following equations for water ratio are the same as those
appearing in Bulletin I with one minor change, the term $(a-c)n$ is
removed from the brackets inclosing the quantity multiplied by $R$

$$x = R \left( \frac{3}{2} p + \frac{30n}{1\ 26^{m}} \right) + (a-c)n \tag{5}$$

Where $x$ = volume of water required (ratio to volume of cement
in batch—cement assumed to weigh 94 lb per cu ft )

$R$ = relative consistency of concrete (or workability
factor")

$p$ = normal consistency of cement (ratio by weight)

$m$ = fineness of modulus of aggregate (an exponent)

$n$ = volumes of mixed aggregate to one of cement (the mix)

$a$ = absorption of dry aggregate (ratio of water absorbed
to volume of aggregate)  Determine $a$ after immersion in water for 3 hr  Average values for crushed
limestone and pebbles may be assumed as 0 02,
porous sandstone may reach 0 08  very light and
porous aggregate may reach 0 25

$c$ = moisture contained in aggregate (ratio of water contained to volume of aggregate)  Assume $c$ = zero
for room dry aggregate

It will be seen that $(a-c)$ is the absorption of the aggregate as used, or
the net absorption  It should be noted that for practical purposes the
absorption of the aggregate need not be determined  However, it is important to make this correction when tests are being made on aggregates of
different types and in establishing the underlying principles

For the usual ranges in fineness modulus essentially the same results
will be obtained from a somewhat simpler formula

$$x = R \left[ \frac{3}{2} p + \left( 22 - \frac{m}{42} \right) n \right] + (a-c)n \tag{6}$$

The water ratio  the function which governs the strength, is the
amount of water which goes to the cement as distinguished from the total

quantity of water including that absorbed by the aggregate It may be determined from either of the above equations by omitting the quantity $(a-c)n$ from the formulas

It is necessary to determine the unit weights of the fine, coarse and mixed aggregate in order to be able to transform proportions expressed in the usual manner to the more correct expression represented by the *Real Mix* The weight of the aggregate in pounds per cubic foot is used in the calculations which follow The unit weight is determined by means of a cylindrical measure having height equal to diameter The measure is filled with the aggregate in three layers Each layer is puddled 25 to 30 times with a ⅜ in round steel bar, pointed at the lower end After the last layer is puddled the measure is heaped and the surplus aggregate struck off with a straight edge Measures having capacities of 1/10 cu ft or more may be used for fine aggregates For the coarse and mixed aggregates measures of not less than ⅓ to ½ cu ft should be used This is the method recommended by Committee C 9 of the American Society for Testing Materials

### PROBLEMS IN DESIGN OF CONCRETE MIXTURES

In the following pages a few examples of the application of Professor Abrams' water-ratio theory to the design of concrete mixtures are given using the principles which have been outlined above Most problems in the design of concrete mixtures can be solved with a reasonable degree of accuracy from Fig 1 or Equations 2 and 5 or 6 if the proportions are reduced to the proper units

Fig 1 is a nomographic chart showing the interrelation of quantity of cement, grading of aggregate, consistency and strength of concrete as expressed by Equations 2 and 5 The use of the chart is made clear in the problems which follow

Let us emphasize, before proceeding with the problems that in order to study a concrete mixture intelligently it is desirable to express

(1) Proportions of cement and aggregate as a ratio of volume of cement to the volume of aggregate with cement expressed as unity (mix 1 4, 1 5, etc )

(2) The size and grading of the aggregate by some finite number The studies at this laboratory have shown the fineness modulus to be the best measure of this quantity

(3) The plastic condition of the concrete as a ratio to the normal plasticity (relative consistency = 1 00).

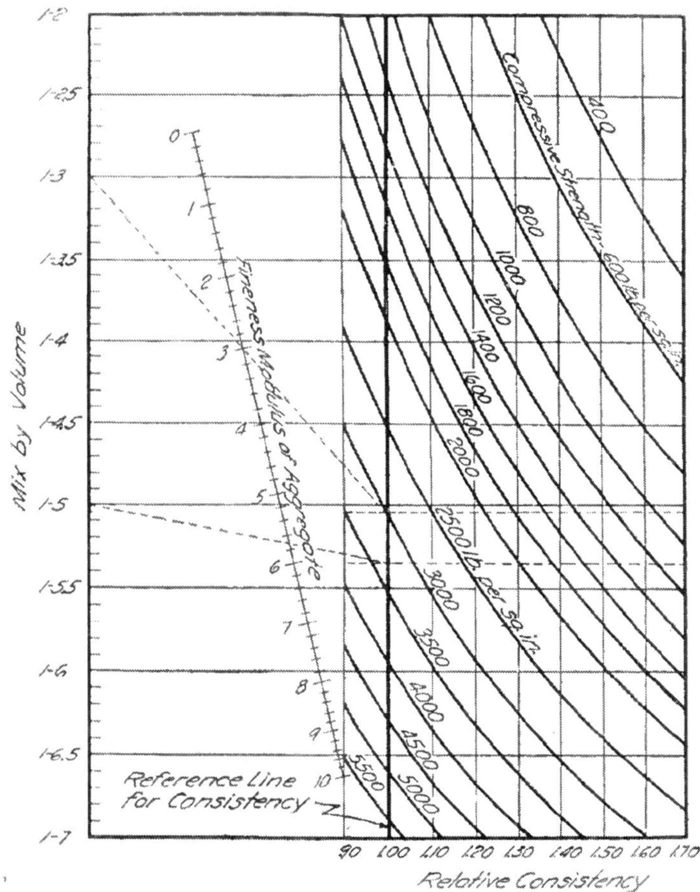



FIG. 1. DIAGRAM FOR THE DESIGN OF CONCRETE MIXTURES.

Same as Fig. 6, Bulletin No. 1, Structural Materials Research Laboratory.

This chart is based on compression tests by 6 by 12-inch concrete cylinders; age 28 days; stored in damp sand.

The cement used gave compressive strengths in 1:3 standard sand mortar as follows, when tested in the form of 2 x 4-in. cylinders:

| Age | Lb. per Sq. In. |
|---|---|
| 7 days | 1,900 |
| 28 days | 3,200 |
| 3 months | 4,200 |
| 1 year | 4,300 |

A study of Equation 5 will show that these three factors fix the water-ratio. Therefore, while the water-ratio does not appear as such in Fig. 1, it is taken into account through the interrelation of these factors.

## PROBLEM 1

Given a fine and a coarse sand. In what proportions must the fine sand be mixed to give the same strength as would be obtained with the coarse sand in a 1 : 2 : 3½ mix? The same coarse aggregate (graded No. 4-1½ in.), cement and relative consistency will be used in each case.

*Solution.* From the water-ratio theory it will be seen that if the fine sand is mixed with the pebbles in the proper proportions to give the same fineness modulus as 2 volumes of the coarse sand mixed with 3½ volumes of the pebbles that the same strength will be obtained for the same *real* mix and relative consistency.

It is therefore necessary to find what real mix represents the 1 : 2 : 3½ mix, and to calculate the fineness modulus of a mixture of the coarse sand and pebbles in these proportions, and the proportions in which to mix the fine sand and pebbles to give the same fineness modulus. The same real mix would be used with the fine sand mixture; from the real mix and the weights of the aggregates the nominal mix may be determined.

On making sieve analyses and unit weight determinations, say we find that

| | |
|---|---|
| Fineness modulus of fine sand | = 2.50 |
| Unit weight of fine sand | = 105 lb. per cu. ft. |
| Fineness modulus of coarse sand | = 3.25 |
| Unit weight of coarse sand | = 114 lb. per cu. ft. |
| Fineness modulus of pebbles | = 7.30 |
| Unit weight of pebbles | = 110 lb. per cu. ft. |
| Unit weight of mixture of coarse sand and pebbles in proportions of 2 volumes of sand, 3½ volumes of pebbles | = 128 lb. per cu. ft. |

First investigate the 1 : 2 : 3½ mix, using the coarse sand.

The total weight of aggregate for one cubic foot of cement divided by the unit weight of the mixed aggregate will give the volume of mixed aggregate, or

$$\frac{2 \times 114 + 3.5 \times 110}{128} = \frac{613}{128} = 4.8 \text{ cu. ft. of mixed aggregate for}$$

one cubic foot of cement. The real mix is then 1 : 4.8.

The ratio of volume of sand to the separate volumes of fine and coarse aggregate for the 1 2 3 5 mix is

$$\frac{2}{2 + 3 5} = 0 36$$

Therefore, from Equation 3 the fineness modulus of the mixed aggregate will be $0 36 \times 3 25 + 0 64 \times 7 30 = 5 83$

It will be noted from Table 1 that this value of fineness modulus is just within the limit for sand and pebbles in a 1 4 8 mix

Calculate the proportions in which the mixture of fine sand and the pebbles will give a fineness modulus of 5 83 by substituting, in Equation 4,

$$, = \frac{7 30 - 5 83}{7 30 - 2 50} = 0 31, \text{ or } 0 31 \text{ cu ft of } fine \text{ sand mixed with } 0 69$$

cu ft of pebbles will have a fineness modulus of 5 83

It is next necessary to determine the volume of mixed aggregate which will be obtained by mixing 0 31 cu ft of fine sand and 0 69 cu ft of pebbles in order to calculate the nominal mix from the real mix

```
0 31 cu ft of the fine sand weighs   33 lb
0 69 cu ft of the pebbles weighs     76 lb
                                     ———
                            Total   109 lb
```

Say the unit weight of the mixture of fine sand and pebbles is found to be 126 lb per cu ft   The weight of fine sand and pebbles divided by the unit weight of the mixed aggregate or

$$\frac{109}{126} = 0 86 \text{ cu ft of mixed aggregate, obtained by mixing } 0 31 \text{ cu ft}$$

of sand and 0 69 cu ft of pebbles

The real mix would be the same as above, therefore 4 8, the volume of mixed aggregate for one cu ft of cement is 0 86 of the separate volumes of sand and pebbles

Then

$$\frac{4 8}{0 86} = 5 6 \text{ cu ft of sand and pebbles (not mixed) for one cu ft}$$

of cement

Then the volume of sand is $0 31 \times 5 6 = 1 73$ cu ft

And the volume of pebbles is $0 69 \times 5 6 = 3 85$ cu ft for one cu ft of cement

The nominal mix is then 1 1 73 3 85

Or a 1 1 73 3 85 mix using the fine sand should give the same strength as a 1 2 3 5 mix using the coarse sand

### PROBLEM 2

Find the probable compressive strength at 28 days of a
1 2 · 4 concrete made from a given sand and pebble aggregate
and mixed to a consistency suitable for reinforced concrete construction   (Relative consistency 1 25 )

*Solution.* This information can be obtained from either Fig 1 or
Equations 2 and 5, if the *real mix* and the fineness modulus of the mixed
aggregate are calculated   In order to do this, it is necessary to make
sieve analyses of the fine and coarse aggregate, and unit weight deter
minations for the fine, coarse and mixed aggregate.  Say that our tests
show that

Fine aggregate, graded 0 No  4 sieve, fineness modulus = 3 10
Unit weight of fine aggregate = 112 lb per cu ft
Coarse aggregate, graded No 4-1½ in  fineness modulus = 7 00
Unit weight of coarse aggregate = 110 lb per cu ft
Unit weight of mixed aggregate = 127 lb per cu ft

The real mix will be found by calculating the volumes of mixed
aggregate for one volume of cement as in Problem 1
The volumes of sand times its unit weight = 2 × 112 = 224 lb of
sand for one cu ft of cement
The volumes of pebbles times its unit weight = 4 × 110 = 440 lb
Total weight of aggregate for one cu ft of cement = 664 lb
The volume of mixed aggregate for one cu ft of cement will be the
total weight of aggregate divided by its unit weight or $\frac{664}{127} = 5\,2$ cu ft.
The real mix is then 1  5 2

The ratio of the volume of sand to the separate volumes of sand and
pebbles is $\frac{2}{2+1} = 0\,33$, and the ratio of volumes of pebbles is $\frac{4}{2+4} +$
0 67   Then from Equation 3 the fineness modulus of the mixture is

$$0\,33 \times 3\,10 + 0\,67 \times 7\,00 = 5\,71$$

We now have the information necessary to obtain the strength of the
concrete from either Fig 1 or Equations 2 and 5

*From Fig 1*   Draw a straight line from the point on the mix scale
representing a mix of 1  5 2 through 5 71 on the fineness modulus scale
until it intersects the reference line for consistency   From this point draw
a horizontal line to the vertical line representing a relative consistency of
1 25   This intersection gives the strength—about 2200 lb per sq in

*From Equations 2 and 5*   Determine the water ratio by substituting
in Equation 5 and solve for the strength from Equation 2   Assume the
cement to have a normal consistency of 22

$$\text{Then } r = 1\,25 \left( \frac{3}{2}\,22 + \frac{30 \times 5\,2}{1\,26^{5\,7}} \right) = 0\,95 \qquad \text{(Equation 5)}$$

$$\text{and } S = \frac{14000}{7^{0\,95}} = 2200 \text{ lb per sq in} \qquad \text{(Equation 2)}$$

It should be emphasized here that the constants in Equation 2 depend on definite conditions of test   While other experimenters should get the same *relation* they should not expect to obtain the same *values*

### PROBLEM 3

Mix the aggregates given in Problem 2 with cement and water in such proportions as to give concrete having a strength of 3000 lb per sq in in Fig 1 for a relative consistency of 1 10

*Solution*   A cut and try method must be used for this problem   Table 1 gives the maximum permissible fineness modulus for a given mix and size of aggregate   Since these values are near the upper limit for sand and pebbles we will choose a fineness modulus 25 below the maximum permissible value

From the intersection of the 3000-lb contour with the 1 10 relative consistency line in Fig 1 draw a horizontal line to the reference line for consistency   With this point as a center, rotate a straight edge until such a position is found that it passes through a fineness modulus which is 0 25 lower than the maximum permissible for the mix given by the intersection on the mixture ordinate   For the conditions given the fineness modulus is found to be 5 70 and the mix 1 : 4 5

We next calculate the ratio of volume of sand to the sum of separate volumes of fine and coarse aggregates from Equation 4

$$r = \frac{7\,00 - 5\,70}{7\,00 - 3\,10} = 0\,333$$

Now determine the number of cubic feet of mixed aggregate obtained from 0 333 cubic foot of sand and 0 667 cubic foot of pebbles

0 333 × 112 + 0 667 × 110 = 111 lb, the weight of 0 333 cu ft of sand and 0 667 cu ft of pebbles

The unit weight of the mixed aggregate in the above proportions is, say, 127 lb per cu ft

$$\text{Then } \frac{111}{127} = 0\,875 \text{ cu ft of mixed aggregate obtained by mixing 0 333}$$

cu ft of sand and 0 667 cu ft of pebbles

Therefore 4 5 is 0 875 of the separate volumes of sand and pebbles required for one cubic foot of cement in the above mix

The volume of unmixed aggregate is therefore $\dfrac{4\,7}{0\,875} = 5\,15$ cu ft of sand and pebbles measured separately

The volume of sand is $0\,333 \times 5\,15 = 1\,72$ cu ft

The volume of pebbles is $0\,667 \times 5\,15 = 3\,44$ cu ft

The nominal mix which will give the required strength is then 1  1 72  3 44

## PROBLEM 4

Given a pit containing a well graded 0 No 4 sand and a well-graded No 4-1½ in pebbles  The material occurs in the proportions of 60% sand and 40% pebbles

What mix must be used with the aggregates in the proportions in which they occur in the pit to obtain the same strength as with a 1  2  3 mix?

*Solution*  This problem involves methods similar to those used in preceding problems  Say it is found that

Fineness modulus of sand       = 3 00
Unit weight of sand            = 112 lb per cu ft
Fineness modulus of pebbles = 7 00
Unit weight of pebbles         = 110 lb per cu ft
Unit weight of mixed aggregate in the 1  2  3 mix = 127 lb per cu ft
Unit weight of aggregate in proportions of 60% sand and 40% pebbles = 124 lb per cu ft

$\dfrac{2}{2+3} = 0\,40 =$ ratio of volume of sand to separate volumes of fine and coarse aggregates in the 1  2  3 mix

$0\,40 \times 3\,00 + 0\,60 \times 7.00 = 5\,40 =$ fineness modulus of aggregate in the 1  2  3 mix

$\dfrac{2 \times 112 + 3 \times 110}{127} = 4.36,$ or the real mix $= 1$  4 36

The fineness modulus of aggregate in the proportions occurring in the pit is, from Eq. 3, $0\,60 \times 3\,00 + 0\,40 \times 7\,00 = 4\,60$

In Fig 1 pass a straight edge through a real mix of 1  4 36 and a fineness modulus of 5 40  Find the intersection on the reference line for consistency  With this point as a center rotate the straight edge until it passes through fineness modulus 4 60  The intersection on the mix ordinate will give the real mix, 1  3 7, which will produce the same strength with the material in the proportions in which they occur in the pit, as the 1 . 2  3 mix.

The nominal mix is calculated as in Problem 1, as follows

$$\frac{0.60 \times 112 + 0.40 \times 110}{124} = 0.895 \text{ cu ft of mixed aggregate}$$

obtained by mixing 0.60 cu ft of sand and 0.40 cu ft of pebbles

Then $\frac{3.7}{0.895} = 4.14$ cu ft of unmixed aggregate per cu ft of cement

The volume of sand for 1 cu ft of cement is $4.14 \times 0.60 = 2.48$ cu ft
The volume of pebbles is $4.14 \times 0.40 = 1.65$ cu ft

The nominal mix using the materials in the proportions in which they occur in the pit, which will give the same strength as the 1 : 2 : 3 mix, is then 1 : 2.48 : 1.65

### Problem 5

Given the following four aggregates

1—A fine sand, having a fineness modulus of 1.20

2—A coarse sand, graded No. 8 to No. 4 mesh sieve, having a fineness modulus of 5.00

3—A gravel graded No. 4 to ¾ in. having a fineness modulus of 6.50

4—A gravel graded No. ¾ to 1½ in. having a fineness modulus of 8.00

Mix these aggregates in a rational manner to obtain a fineness modulus of 5.75

*Solution.* For this problem no hard and fast rules may be laid down. It permits of an infinite number of solutions and the engineer must exercise judgment as to which is the best in each specific case. Information obtained from observation or elsewhere tells us that the average well graded sand, passing through a No. 4 mesh sieve has a fineness modulus of about 3.00 and that the average well-graded pebbles sized between a No. 4 sieve and 1½ in. has a fineness modulus of about 7.00

Then the desired result may be obtained as follows

The proportions in which to mix the two sands to give a fineness modulus of 3.00 may be determined by substituting in Equation 4

Then $r = \dfrac{5.00 - 3.00}{5.00 - 1.20} = 0.53$, or aggregates No. 1 and 2, mixed in the proportions of 0.53 volumes of No. 1 and 0.47 volumes of No. 2 will give a fine aggregate having a fineness modulus of 3.00

In like manner determine the proportions in which to mix the coarse aggregates to give a fineness modulus of 7.00,

Then $i = \dfrac{8.00 - 7.00}{8.00 - 6.50} = 0.67$, or aggregates No. 3 and 4, mixed in proportions of 0.67 volumes of No. 3 and 0.33 volumes of No. 4 will give a coarse aggregate having a fineness modulus of 7.00.

The proportions in which to mix the resulting fine and coarse aggregates are found from the same equation

$$i = \dfrac{7.00 - 5.75}{7.00 - 3.00} = 0.31,$$ or 0.31 volumes of the mixture of Nos. 1 and 2, and 0.69 volumes of the mixture of Nos. 3 and 4 will give the desired fineness modulus of 5.75.

The individual ratios of the whole will then be

Volumes of aggregate No. $1 = 0.31 \times 0.53 = 0.165$

Volumes of aggregate No. $2 = 0.31 \times 0.47 = 0.147$

Volumes of aggregate No. $3 = 0.69 \times 0.67 = 0.460$

Volumes of aggregate No. $4 = 0.69 \times 0.33 = 0.228$

## Problem 6

*Relative Costs of Different Mixtures.*—The application of the principles illustrated in the foregoing problems to the calculation of the relative costs of different mixtures should be apparent.

Other than the cost of materials, information is needed on one other factor, the volume of concrete produced by given volumes of materials—the "yield" or "over run." This quantity should be determined experimentally.

As an illustration let us compare the cost of the two mixtures given in problem 4. The following quantities should not be confused with similar quantities given in various handbooks. These are the actual quantities of materials in the concrete in place. They should not be used in estimating the cost of concrete materials unless allowance is made for wastage, however they serve for a comparison of costs.

Suppose that it is found by experiment that one bag of cement in the 1:2:3 mix produces 4.6 cu. ft. of concrete and that the 1:2.48:1.65 mix produces 4.2 cu. ft. of concrete for one bag of cement.

Assume the cost of materials delivered on the job for the 1:2:3 mix as follows:

Pebbles, $2.00 per cu. yd.

Sand, $2.00 per cu. yd.

Cement, $3.00 per bbl.

Then for the 1:2:3 mix the quantity of cement for 1 cu. yd. of concrete will be $\dfrac{27}{4.6} = 5.86$ bags $= 1.47$ bbl., since there is twice as much sand

and three times as much pebbles as cement $\dfrac{5\ 86 \times 2}{27} = 0\ 435$ cu yd of sand

per cu yd of concrete and $\dfrac{5\ 86 \times 3}{27} = 652$ cu yd of pebbles per cu yd of concrete

The total cost of materials per cu yd of 1  2  3 concrete will be.

$$1\ 47 \times 3\ 00 + 0\ 435 \times 2\ 00 + 0\ 652 \times 2\ 00 = \$6\ 58$$

It will be remembered that in Problem 4 we were dealing with a pit in which the sand was 60% of the whole  It is evident that if the 1  2  3 mix is used, either a considerable amount of the sand must remain unused or additional coarse aggregate imported  Suppose that the former is the case, and that if the material is used in the proportions in which it occurs in the pit—that is, in the 1  2 48  1 65 mix, the cost of aggregate can be reduced 50 cents per cu yd  for both fine and coarse

Then

$$\frac{27}{4\ 2} = 6\ 42 \text{ bags} = 1\ 61 \text{ bbl of cement per cu yd of concrete,}$$

$$\frac{6\ 42 \times 2\ 48}{27} = 0\ 59 \text{ cu yd of sand per cu yd of concrete,}$$

$$\frac{6\ 42 \times 1\ 65}{27} = 0\ 39 \text{ cu yd of pebbles per cu yd of concrete}$$

Then the cost per cu yd of the 1  2 48  1 65 mix equals

$$1\ 61 \times 3\ 00 + 0\ 39 \times 1\ 50 + 0\ 39 \times 1\ 50 = \$6\ 30$$

Or for the prices assumed there would be a saving of over 4% in cost of materials by using the aggregates in the proportions in which they occur in the pit

DISCUSSION

The Chair—It is a matter of conservation to make use of aggregates as they exist in gravel pits. Where nature has given us more sand than pebbles if we use a specification calling arbitrarily for a 1 2 4 mix, we are wasting a lot of the material in the pit. For these reasons engineers have been trying to get away from arbitrary mixtures. The work of Prof Abrams as explained here by Mr Walker, the work of Messrs Young and Edwards, have all been along this line of allowing us intelligently to compute how to vary our mixtures so as to get concrete of equal strength and equal consistency when the aggregate varies, and so the matter is of great importance, not especially perhaps to the building industry, but to the industry of building concrete roads.

Mr W A Slater—I would like to ask Mr Walker if he can state any limit within which he would expect he would be able to produce concrete of the strength that has been specified. How effective a system of inspection could he outline which would accomplish what is desired? If we are going to get away from the arbitrary specification of 1 2 4 concrete and specify the strength of concrete as delivered on the job how closely can we come to guaranteeing that that strength will be delivered? In other words, has he had any chance of following up, on any job, the actual production of concrete and finding out how closely the strengths obtained with this method, or something of the kind, agreed with the strengths predicted?

Mr R C Yeoman—The question Mr Slater brings up I think, brings in the idea of administration of the job. In the production of sand and gravel for concrete large plants have been built for the purpose of keeping that production uniform, and division on the ¼-in or ⅛-in screen has been devised in order to help out that uniformity. If we are going to allow the plants just to wash the material and send it off to the job as it comes we are going to find another factor which is troublesome. The pits usually vary from day to day in their operation, and one day there will be 40% sand and the next day 60%. The administration on the job is continually testing the material and determining the proper relation of cement and aggregate. That is going to be a problem of administration not heretofore handled, and I am wondering if they have had any experience in administering a job of that kind, for changes that are made frequently, say, during the work or two or three times a day.

Mr H H Knouse—Four years ago, in Omaha, we put in some reinforced concrete linings for a water works reservoir, and on account of certain physical conditions that entered into the placing of the concrete it was necessary that the consistency be controlled very closely to a certain predetermined point. Working back from that point, we evolved a rather crude method of checking what we termed the percentage of voids, which

( 103 )

is now practically an obsolete term by measuring accurately all the materials that went into the concrete mixer on every batch and measuring accurately the amount of concrete which came out. We had a calibrated hopper, and at frequent periods during the day we would get that hopper entirely clean and throw one batch from the mixer into it quickly, measuring it. We had a series of curves from which we were able to check back and determine with a fair degree of accuracy what the percentage of the voids was running in our coarse aggregate. We assumed that the grading of our fine aggregate was approximately constant, which I believe it was. The proportion of the cement to the fine aggregate was held constant and we then controlled the percentage of mortar in excess of the percentage of voids. We were striving first for a water tight concrete, strength was rather a secondary consideration. I never have had the opportunity to follow that up in a really scientific or careful manner but I believe that in that particular case it served the purpose of controlling the properties of the concrete, which we were looking for, and I think it is adaptable to a wide range of uses.

Mr S. H. Wightman—I have a suggestion to offer which is a practical means of rectifying an aggregate. In Detroit, both the river gravel and the bank gravel ran very high in sand, it ran from 70% to 35% in sand, and I tried to evolve a practical way on the job whereby the gravel as it came, the bulk of our material, could be rectified. The first step I took in doing that was to develop what is called an ideal curve, in which we took the screens running from 100. We developed by a series of tests what we considered the proper percentages of sand and aggregate for those various sized screenings. Then we purchased our gravel in boatload lots and made a sieve analysis. We found that in all cases it ran very high in the 40% sand. We also found that the proportion of sand was very high. The matter of rectification presented itself as an easy way of simply adding enough stone and in the proper size.

We were able to purchase ⅝-in, ¾-in and 1-in stone, and by the analysis of the gravel or the bulk of the material that we used it was just a question of adding three parts of stone to two parts of gravel as it came, or equal parts or whatever the sieve showed. On getting a boatload of material, we could make one sieve analysis and with slide-rule calculation immediately determine how much stone would approximate our curve, so for that whole boatload of gravel we could rectify and approximate our true strength or ideal curve as developed.

That worked out so nicely that the people manufacturing stone wanted to get it in general use, and I wrote a little pamphlet on the subject. We took it up with several of the contractors, and they simply reduced it to a sieve analysis of gravel eliminating the various sizes and just using the ¼-in screen. It was then a question of determining whether they had 80% or 70% of sand in their gravel, and we gave them a little schedule which showed if they had 80% sand how many wheelbarrows they would have to add of stone. If it was footings they could

use 2 in stone and if it was reinforced concrete 1-in stone  That worked
out and we sold every large contractor in Detroit crushed stone and he
found an economy in the cement by replacing the high sand content and
bringing that back to a mix which might be represented in the 1 2 4
mix the specifications called for, or could follow an ideal curve

Mr Walker—You kept the quantity of the cement constant in each
case, I take it and made your aggregate conform to a given sieve analysis?

Mr Wightman—Yes, what we called rectifying the gravel  We did
not try to get down to the decimal points, or anything of that kind, it
was just to make a rough approximation  For instance, one contractor
had three mixers working for a number of years in which he was using one
bag of cement and two wheelbarrows of gravel  I was inspector for some
gravel works at that time, and I said  "You are getting about the proper
proportion of mortar all right, but you would get just as strong concrete
or even stronger, if you had a greater percentage of stone, and I will per
mit you to use another wheelbarrow of crushed stone in your mixture"
and that is what started the ball rolling  He calculated that during the
several years he had been working on that mix he had lost a great many
thousands of dollars, and he calculated that on that one job, when he
got through, that he saved some $2000 in the saving of cement  I know
that the concrete was just as strong, because his mortar ratio was right,
and the mortar was in sufficient quantity to fill a much larger volume of
the larger aggregates

Mr Slater—May I ask Mr Wightman if he has the figures for the
strength of concrete produced before and after that change was made, and
if they are available for report in this discussion?

Mr Wightman—The figures I received on tests were made in devel
oping a curve, and after I established that this curve gave a certain
strength, in my own work I followed the curve  I have not had tests
made on the rectifying of gravel, but when you have been used to having
concrete tested and made those tests for a number of years, you reach a
point where you can judge within 500 or 600 lbs  the way your concrete
is running to a strength of 2000 to 3000 lb, just about what you are
getting, so I cannot give you the accurate figures

Mr Slater—The reason for my questions in both cases was to get at
some idea of what strength we actually get on concrete jobs  I want to find
if anybody here has information of strengths determined from tests of
specimens taken from the mixer on the job, and representing a fair average
all through any given job for comparison with the strength predicted on
the same mix

Mr Wightman—I have noticed in our discussion today on this mat
ter of grading that very little is said of the benefits of saving money  It is
very hard to interest the architect and the contractor in the theory of
grading and proportioning  If more is said about the saving of cement in
the work, which means a saving in cost in dollars and cents, I think it
would bring about a more immediate use and practice of the recognition

of these various methods of grading and proportioning We all know that specifications laid down by architects and engineers generally call for an excess use of cement due to the fact that they do not know what the exact conditions on the field are going to be We know that if a scientific method of proportioning was used in most cases a great deal of cement could be saved The price of cement today is a real item of cost

MR WALKER *(by letter)*—We have not had the opportunity to test concrete from jobs where the water ratio theory was used in proportioning the concrete However, we have tested concrete from a number of projects where given aggregates were used throughout the work and where one would expect the specifications to be followed with reasonable faithfulness

Test pieces were molded in 6 x 12-in paraffined cardboard cylinders, and the concrete was taken directly from the batch after it was in place Specimens were made each day as the work progressed The following table gives the strengths of concrete from 5 different jobs

COMPRESSIVE STRENGTH FOR CONCRETE FROM DIFFERENT JOBS

(lb per sq in)

| 1 | 2 | 3 | 4 | 5 |
|---|---|---|---|---|
| 1300 | 2250 | 3250 | 1300 | 2160 |
| 4090 | 1960 | 4480 | 2020 | 3060 |
| 2710 | 3400 | 3180 | 2360 | 2610 |
| 4250 | | 3710 | 2840 | 1800 |
| 3050 | | 2390 | 3150 | 2340 |
| 3850 | | 3220 | 2270 | 3420 |
| 3620 | | 1580 | 3380 | 2100 |
| 3170 | | 2220 | 3550 | 3760 |
| 3430 | | | 1270 | 2930 |
| 2700 | | | 3770 | 3410 |
| 3010 | | | 3110 | 3090 |
| 2970 | | | | 2630 |
| | | | | 2780 |
| | | | | 2140 |
| | | | | 2930 |
| | | | | 2030 |
| | | | | 3000 |
| | | | | 3550 |
| | | | | 2050 |
| 3180 | 2540 | 3000 | 2640 | 2730 |

Grand Average for Jobs 1 2, 3 and 4   2900

On Jobs 1, 2, 3 and 4 the aggregates were a well graded 0 ¼ in sand and crushed limestone graded ¼ to 2 in The mix was 1 2 3 One specimen was made each day and stored on the job over night, after which they were removed to the basement of an office building and stored for about 14 days They were then removed to the laboratory, where they were stored in the air until tested at 28 days The same materials were used on the four jobs The work extended over a period of about 40 days This concrete was used in road constructions and was placed during the months of July and August

On Job No 5 the aggregates were well graded 0-¼ in sand and pebbles graded from ¼ to 2 in  The mix was 1 2 4  Two specimens were made on each day at intervals varying from 2 days to a week  The work extended over a period of about 1 month  The specimens were stored on the job for about 14 days when they were removed to the laboratory  They were then stored in the air of the laboratory until tested at the age of 28 days  This concrete was used in road work and was placed during the latter part of September and the early part of October

Since the brand of cement and the conditions of storage were different than used in our laboratory tests it is not possible to make a direct comparison of the strength obtained with the laboratory strengths  However, with aggregates similarly graded, using a cement of average strength and storing the specimen in damp sand until test, we would expect to obtain about 3400 lb per sq in for the 1 · 2 3 mix and 3000 lb for the 1 2 4 mix  If these values are taken as a basis, the 1 2 3 mix may be considered as 15% lower than the predicted laboratory strength and the 1 2 4 mix 9% lower  However, it must be remembered, as pointed out above that parallel tests were not made in the laboratory using the same materials

It will be noted that about 30% of these results are more than 10% below the average  The mean variation for Jobs 1, 2, 3 and 4 is 23 5% and for Job 5 it is 17 8%

I would like to call attention to the fact that the use of the ideal curve is merely a limited application of the fineness modulus theory  Mr Wightman obtained the same fineness modulus by making his aggregates follow the same sieve analysis curve, whereas he might have obtained the fineness modulus with much less variation in the proportions without special attention to the exact path of the sieve analysis

## WEAR AND COMPRESSION TESTS OF CONCRETE.

By Ray B. Crepps.[*]

This paper gives results and curves taken from a series of tests conducted in the Testing Materials Laboratory of Purdue University in coöperation with the Indiana Sand and Gravel Producers Association. The tests were originally designed with a view of placing before the members of that association some underlying principles in concrete mixtures. However, a number of tests taken from the different series are comparable under this heading.

FIG. 1.—DRUM AND INSIDE BAND OF CONCRETE WEAR TEST MACHINE.

These are the first tests to be conducted on the concrete wear machine recently installed in this laboratory. The type of wear block designed for this machine is wedge-shaped instead of rectangular, as used by other experimenters. Although the tests are limited in number, certain indications are brought out which may be of interest.

The wear machine is essentially a Talbot-Jones rattler, modified in the details. It consists of a cast-iron cylindrical drum 3 ft. 6 in. in diameter

* Instructor in the Testing Laboratory, Purdue University, Lafayette, Ind.

FIG. 2.—DRIVING MECHANISM AND DRUM ATTACHMENT.

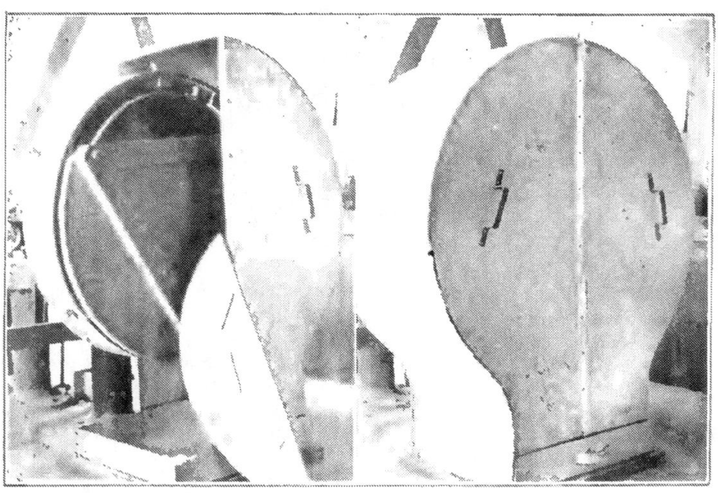

FIG. 3.—WOODEN COVER AND HALF
OF ENCASEMENT.

FIG. 4.—ENCASEMENT OF WEAR TEST
MACHINE.

with an inside depth of 8 in. There are six 2 x 1½ in. lugs cast on the inside of the circumference at the sixth points. The shell is about 1 in. in thickness; illustration is shown in Fig. 1. Fig. 1 also shows an 8 x ¼ in. sheet steel band in the form of a ring, with a diameter of 3 ft., setting inside the drum which is held in place by set screws which pass through the lugs. The adjustment of this band around the concrete wear blocks is made by means of three bolts which pass through the 2 x 2½ x 14 in. angle irons fastened to the ends of the band.

Fig. 2 shows the driving mechanism and the drum attached to a shaft of an overhung brick rattler, which was introduced at Purdue in 1889.

In Fig. 3 is shown a circular wooden cover 1 in. in thickness, supported on a 2 x 4 in. oak triangular frame, which is fastened to the front of the drum by means of four stud bolts.

FIG. 5.—WEDGE-SHAPED BLOCKS AR-
RANGED IN BAND.

The revolving drum and cover is inclosed in a removable galvanized iron case, made in two sections. The case is easily removed, allowing access to the drum. A pan 1 in. deep at the bottom catches the dust resulting from the test. The encasement is shown in section in Fig. 3, and closed in Fig. 4.

The test pieces are wedge-shaped, having a wearing surface of 8 x 3 in., circular bottom, and a depth at the middle of 5 11/16 in. The ten wedge-shaped blocks, which constitute a test set, are arranged around the perimeter of the band, as illustrated in Fig. 5. The surface of contact between the blocks lies in a plane which passes through the axis of the drum. The distance from the surface of the blocks and the center of the drum is 12 5/16 in.

The advantages claimed for the wedge-shaped block over the rectangular block are: 1. The chipping action at the edge of contact is reduced. 2. No wooden wedges are required to hold the blocks in place.

The abrasive charge is made up of 200 lb. of cast-iron balls, ten ot

which are 3¾ in in diameter and about 133 are 1⅞ in in diameter
These balls conform to the requirements of the American Society for Test
ing Materials for the standard rattler test of paving brick

The tests covered in this paper were made on wedge shaped blocks
and 8 x 16 in cylinders  The proportions in each test were 1 part cement,
2 parts sand, and 3 parts gravel  The aggregates were taken from the
washed output of a gravel plant at Lafayette, Ind  The cement used was
a standard brand of portland cement, which passed the requirements of the
American Society for Testing Materials.

Table I —Physical Properties of Cement

| | |
|---|---|
| Normal consistency (percent by weight) | 23% |
| Initial set (Gilmore needle) | 3 hr 12 min |
| Final set (Gilmore needle) | 5 hr 02 min |
| Fineness (residue on a 200 sieve) | 17 98 |
| Soundness (over boiling water) | O K |
| Tensile strength (1 3 standard sand mortar) | |
| 7 day | 233 lb per sq in |
| 28 day | 328 lb per sq in |

Table II —Sieve Analysis of Aggregates

| Test No | Per Cent Coarser than Sieves * | | | | | | | | | Fineness Modulus |
|---|---|---|---|---|---|---|---|---|---|---|
| | No 100 | No 48 | No 28 | No 14 | No 8 | No 4 | ⅜ in | ¾ in | 1½ in | |
| 1 | 98 4 | 97 4 | 91 7 | 75 8 | 62 0 | 52 4 | 17 2 | 0 | 0 | 5 05 |
| 2 | 99 6 | 99 2 | 93 5 | 77 7 | 65 1 | 59 1 | 42 8 | 0 | 0 | 5 37 |
| 3 | 99 6 | 99 2 | 93 6 | 78 1 | 65 7 | 60 3 | 19 9 | 13 0 | 0 | 5 61 |
| 4 | 99 6 | 99 2 | 93 7 | 78 4 | 66 2 | 61 5 | 54 0 | 15 8 | 0 | 5 68 |
| 5 | 99 6 | 99 2 | 93 7 | 78 4 | 66 2 | 61 5 | 45 0 | 14 0 | 3 5 | 5 66 |
| 6 | 99 5 | 97 7 | 88 3 | 77 7 | 66 4 | 55 3 | 18 1 | 30 0 | 0 | 5 64 |
| 7 | 99 5 | 97 8 | 89 0 | 79 1 | 68 9 | 61 1 | 18 3 | 15 9 | 0 | 5 60 |
| 8 | 99 5 | 97 7 | 88 1 | 77 3 | 66 4 | 58 7 | 51 6 | 18 4 | 0 | 5 58 |
| 9 | 99 5 | 97 6 | 87 9 | 77 0 | 65 8 | 57 0 | 49 9 | 22.3 | 0 | 5 57 |
| 10 | 99 5 | 97 7 | 88 3 | 77 7 | 66 7 | 56 8 | 49 7 | 26 7 | 0 | 5 63 |
| 11 | 99 6 | 93 5 | 73 3 | 66 1 | 61 6 | 54 9 | 31 9 | 4 1 | 0 | 4 85 |
| 12 | 99 4 | 96 1 | 83 3 | 75 3 | 69 6 | 61 2 | 10 6 | 15 2 | 0 | 5 41 |
| 13 | 99 3 | 93 7 | 80 6 | 73 2 | 66 6 | 66 6 | 29 9 | 10 1 | 0 | 5 09 |
| 14 | 99 6 | 97 9 | 87 9 | 77 1 | 66 6 | 57 4 | 31 1 | 12 2 | 0 | 5 33 |
| 15 | 98 4 | 90 0 | 77 4 | 67 4 | 59 1 | 45 7 | 11 4 | 5 5 | 1 7 | 4 65 |
| 16 | 97 9 | 92 4 | 78 1 | 64 8 | 55 6 | 41 3 | 10 2 | 0 | 0 | 4 40 |
| 17 | 97 9 | 92 1 | 78 4 | 67 0 | 59 7 | 50 5 | 31 1 | 0 2 | 0 | 4 77 |
| 18 | 97 9 | 92 4 | 78 2 | 67 0 | 60 6 | 53 1 | 38 2 | 11 7 | 0 | 4 94 |
| 19 | 97 9 | 92 5 | 78 5 | 68 1 | 63 3 | 60 9 | 52 6 | 29 3 | 0 | 5 43 |
| 20 | 97 9 | 92 6 | 78 8 | 68 1 | 62 2 | 56 3 | 41 8 | 24 6 | 0 | 5 25 |

* Tyler Standard Sieves

A separate batch of concrete was made for each test piece, each batch
being hand-mixed in a shallow pan  The materials were weighed separately
and mixed dry, after which water was added until the concrete gave a
slump of from ½ to 1 in in a freshly molded 6 x 12 in cylinder  This
method for obtaining the slump is the same as used at the Structural
Materials Research Laboratory Lewis Institute, Chicago  The concrete
was tamped in the molds with a steel tamper that weighed approximately
2½ lb and had an end 1 in square  After the operation of filling and
tamping was complete, the top was struck off with a mason's trowel

Both the wear blocks and cylinders received the same curing treatment
They were removed from the molds in 24 hours, stored in damp sand for a
period of 10 days and then placed in air in the laboratory until tested
The testing was done at 28 days

The wear test consists of exposing the inner surface of the ten blocks
to the action of the 200 lb abrasive charge for 1800 revolutions at the rate
of 30 r p m   The machine was run in one direction for 900 revolutions
and then reversed.

TABLE III—RESULTS OF TESTS OF CONCRETE

Wear tests of wedge shaped concrete blocks 8 x 8 in  on original surface
Compression tests of 8 x 16 in  concrete cylinders
Mix 1  2  3, by volume, age at test, 28 days  stored 10 days in damp sand  17 days in air in the laboratory
Materials weighed separately  concrete mixed by hand, concrete tamped in forms
Consistency was such as to give a slump of ½ in  to 1 in  in a freshly molded 6 x 12 in  concrete cylinder
Each wear test value is the average from ten wear blocks
Each compression test is the average of two cylinders

| Test No | Fineness Modulus | Water Ratio | Depth of Wear (in ) | Compressive Strength (lbs  per  sq  in ) |
|---|---|---|---|---|
| 1 | 5 03 | 0 767 | 0 714 | 3452 |
| 2 | 5 37 | 0 786 | 0 683 | 3474 |
| 3 | 5 61 | 0 778 | 0 651 | 4115 |
| 4 | 5 68 | 0 757 | 0 673 | 3785 |
| 5 | 5 66 | 0 640 | 0 642 | 4075 |
| 6 | 5 64 | 0 719 | 0 554 | 3870 |
| 7 | 5 60 | 0 656 | 0 560 | 3544 |
| 8 | 5 58 | 0 759 | 0 661 | 3450 |
| 9 | 5 57 | 0 765 | 0 571 | 3511 |
| 10 | 5 63 | 0 741 | 0 602 | 3703 |
| 11 | 4 85 | 0 777 | 0 841 | 2805 |
| 12 | 5 41 | 0 844 | 0 738 | 3033 |
| 13 | 5 09 | 0 618 | 0 658 | 3455 |
| 14 | 5 33 | 0 770 | 0 710 | 3228 |
| 15 | 4 65 | 0 904 | 0 880 | 1744 |
| 16 | 4 40 | 1 020 | 1 025 | 1990 |
| 17 | 4 77 | 0 883 | 0 804 | 2470 |
| 18 | 4 99 | 0 894 | 0 774 | 2207 |
| 19 | 5 43 | 0 841 | 0 701 | 2430 |
| 20 | 5 25 | 0 835 | 0 715 | 2462 |

The compressive strength tests were made on a 200,000 lb Riehle testing machine   All cylinders were capped with plaster of paris and were
tested on a spherical bearing block

Table II gives the sieve analysis of the aggregates, showing the
percents coarser than certain Tyler standard sieves  The following sieves
were taken:  100, 48, 28, 14, 8, 4, ⅜, ¾, 1½   Each sieve is made of
square mesh cloth, having an opening double the width of the preceding one

The fineness modulus, as shown in this table, was determined by dividing the sum of the percents retained on the sieves by 100   It varies from
4 40 to 5 68 for these tests

Table III gives the results of the tests on concrete   The water-ratio as used in this table is an expression for the ratio of the volume of water to the volume of cement, considering the cement to weigh 94 lb. per cu ft.

The depth of wear is based on the loss in weight after abrasion.  The wear blocks were weighed before and after being submitted to the wear test, and the loss in weight determined   The depth of wear is expressed by the formula

$$D = \sqrt{\dfrac{L \times 24\,97}{W}}$$

where

$D$ = the depth of wear
$L$ = loss in weight in pounds
$W$ = weight per cubic foot of concrete

This formula takes into account the increase in the surface due to the increase in the depth of wear

Some of the points on the accompanying curve sheets represent tests upon stone while the data for these tests have not been included in the tables   However, the curves would only be slightly affected

It is recognized by the writer that the number of tests reported on in this paper is insufficient from which to establish any definite conclusions and therefore in the discussions of the curves reference is made to curves from the recent works of Prof Duff A  Abrams  Lewis Institute  Chicago

Fig  6  which compares the compressive strength to the water-ratio, shows the influence of water on the strength, under the conditions and range of these tests, i  e , for one mix  one curing condition and one consistency   It is seen from the curve that a concrete having a low water ratio has a higher strength than one with a greater water ratio.  The curve A taken from 'The Effect of Time and Mixing on the Strength of Concrete," by Prof  Abrams, has the same general slope and covers, approximately  the same area as the curve from these data, the variation being due to the difference in the mixtures, methods, and cement   In curve A the mix and grading were maintained constant, but the water content varied, giving different consistencies   The comparison shows two ways of affecting the quantity of water in a concrete mixture, in the case of these tests, it being accomplished by different grading and in the other case by different consistencies

A comparison of the wear to the water-ratio is made in Fig  7   This curve shows that with an increase in the water content of a concrete the depth of wear is also increased   This curve coincides with a portion of the curve taken from Fig 8 of Bulletin No  2 of Lewis Institute   The conditions under these tests were the same as those mentioned for the strength water ratio curves

Strength and wear are combined in a curve shown in Fig 8   From this curve it is seen that a concrete giving a high strength shows a low wear and one giving a low strength shows a high wear.  Recalling the two

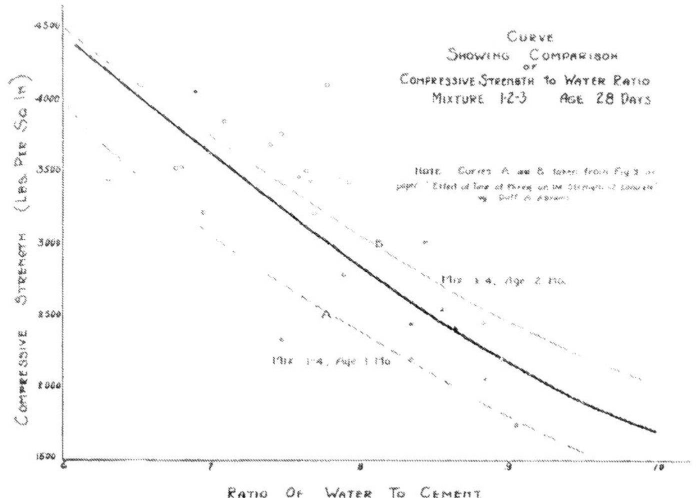


FIG. 6.—CURVE SHOWING COMPARISON OF COMPRESSIVE STRENGTH TO WATER-RATIO.

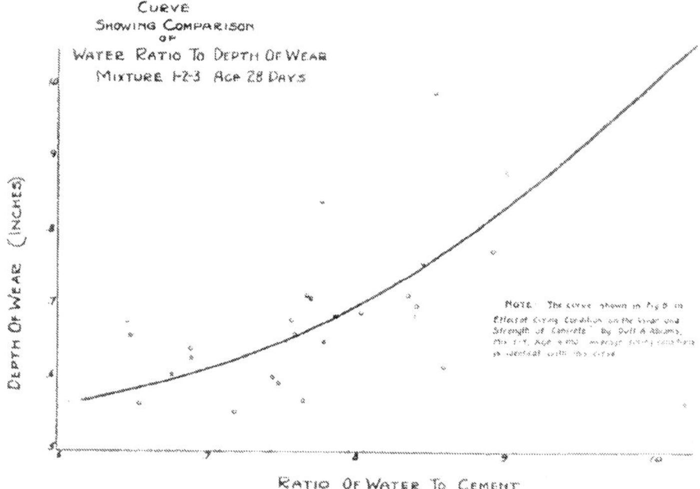


FIG. 7.—CURVE SHOWING COMPARISON OF DEPTH OF WEAR TO WATER-RATIO.

preceding curves, it is seen that the reason for this relation lies in the water ratio, since both the strength and wear are controlled by the water content.

A comparison curve (A) is taken from Fig 10 in Bulletin No 2, Lewis Institute  This is a curve of a 1 4 mix of various consistencies and different curing conditions  Both curves are similar in character

Studying these curves we see that it is the water content which produces the marked effect on the strength and wear, regardless of the factors

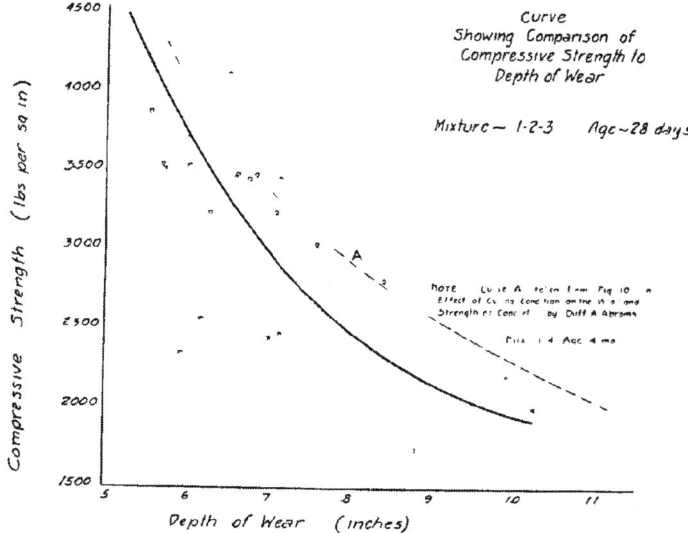


FIG  8 —CURVE SHOWING COMPARISON OF COMPRESSIVE STRENGTH TO DEPTH<br>OF WEAR

producing the change, since in one case the grading varies and in the other case the consistency changes, both affecting the water ratio

Fig 9 shows a curve comparing the compressive strength to fineness modulus  Fig 10 shows a curve comparing the depth of wear to the fineness modulus  These relations can be compared since the same consistency was used in all concretes  It is also seen from the data that, for one mix, as the fineness modulus increases the water ratio decreases  Evidence for this latter relation has been observed in the standard tensile strength tests of Indiana sands, at Purdue University

The results obtained from this method of wear test are not entirely satisfactory  It has been observed by inspecting the wear blocks after

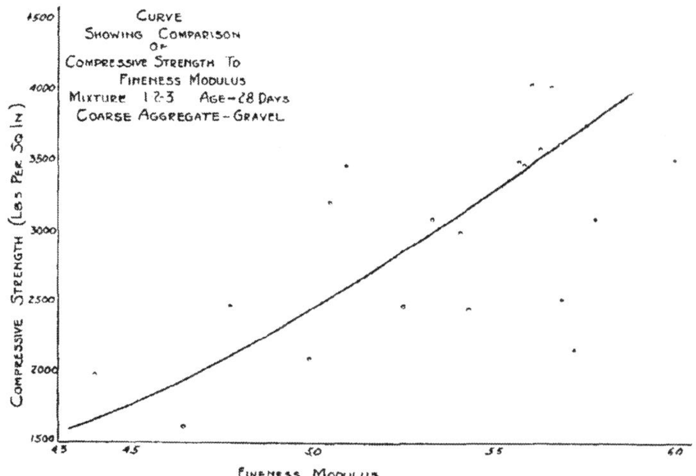



FIG 9—CURVE SHOWING COMPARISON OF COMPRESSIVE STRENGTH TO FINE-
NESS MODULUS

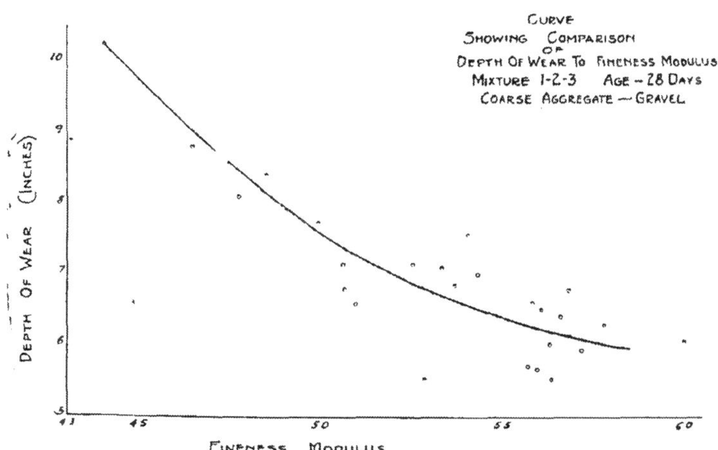



FIG 10—CURVE SHOWING COMPARISON OF DEPTH OF WEAR TO FINENESS
MODULUS

going through the test that the edges of the blocks next to the drum and
cover have received an extra amount of wear, and in a number of cases
particles of the coarse aggregate have been knocked out   This is especi
ally noted in cases where the maximum size of the coarse aggregate is
large   This effect is not noticed on blocks in which the maximum size is
small   Since the depths of wear range from $\frac{1}{4}$ to 1 in for a 1 2 3 mix or
a slump between $\frac{1}{2}$ to 1 in , any chipping or knocking out of the larger
particles from the edge seems objectionable

In conclusion, the results of these tests indicate that, for a 1 2 3 mix
in which the fineness modulus varies and the consistency is constant.
general relations exist between·

1   Compressive Strength and Water Content.
2   Wear and Water-Ratio
3   Compressive Strength and Wear
4   Compressive Strength and Fineness Modulus
5   Wear and Fineness Modulus

## DISCUSSION

Mr Stanton Walker—I should like to ask whether you have made enough tests at Purdue to show that there is a general relation between strength and wear for different sources of aggregate? At the Lewis Institute we have made a great number of tests for different gradings of sand-pebble aggregates, and a few good grades of aggregates of different nature, but I do not know of any considerable number of tests where the quality of the aggregate has extended over any considerable range I should like to ask if your tests answer the question whether or not the strength is a function of the wear over any wide ranges in quality of aggregate?

Mr R. B. Crepps—The tests at Purdue University do not cover a large enough scope to finally justify that conclusion The materials tested so far in the wear tests have been practically of one quality We have made a small comparison with materials from different parts of the state, but the tests are rather limited However, the indications are that the different qualities of gravel do not make a very marked change in the strength and wear

Mr Walker—We have made tests on about four different aggregates, all of them rather good grade, and we have found that the strengths are as nearly the same as one could expect, for the same fineness of modulus and the same mix and the same consistency There has been some little variation in wear, the softer aggregates seem to give somewhat higher wear than the harder aggregates. I think we will hardly be justified in making only the one test until we are absolutely sure that the strength is a criterion for the wear

Mr K H Talbot—I was particularly interested in the statement that these specimens were stored in sand for only ten days and then broken Within the past year I have been questioning whether a concrete pavement subjected to curing, due to moisture underneath and all around, was given a much better chance to harden than specimens made in this way If any one has tests of specimens kept in moist sand for a year or even six months and tests made as in Mr Crepps' series, on which they can pass judgment as to the relative effect of water content on wear, it would be interesting

Mr Fuller—I think that the answer will be found in Bulletin No 2 of the Structural Materials Research Laboratories In this bulletin tests are reported for concrete three or four months old Some of the specimens were stored in damp sand for the entire time, some were stored in air for the entire period, some were stored first in sand and then in air for various periods The tests show an increase in strength and a decrease in wear for the longer periods of storage in damp sand, with one exception—the wear tests on the four months blocks— which were made while the blocks were still moist  In them there is a slight increase in wear, probably due to the moisture in the surface of the concrete  Had those blocks been dried out three or four days before the tests  the same relations would probably have obtained  For periods up to very nearly the whole time of the storage you will find an increase in strength and a decrease in wear with the storage of the specimen

COMPRESSIVE STRENGTH OF CONCRETE IN FLEXURE

By W A Slater* and R R Zipprodt *

For calculations of strength in the design of reinforced concrete beams,
the use of the "straight line" formula has become almost universal   In
adopting this formula it has been generally recognized that the compressive stresses calculated by its use were greater than those actually
developed under the conditions assumed

As time has passed it seems as if this feature has been lost sight of
by many designers, and as if a beam is supposed to be on the point of
failure by compression in the concrete if calculations by the straight line
formula show a compressive stress equal to the ultimate cylinder strength
of the concrete   The few published test results in which failure occurred
primarily by compression indicate clearly that this is not the case   Further,
there have been indications that for beams with sufficient longitudinal
reinforcement to develop the compressive strength of the concrete, failure
by compression would not occur until the compressive stress calculated
by the parabolic formula was higher than the cylinder strength of the
concrete   In tests of concrete cylinders in direct compression it seems
likely that failure is precipitated in many cases by the reaching of the
ultimate strength at some portion of the cylinder while the cylinder is
given credit for having a strength equal only to the average stress at
failure   In a beam it is upon the development of the maximum (extreme
fiber) stress that failure should occur when the extreme fiber stress is
equal to the average cylinder strength if in the latter it is a higher stress
than the average which precipitates failure

If these indications are to be relied upon it would seem a safe pro
cedure to permit an increase in the working stress in compression above
that generally used in reinforced concrete design

To obtain some information on this subject tests were made by the
United States Bureau of Standards at the John Fritz Civil Engineering
Laboratory of Lehigh University in 1919 on four reinforced concrete
beams

Tests made at about the same time on four beams at Lafayette Col-
lege, Easton, Pennsylvania  also gave some information on this subject
These tests were carried out by Messrs H E Baugh, P D Kern and
C B Kidney as thesis work under the direction of Professor A H Fuller
Acknowledgment is made to these men and to Professor Fuller for per
mission to use the data in this paper

Since the carrying out of these tests it has been learned that in
a considerable number of beams tested in 1908 by the United States
Geological Survey in the structural materials investigation at St Louis

*U S  Bureau of Standards, Washington, D C

from 1905 to 1908, under the direction of Mr. Richard L. Humphrey, failure occurred by compression in the concrete. Some of these hitherto unpublished data have been available for this paper, but there are others for which certain information, which is essential if the data are to be used, has not yet been found.

*Test Specimens:* - Fig. 1 gives the details of the beams tested at Lehigh University. The beams were 10 ft. 8 in. in length. At the center

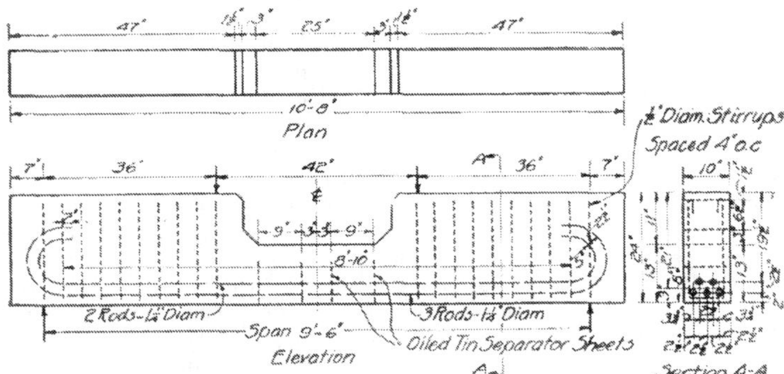


FIG. 1—DETAILS OF BEAMS TESTED BY THE BUREAU OF STANDARDS AT LEHIGH UNIVERSITY.

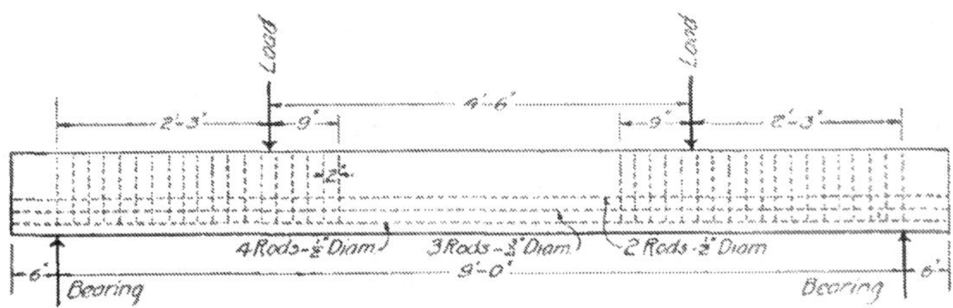


FIG. 2—ELEVATION OF BEAMS TESTED AT LAFAYETTE COLLEGE.

the beams had a cross-section 10 in. wide and 13 in. high. The beams were reinforced for longitudinal tension by five 1¼-in. round rods, hooked at the ends for anchorage. The yield-point stress for this reinforcement was about 55,000 lb. per sq. in. Two of the rods were in the upper layer, 8½ in. below the compression surface, and three were in the lower layer, 11 in. below the compression surface. Between the load points and the points of support, the ends of the beams were reinforced with ½-in. round vertical U stirrups, spaced 4 in. on centers. One ½-in. rod was placed longitudinally in the top of the enlarged portion of the beam on each side of the center to maintain the spacing and level of the stirrups  In each beam, oiled tin separator sheets were placed 3 in  and 9 in  on either side of the center line of the beam  These extended upward from the bottom of the beam for a distance of 8 in  thus effectively cutting the concrete in the tension portion of the beam at four places  Control cylinders 8 in  by 16 in  were made at the same time that the beams were made and were stored under conditions as nearly like the storage conditions of the beams as seemed feasible

Figs  2 and 3 give the details of the beams made at Lafayette College Easton, Pa  These beams were rectangular in cross-section, being 8 in wide  11 in  deep over all  and 10 ft  0 in  in length  The reinforcement consisted of three 3 in  round rods and six ½ in  round rods distributed in three layers  The distance from the center of gravity of the steel to the compression surface was 8½ in  The ends of the beams, from the points of support to a point 9 in  beyond the load points, were reinforced by ¼ in  vertical U stirrups spaced 2 in  on centers

All the beams were made of 1 2 4 concrete, the proportions being by weight  The forms of beams 1A and 2A (see Table I) were mechanically vibrated while the beams were being poured  The forms of beams 1B and 2B were hand tamped during pouring  The percentage of water used in beams 1A and 1B was 9 0  that in 2A and 2B was 8 0  The control specimens were 8 x 16 in  cylinders

The beams made and tested by the United States Geological Survey consisted of two series  In Series 21 there were 90 beams, in Series 21A there were 48 beams  Of these only those which were reported to have failed by compression in the concrete were reported in this paper in Tables II and III  Fig  4 shows the details of the beams  All the beams of these two series were rectangular in cross section, 8 in  wide, 11 in  high and 13 ft  0 in  in length  Three 1 in  round rods were used as tension reinforcement in all beams  The yield point stress for the reinforcement as determined by the average of 15 tests was 38 200 lb  per sq  in  The sketch giving the design of the specimens and certain photographs which are available show each rod bearing a 1-in  hexagonal nut at either end of the beam  Evidence, in the form of notes of these tests showing that these nuts were used, has not been found  and since failure of a number of the beams was due to slipping of the rods  it is open to question whether the nuts were used on all the beams *  Each end of each beam between the load point and the point of support was reinforced by ¼-in  round stirrups spaced 4 in  on centers

In Series 21, two kinds of aggregate were used, gravel and limestone  Both were combined in proportions by volume of 1 3 6  In Series 21A gravel only was used, and in the proportions by volume of 1 2 4  Tables

---

* Since the publication of this text, Mr  Richard L  Humphrey, who was in charge of the investigation, has stated that nuts, as required by Fig  4, were used in all beams

II and III give the details of the making of the beams in the two series. One of the original purposes in the tests made at St. Louis was to obtain data showing a comparison between the results of laboratory tests and results obtained by several contractors using their own methods of pouring. The companies making the beams are designated in Tables II and III as

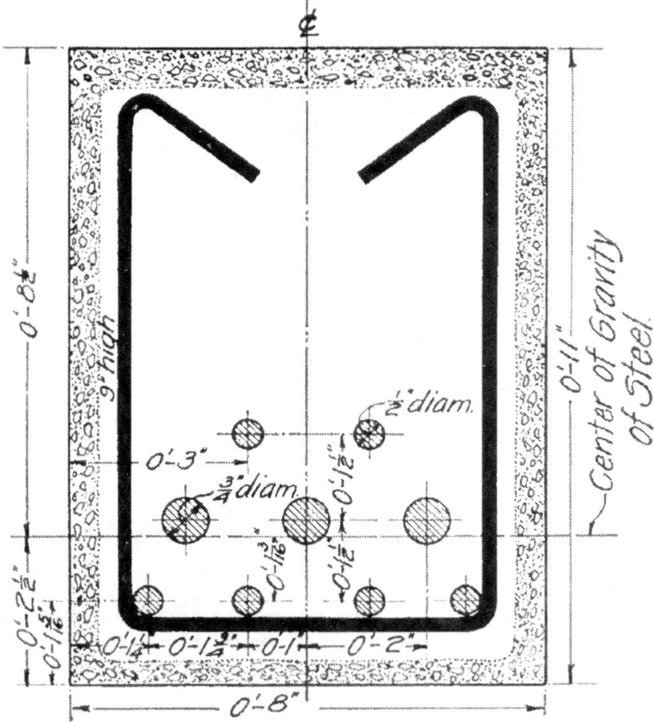


FIG. 3.—CROSS-SECTION OF BEAMS TESTED AT LAFAYETTE COLLEGE.

Company A, Company B and Company C. The Structural Materials Testing Laboratory is indicated by the initials S. M. T. L.

In both Series 21 and 21A, 8 by 16-in. control cylinders were made with the beams and were stored under conditions similar to the storage of the beams.

*Testing:* The beams at Lehigh University were tested at an age of 28 days, and on a span of 9 ft. 6 in. The load points were 42 in. apart, the distance from each load point to the corresponding support thus being

## TABLE I

### DATA OF BEAMS TESTED AT LAFAYETTE COLLEGE AND AT LEHIGH UNIVERSITY

(All stresses are given in pounds per square inch )

| Beam No | Maximum Load, lb | Cylinder Strength, lb per sq in | Computed Stress | | | Ratio fc to Cylinder Strength | | Ratio-Secant Modulus to Initial Modulus | Unit Deformation at Maximum Load | |
| | | | Tension | Compression | | | | | | |
| | | | Straight Line | Straight Line | Parabolic | Straight Line | Parabolic | | Steel | Concrete |
|---|---|---|---|---|---|---|---|---|---|---|
| | | | | TESTS AT LAFAYETTE COLLEGE | | | | | | |
| 1A | 40,980 | 1,321 | 33,000 | 3 840 | 2 780 | 2 90 | 2 10 | | | |
| 1B | 41,950 | 1,490 | 33,800 | 3 930 | 2,840 | 2 64 | 1 91 | | | |
| 2A | 47,770 | 2,060 | 38,500 | 4 460 | 3,210 | 2 16 | 1 57 | | | |
| 2B | 44 200 | 1 840 | 35,700 | 4,110 | 3 000 | 2 19 | 1 59 | | | |
| | | | BUREAU OF STANDARDS TESTS AT LEHIGH UNIVERSITY | | | | | | | |
| 14AA11 | 91 200 | 3 280 | 33,600 | 6 250 | 4,560 | 1 91 | 1 39 | 0 79 | 0 00146 | 0 00316 |
| 14AA12 | 87,750 | 3 300 | 32 300 | 6,000 | 4,390 | 1 82 | 1 33 | 0 79 | 0 00120 | 0 00269 |
| 14AB21 | 79 060 | 2,480 | 27 700 | 4 660 | 3 450 | 1 58 | 1 39 | 0 81 | 0 00111 | 0 00284 |
| 14AB22 | 74 100 | 2,410 | 26 000 | 4 380 | 3 240 | 1 82 | 1 35 | 0 46 | 0 00106 | 0 00238 |

## TABLE II.

### DATA OF BEAMS OF SERIES 21 TESTED BY THE UNITED STATES GEOLOGICAL SURVEY AT ST LOUIS IN 1908.

Proportions of Concrete 1 . 3  6

| Beam No | Made by | Forms | Aggregate | Mixing | Storage | Age, weeks | Maximum Load lb | Cylindrical Strgth lb per sq in | Computed Stress Tension Straight Line | Computed Stress Compression Straight Line | Computed Stress Compression Parabola | Ratio to Cylinder Strength Straight Line | Ratio to Cylinder Strength Parabola | Ratio Secant to Initial Modulus | Unit Deformation at Maximum load Steel | Unit Deformation at Maximum load Concrete |
|---|---|---|---|---|---|---|---|---|---|---|---|---|---|---|---|---|
| 779 | Co A | Wood | Gravel | Hand | Outside | 4 | 16,310 | 833 | 21 800 | 2 190 | 1,580 | 2 63 | 1 90 | 0 30 | 0 00130 | 0.00220 |
| 780 | " A | " | " | | | 4 | 12 920 | 789 | 17,300 | 1 740 | 1 250 | 2 20 | 1 58 | 0 58 | 0 00115 | 0 00280 |
| 800 | " A | Steel | " | | Inside | 13 | 19 000 | 660 | 23 400 | 2 550 | 1 840 | 3 86 | 2 79 | 0 38 | 0 00120 | 0 00327 |
| 791 | " A | " | " | Machine | | 4 | 14,500 | 885 | 19 350 | 1,950 | 1 400 | 2 20 | 1 58 | 0 41 | 0 00092 | 0 00215 |
| 792 | " A | | " | " | | 4 | 11 610 | 650 | 15 500 | 1 560 | 1 120 | 2 40 | 1 72 | 0 49 | 0 00078 | 0 00254 |
| 795 | " A | " | " | | " | 13 | 16 700 | 1 470 | 22,300 | 2 240 | 1 620 | 1 52 | 1 10 | 0 50 | 0 00110 | 0 00200 |
| 811 | " B | Wood | Limestone | Hand | Outside | 13 | 10,560 | 581 | 14 100 | 1 420 | 1 020 | 2 43 | 1 75 | 0 43 | 0 00083 | 0 00243 |
| 856 | " B | Steel | Gravel | " | Inside | 4 | 10 750 | 537 | 14 350 | 1 440 | 1 040 | 2 68 | 1 94 | 0 44 | 0 00076 | 0 00174 |
| 858 | B | " | " | | | 4 | 8 400 | 672 | 11 200 | 1 130 | 810 | 1 68 | 1 21 | 0 46 | 0 00068 | 0 00268 |
| 822 | " B | " | " | Machine | | 4 | 8 160 | 577 | 10,900 | 1,100 | 790 | 1 91 | 1 37 | 0 24 | 0 00049 | 0 00213 |
| 827 | " C | Wood | Limestone | Hand | Outside | 4 | 9 700 | 607 | 12 900 | 1 300 | 940 | 2 56 | 1 85 | 0 22 | 0 00042 | 0 00194 |
| 829 | C | | " | | " | 13 | 8 000 | 1,380 | 10,700 | 1 070 | 775 | 0 78 | 0 56 | 0 48 | 0 00059 | 0 00265 |
| 830 | C | " | " | " | " | 13 | 10,300 | 636 | 13 750 | 1 380 | 1 000 | 2 17 | 1 57 | 0 56 | 0 00058 | 0 00236 |
| 838 | " C | Steel | Gravel | Machine | Inside | 4 | 9 450 | 725 | 12,600 | 1 270 | 915 | 1 75 | 1 26 | 0 44 | | |
| 839 | " C | | " | " | " | 4 | 8 200 | 684 | 10,900 | 1,100 | 790 | 1 60 | 1 15 | 0 54 | | |
| 840 | " C | " | " | | " | 4 | 9 360 | 623 | 12 500 | 1 960 | 910 | 2 02 | 1 46 | 0 23 | | |
| 841 | " C | " | " | | " | 13 | 18 030 | 956 | 24 100 | 2 420 | 1 750 | 2 53 | 1 83 | 0 44 | | |
| 842 | C | " | " | | " | 13 | 20 500 | 1,243 | 27 400 | 2 760 | 1 980 | 2 22 | 1 59 | 0 52 | | |
| 843 | C | " | " | | " | 13 | 19,570 | 1,214 | 24,800 | 2,490 | 1 790 | 2 05 | 1 47 | 0 30 | | |
| 805 | S M T L | " | " | | Outside | 4 | 15 150 | 789 | 20 200 | 2 030 | 1 470 | 2 58 | 1 86 | 0 47 | 0 00068 | 0 00182 |
| 807 | | " | " | | " | 4 | 16 750 | 658 | 22 400 | 2,250 | 1 620 | 3 42 | 2 46 | 0 28 | 0 00082 | 0 00201 |
| 804 | " | " | " | | " | 13 | 17 150 | 1 210 | 22 900 | 2,300 | 1 660 | 1 90 | 1 37 | 0 60 | 0 00087 | 0 00222 |
| 853 | " | " | Limestone | | " | 13 | 15,000 | 1,200 | 20 000 | 2 010 | 1 450 | 1 68 | 1 21 | 0 52 | 0 00073 | 0 00185 |
| 863 | " | " | Gravel | | Inside | 4 | 16 700 | 961 | 22,300 | 2,240 | 1 620 | 2 43 | 1 69 | 0 43 | 0 00093 | 0 00239 |
| 864 | " | " | " | | " | 4 | 13 000 | 1 074 | 17 350 | 1 740 | 1 260 | 1 62 | 1 17 | 0 59 | 0 00065 | 0 00199 |

36 in   The initial load applied to all beams was 5,000 lb, at which load the initial strain gage readings were taken   Load was applied thereafter in increments of 15,000 lb for all beams except 14AA11, in which the load was applied in increments of 20,000 lb

Strain gage readings for the determination of the deformations in the concrete were taken on two gage lines on the top (the compression) surface of the beam   These readings were over 4-in gage lengths and were taken on brass plugs set into the concrete with the surface of the plug flush with the top surface of the beam   Strain gage readings for the determination of the stresses developed in the tension reinforcement were taken on each side of the beam at the center line of the lower outside rods   The location of the gage line on the reinforcement on one side of each beam is shown in Fig 5   Center deflections were also taken on all the beams

The beams of the series made at Lafayette College were tested at an age of 30 days   The span length was 9 ft 0 in and the beams were loaded at the one-quarter points of the span   The distance between load points being 4 ft 6 in in the distance between load point and the corresponding support was 2 ft. 3 in.

The beams made at the Structural Materials Testing Laboratory were all tested on a span of 12 ft 0 in   A number of the beams were tested at an age of 4 weeks, and the remainder at the age of 13 weeks   The beams were all loaded at the one-third points of the span

Longitudinal deformations ½ in below the upper fiber and approximately at the elevation of the reinforcement (9¾ in below the upper surface of the beam) were measured by means of a friction roller extensometer   The gage length over which the deformations were measured was 29¼ in   The method of attaching the instruments is shown in Technologic Paper No 2, U S Bureau of Standards   Center deflection of the beams and end slip of the rods were measured also

*Manner of Failure*   In the beams tested at Lehigh University large quantities of longitudinal reinforcement were used to preclude failure by tension in the reinforcement   An enlarged section outside the load points was used to preclude failure due to high shearing stresses   The phenomena of the tests indicated conclusively that failure was by compression   The yield point stress of the reinforcement was around 55 000 lb per sq in and both the computed and measured tensile stresses were so much below this (see Table I) that there is no chance of compression failure having been brought on by reaching the yield-point stress in the reinforcement   Fig 5 is a view showing the beams after completion of the test

For the beams tested at Lafayette College the yield-point stress of the reinforcement is not known   Inspection of the beams after the test showed that all cracks, both vertical and diagonal, had so nearly closed that failure by either longitudinal or diagonal tension could not have been imminent   Failure was reported to have been by compression and it seems as though there can be no question that such was the case

| Beam No | Made by | Forms | Aggregate | Mixing | Storage | Age weeks | Maximum load lb | Cylindrical Strgth lb per sq in | Computed Stress Tension Straight Line | Computed Stress Compression Straight Line | Computed Stress Compression Parabola | Ratio fc to Cylinder Strength Straight line | Ratio fc to Cylinder Strength Parabola | Ratio Secant to Initial Modulus | Unit Deformation at Maximum Load Steel | Unit Deformation at Maximum Load Concrete |
|---|---|---|---|---|---|---|---|---|---|---|---|---|---|---|---|---|
| 1095 | Co. A | Wood | Gravel | Machine | Outside | 1 | 15,400 | 1,285 | 20,600 | 2,070 | 1,490 | 1 61 | 1 16 | 0 43 | 0 00104 | 0 00117 |
| 1096 | " A | " | " | " | " | 4 | 18,800 | 1,260 | 25,100 | 2,520 | 1,820 | 2 00 | 1 43 | 0 11 | 0 00106 | 0 00175 |
| 1097 | " A | " | " | " | " | 4 | 19,750 | 1,338 | 26,400 | 2,650 | 1,910 | 1 98 | 1 43 | 0 45 | 0 00105 | 0 00217 |
| 1098 | " A | " | " | " | " | 13 | 25,590 | 1,720 | 34,200 | 3,440 | 2,470 | 2 00 | 1 44 | 0 45 | 0 00130 | 0 00151 |
| 1099 | " A | " | " | " | " | 13 | 21,800 | 1,830 | 29,100 | 2,920 | 2,110 | 1 60 | 1 15 | 0 44 | 0 00106 | 0 00223 |
| 1100 | " A | " | " | " | " | 13 | 25,000 | 1,670 | 33,400 | 3,360 | 2,420 | 2 01 | 1 15 | 0 57 | 0 00117 | 0 00190 |
| 1101 | " A | Steel | " | " | Inside | 4 | 22,750 | 1,163 | 30,400 | 3,060 | 2,200 | 2 63 | 1 89 | 0 38 | 0 00115 | 0 00174 |
| 1102 | " A | " | " | " | " | 4 | 19,900 | 1,596 | 26,600 | 2,670 | 1,920 | 1 75 | 1 26 | 0 52 | 0 00103 | 0 00163 |
| 1103 | " A | " | " | " | " | 4 | 21,950 | 1,659 | 29,300 | 2,950 | 2,120 | 1 78 | 1 28 | 0 53 | 0 00116 | 0 00145 |
| 1107 | " B | Wood | " | " | Outside | 4 | 20,760 | 1,750 | 27,700 | 2,790 | 2,010 | 1 60 | 1 15 | 0 50 | 0 00098 | 0 00115 |
| 1110 | " B | " | " | " | " | 13 | 23,950 | 2,130 | 37,000 | 3,210 | 2,320 | 1 51 | 1 09 | 0 50 | 0 00129 | 0 00116 |
| 1112 | " B | " | " | " | " | 13 | 28,240 | 2,100 | 37,700 | 3,790 | 2,730 | 1 80 | 1 30 | 0 15 | 0 00127 | 0 00148 |
| 1113 | " B | Steel | " | " | Inside | 4 | 19,020 | 1,935 | 26,600 | 2,680 | 1,930 | 1 39 | 1 00 | 0 48 | 0 00089 | 0 00127 |
| 1111 | " B | " | " | " | " | 4 | 19,410 | 1,757 | 25,900 | 2,610 | 1,880 | 1 49 | 1 07 | 0 45 | 0 00089 | 0 00179 |
| 1115 | " B | " | " | " | " | 4 | 20,960 | 1,700 | 28,000 | 2,810 | 2,030 | 1 65 | 1 20 | 0 49 | 0 00092 | 0 00171 |
| 1116 | " B | " | " | " | " | 13 | 30,750 | 2,600 | 41,000 | 4,130 | 2,970 | 1 59 | 1 14 | 0 62 | 0 00139 | 0 00179 |
| 1119 | " C | Wood | " | " | Outside | 4 | 21,720 | 2,388 | 29,000 | 2,910 | 2,100 | 1 22 | 0 88 | 0 18 | 0 00108 | 0 00182 |
| 1120 | " C | " | " | " | " | 4 | 20,750 | 2,282 | 27,700 | 2,780 | 2,010 | 1 22 | 0 88 | 0 41 | 0 00115 | 0 00164 |
| 1121 | " C | " | " | " | " | 1 | 18,340 | 1,998 | 21,500 | 2,160 | 1,780 | 1 23 | 0 89 | 0 42 | 0 00091 | 0 00168 |
| 1123 | " C | " | " | " | " | 13 | 21,500 | 2,150 | 32,700 | 3,290 | 2,370 | 1 53 | 1 10 | 0 58 | 0 00118 | 0 00177 |
| 1125 | " C | Steel | " | " | Inside | 4 | 22,880 | 1,917 | 30,600 | 3,070 | 2,210 | 1 60 | 1 15 | 0 41 | 0 00117 | 0 00177 |
| 1126 | " C | " | " | " | " | 1 | 20,900 | 1,996 | 27,900 | 2,810 | 2,020 | 1 43 | 1 03 | 0 50 | 0 00092 | 0 00180 |
| 1127 | " C | " | " | " | " | 4 | 17,950 | 1,624 | 21,000 | 2,110 | 1,710 | 1 48 | 1 07 | 0 38 | 0 00088 | 0 00158 |
| 1128 | " C | " | " | " | " | 13 | 27,670 | 2,230 | 37,000 | 3,710 | 2,680 | 1 66 | 1 20 | 0 42 | 0 00113 | 0 00233 |
| 1129 | " C | " | " | " | " | 13 | 26,900 | 2,400 | 35,900 | 3,610 | 2,500 | 1 50 | 1 08 | 0 60 | 0 00114 | 0 00213 |
| 1130 | " C | " | " | " | " | 13 | 25,790 | 2,330 | 31,400 | 3,160 | 2,590 | 1 49 | 1 11 | 0 48 | 0 00139 | 0 00216 |
| 1131 | S M T I | " | " | " | Outside | 4 | 22,610 | 2,600 | 30,200 | 3,040 | 2,190 | 1 17 | 0 84 | 0 51 | 0 00106 | 0 00157 |
| 1132 | " | " | " | " | " | 1 | 23,770 | 2,560 | 31,700 | 3,180 | 2,300 | 1 24 | 0 90 | 0 50 | 0 00113 | 0 00165 |
| 1133 | " | " | " | " | " | 4 | 21,050 | 2,583 | 32,100 | 3,220 | 2,330 | 1 25 | 0 90 | 0 57 | 0 00108 | 0 00190 |
| 1134 | " | " | " | " | " | 13 | 28,490 | 2,698 | 38,000 | 3,820 | 2,760 | 1 42 | 1 02 | 0 52 | 0 00114 | 0 00200 |
| 1135 | " | " | " | " | " | 13 | 26,710 | 2,648 | 35,600 | 3,580 | 2,580 | 1 35 | 0 97 | 0 51 | 0 00131 | 0 00200 |
| 1136 | " | " | " | " | " | 13 | 21,990 | 2,712 | 33,300 | 3,360 | 2,120 | 1 21 | 0 89 | 0 68 | 0 00123 | 0 00168 |
| 1137 | " | " | " | " | Inside | 4 | 24,000 | 2,500 | 32,000 | 3,220 | 2,320 | 1 29 | 0 93 | 0 65 | 0 00127 | 0 00220 |
| 1138 | " | " | " | " | " | 4 | 24,540 | 2,371 | 32,800 | 3,300 | 2,380 | 1 39 | 1 00 | 0 64 | 0 00139 | 0 00196 |
| 1139 | " | " | " | " | " | 4 | 24,000 | 2,100 | 32,000 | 3,220 | 2,320 | 1 54 | 1 11 | 0 47 | 0 00122 | 0 00206 |
| 1140 | " | " | " | " | " | 13 | 32,000 | 2,900 | 42,700 | 4,300 | 3,100 | 1 48 | 1 07 | 0 52 | 0 00156 | 0 00202 |
| 1141 | " | " | " | " | " | 13 | 31,000 | 2,770 | 41,400 | 4,160 | 3,000 | 1 51 | 1 09 | 0 60 | 0 00152 | 0 00205 |
| 1142 | " | " | " | " | " | 13 | 32,990 | 2,808 | 41,000 | 4,120 | 3,190 | 1 57 | 1 14 | 0 54 | 0 00148 | 0 00203 |

The St Louis beams included in this paper are those which out of a larger series were reported by the test observers to have failed by compression  For the majority of cases there seems to be no reason for questioning the correctness of this opinion  However for the beams having concrete of a high strength the tensile stresses were so high in some cases (see Tables II and III) that it seems probable that the primary failure was by tension and that the compression failure followed as a result of the tension failure  This opinion is confirmed by the fact that in two cases the neutral axis rose after the maximum load had been passed, instead of falling as would have been expected if failure had been primarily by compression  If with the concrete of higher strengths, tension was a factor in the development of failure this may help to account for the

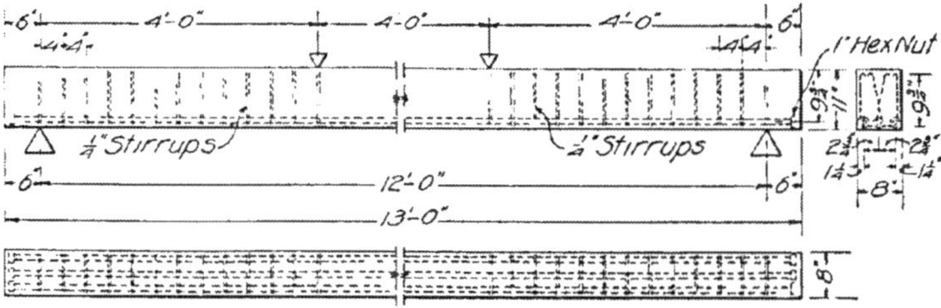


FIG. 4—DETAILS OF BEAMS TESTED BY THE UNITED STATES GEOLOGICAL SURVEY AT ST LOUIS IN 1908

tact that the points of Figs 8 and 9 which represent beams of the St Louis series fall below those of the beams which were tested at Lehigh University and at Lafayette College

*Tables and Diagrams*  Tables I, II and III give the general data of the tests reported in this paper  The calculated values are based upon average dimensions for beams of a given group rather than measured dimensions of individual beams  For the St Louis beams the average measured depth was 9 56 in and the average width was 8 1 in  The maximum variation from the average was 4 per cent and the average variation from the average was 2 2 per cent  The ratio of reinforcement for the St Louis beams was taken as 0 0304 for all beams

The dimensions of beams tested at Lehigh University varied somewhat and separate averages for the two groups were used  For beams 14AA11 and 12 the average width was 10 05 in, the average depth from the compression surface to the center of gravity of the reinforcement was 10 12 in and the average ratio of reinforcement was 0 0605  For beams 14AB21 and 22 the average width was 10 05 in, the average depth was 10 77 in, and the average ratio of reinforcement was 0 057

For the Lafayette College beams the dimensions used were those shown in Figs. 2 and 3. The ratio of reinforcement based on these dimensions is 0.0368.

Tables I, II and III give stresses computed by the straight line and parabolic formulas. In using the parabolic formula for these and all other computations in this paper, it was assumed that the vertex of the parabola, representing the stress distribution above the neutral axis, was at the top of the beam.

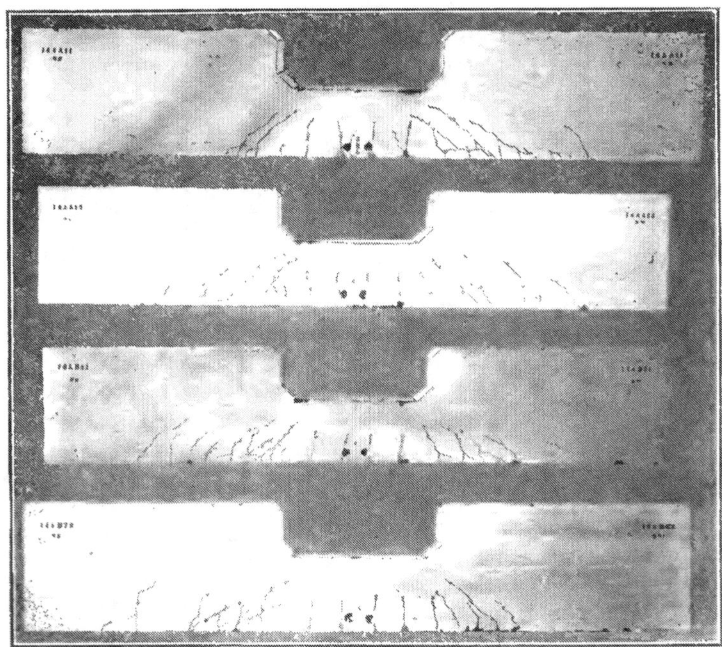

FIG. 5—VIEW OF BEAMS AT LEHIGH UNIVERSITY.

The columns in Tables II and III headed "Ratio $f$ to Cylinder Strength" give the ratios of the computed extreme fiber stresses for the maximum loads on the beams to the strengths of the control cylinders. In the column giving the ratios of the secant modulus to the initial modulus, the moduli referred to are those of the control cylinders. The secant modulus was that for the maximum load on the cylinder.

Fig. 10 shows the stress-strain curves for the control cylinders tested with the beams made at Lehigh University. Figs. 11 and 12 show the average unit deformations in the concrete at the top (compression) surface and in the reinforcement of these beams The center deflections are also shown in these diagrams The straight lines shown in these figures permit a comparison to be made between the calculated and the observed tensile stresses

Figs 13 to 24 show the average unit deformations in the concrete at the top surface and at the elevation of the reinforcement for the St Louis beams They show also the center deflection of the beams, the end slip of the reinforcing rods, and the change in position of the neutral axis during the test These diagrams have been traced directly from those prepared by the Structural Materials Testing Laboratory organization without detailed rechecking This work seems to have been done carefully and systematically The ordinates in these diagrams are in terms of

$\dfrac{M}{bd^2}$ This can be converted into load on the beam with a fair degree of accuracy by placing each thousand pounds of load equal to $\dfrac{33M}{bd^2}$

*Effect of Variation in Form of Distribution of Compressive Stresses on Intensity of Extreme of Fiber Stress* For a given load on a given beam a variation in the assumed form of the distribution of compressive stress above the neutral axis may result in a considerable variation in the intensity of the calculated compressive stress which is developed at the extreme fiber To illustrate this, Fig 6 was prepared using the data of beam 14AB21. For this purpose, it was assumed that the compressive stresses in the beam varied from zero at the neutral axis to a maximum at the extreme fiber according to the ordinates of (*a*) a straight line, (*b*) a second degree parabola with the vertex at the top of the beam, and (*c*) a fourth degree parabola with the vertex at the top of the beam The resulting stresses in the concrete and the steel based on these three assumptions are shown for the maximum load on the beam of 79,060 lb With the straight line distribution this load would have caused an extreme fiber stress of 4,900 lb per sq in With the distribution according to a second degree parabola, the extreme fiber stress would have been 3,550 lb per sq in, while with a fourth degree parabola it would have been only 2,920 lb per sq in

The calculated stresses shown in Tables I, II and III for many of the beams were considerably higher than the ultimate strengths of the control cylinders This may be due to several things

(1) As the compressive deformation in the extreme fiber increases beyond the deformation at which the corresponding cylinder would fail, there must be little corresponding increase in the stress This is generally indicated by the flattening of the stress-strain curve for high loads on a cylinder under direct compression This would bring about a distribution

of the compressive stress in the beam somewhat similar to that shown in Fig. 6 for the fourth degree parabola.

It is apparent that this form of distribution of compressive stresses would help to explain the high stress found when calculated by either the straight line or the parabolic formula. However, for this beam the stress calculated at the maximum load even by the fourth degree parabola was greater than the strength of the cylinders for the same beam, and it seems that the compressive strength in the beam must really have been greater than the cylinder strength. It is very difficult to make the curing

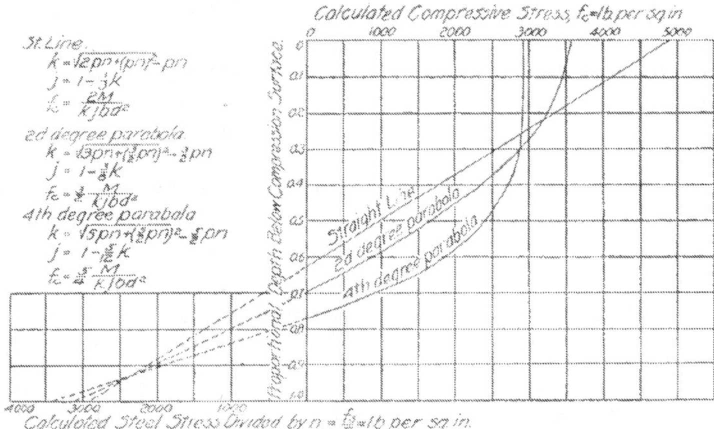


FIG. 6—STRESSES IN BEAM [4AB2] ACCORDING TO VARIOUS ASSUMPTIONS AS TO DISTRIBUTION.

conditions the same for the cylinders as for the beams, and in this way such a condition may have been brought about.

(2) The strength shown by the cylinders is an average for the entire cross-sectional area, and this average may be considerably less than the maximum stress at some point in the cylinder. This is brought out by reference to Figs. 11, 12 and 13, which give the stress-strain curves for the cylinders made with the Lafayette beams. For each cylinder the two curves show the deformations measured on opposite sides of the cylinder. In all cases the deformation on one side was greater than the average deformation. In some cases the deformation was so great that the maximum stress developed at the maximum load must have been much greater than the stress presented as the ultimate strength of the cylinder. Somewhat the same relation would have been brought out by the stress-strain curves for the cylinders made with the Lehigh beams, but for the fact

that for these tests the curves are the averages of six cylinders for each beam. The variation in stresses on opposite sides of the cylinders has been obscured by using average values for both sides and for all cylinders. No cylinder deformations are shown for the St. Louis beams, but examination of the data shows that differences in deformations existed for opposite sides of the same cylinder. Compression failure did not occur in many of the beams until the unit-deformation was nearly twice as great as that which caused failure in the cylinders. This may be seen by reference to Figs. 16 to 27.

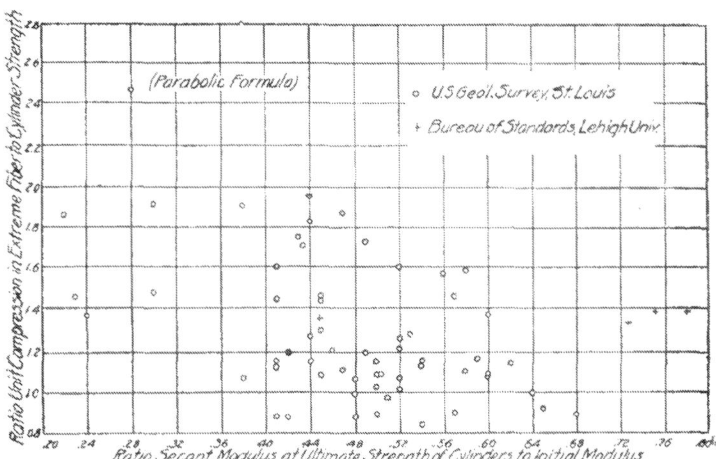


FIG. 7.—RELATION BETWEEN RATIO OF FLEXURAL STRENGTH TO CYLINDER STRENGTH, AND RATIO OF SECANT MODULUS TO INITIAL MODULUS OF ELASTICITY. FLEXURAL STRESS COMPUTED BY PARABOLIC FORMULA.

*Relation Between Form of Stress-Strain Curve and Flexural Strength:* With a low ratio secant modulus of elasticity to initial modulus a large increase in deformation with a relatively small increase in load when nearing the ultimate strength should be found to be a characteristic of the stress-strain curve for a cylinder in direct compression. With such a stress-strain curve for the concrete the form of distribution of the flexural compressive stress in a beam may be expected to resemble the conditions represented in Fig. 6 by the fourth degree parabola. If this form of stress-strain curve is associated with this form of distribution of flexural compression, then a low ratio of secant modulus to initial modulus should be accompanied by a high ratio of flexural compressive strength to cylinder strength. Fig. 7 was prepared to show what the relations in this respect were. It will be seen that in general the low ratios of moduli *do* correspond to high ratios between compressive strengths. In other words it would appear that the high ratios of flexural compressive strength to cylinder strength for the weaker concretes probably is due in some measure to the sharper curvature of their stress-strain curves. This is probably another way of saying that it is due to their lack of elasticity.

*Analysis to Determine Working Stress:* The ratios of the strengths calculated by the straight line formula and by the parabolic formula to

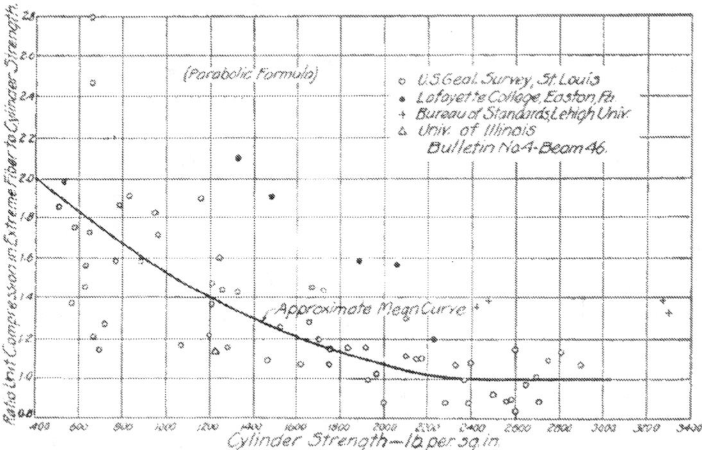


FIG. 8.—RELATION BETWEEN FLEXURAL STRENGTH BY PARABOLIC FORMULA AND CYLINDER STRENGTH OF CONCRETE IN COMPRESSION.

the cylinder strengths are shown in Tables I, II and III. These ratios for the parabolic formula have been plotted in Fig. 8 as ordinates and the compressive strengths of the corresponding cylinders as abscissas. It will be seen that generally this ratio was higher for concrete of low strength than for concrete of high strength. A small portion of the increase in this ratio may be due to the use of too high values of $n$ in the computations for the weaker concretes. Generally $n$ will be greater for the weaker than for the stronger concretes, but at most this effect would be small (perhaps 10% in extreme cases). Even so, the values of $n$ used in the calculations are those recommended by the Joint Committee,[1] and since these are the values ordinarily used for concretes of these strengths, the diagram presents a fair basis for study.

[1] See "Final Report of Joint Committee on Concrete and Reinforced Concrete," Chapter VIII, Section 8.

This diagram shows that in all cases the beams tested at Lehigh University and at Lafayette College developed higher flexural compression than did any other beams for which the cylinder strength of the concrete was the same. Why this is so is not clear, unless as suggested in the article "Manner of Failure," some of the beams of the St. Louis series having concrete of high strength failed in tension. Even though less weight be given to the beams tested at Lehigh University and Lafayette College than to the St. Louis beams (as is indicated by the approximate

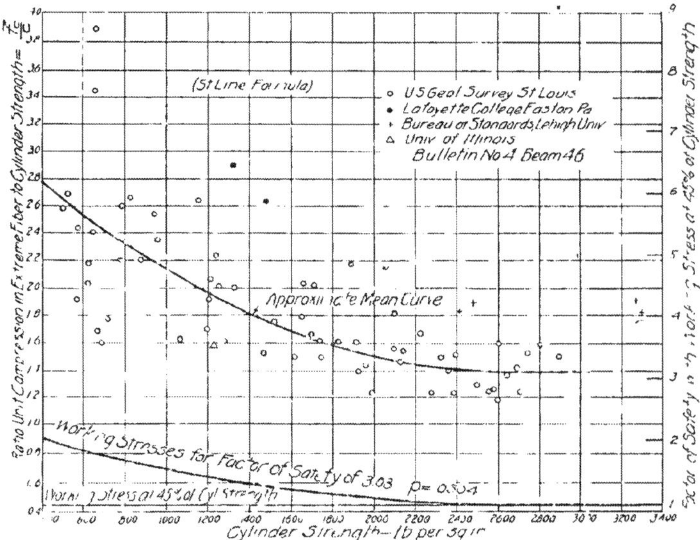


FIG 9 —RELATION BETWEEN FLEXURAL STRENGTH BY STRAIGHT LINE FORMULA AND CYLINDER STRENGTH OF CONCRETE IN COMPRESSION

mean curve in Fig 8), it may be said that for concretes of a strength of 2,600 lbs per sq in or more the flexural compression (computed by the parabolic formula) developed in the beams was about equal to the cylinder strengths, and that for the concrete of lower strengths it was much greater. The equation of this approximate mean curve is

$$\frac{f_c}{c} = 1 + \left(\frac{2600-c}{2200}\right)^2 , \text{ where}$$

$f_c$ = computed compressive stress in extreme fiber at maximum load

$c$ = compressive strength of corresponding control cylinder

In Fig 9 the ratios of flexural strength of the concrete by the straight line formula to the cylinder strengths have been plotted. The approximate mean curve shown in this figure is the same as the curve of Fig 8, but the scale of ordinates corresponds to calculations by the straight line formula. The equation of this curve referred to the new scale of ordinates is

$$\frac{f_c}{c} = 1\ 395\left\{ 1 + \left(\frac{2600 - c}{2200}\right)^2 \right\}$$

If the approximate curve be taken to represent flexural compression which could be developed in beams having concretes of varying strengths, it may be used as a basis for determining what working stresses might have been used in these beams securing at the same time the necessary factor of safety. For structural grade steel with the usual working stress the factor of safety against failure by tension is usually $\dfrac{40\ 000}{16\ 000}$ or 2 5

A larger factor of safety for compression in concrete should undoubtedly be used. On this basis the use of the lower curve of this figure to indicate the safe working stresses would give a factor of safety of 3 08 for strengths of concrete shown in the diagram. The equation of this curve is

$$\frac{f_c}{c} = \frac{1\ 395}{3\ 08}\left(1 + \left(\frac{2600-c}{2200}\right)^2\right) = 0\ 453\left\{1 + \left(\frac{2600-c}{2200}\right)^2\right\},\ \text{where}$$

All the beams shown by open circles had slightly more than three per cent of longitudinal reinforcement, and question may arise as to what effect on the results would have been produced if with the weaker concretes smaller percentages had been used. For beams of weaker concretes smaller percentages could have been used and at the same time compression failure could have been secured. In fact in most cases of actual construction much smaller percentages would be used. An examination of the computed stresses for beams with smaller amounts of reinforcement indicates that if these beams had had only sufficient reinforcement to bring about compression failure no change in the nature of the conclusions would have been necessitated

The use of the above equation for working stresses would indicate that for concrete having a strength of only 500 lb per sq in, a working stress in compression of 87 per cent of the cylinder strength could be used still maintaining the necessary factor of safety. For concrete having a cylinder strength of 2 600 lb per sq in or more the safe working stress would be 45 per cent of the cylinder strength. The writers do not believe it is desirable at the present time to go to such lengths as this in increasing working stresses but it does seem that a safe procedure would be to base the working stress on the assumption that compression failure would not occur before the compressive stress calculated by the parabolic formula becomes equal to the cylinder strength. This would give 45 per cent of the cylinder strength as a safe value for the working stress, and the additional toughness of the beams with weaker concrete would come in as an additional safeguard against accidental variations in strength

For example assume that for a given case the working stress was based upon a cylinder strength for the concrete of 2,000 lb per sq in and that the actual strength of the cylinders taken from the job proved to be only 1,300 lb per sq in. The working stress in this case would be 900 lb per sq in, and from the diagram it appears that with concrete having a cylinder strength of 1,300 lb per sq in compression failure would not be likely to occur before the compressive stress (computed by straight line formula) reached 1.88 times the cylinder strength, or 2,440 lb per sq in

Under these circumstances the factor of safety would be $\dfrac{2,440}{900}$, or 2.71

At the bottom of Fig 9 the horizontal line representing 45 per cent of the cylinder strength corresponds to this proposed working stress. On the right of this figure are given as ordinates the factors of safety which correspond to this working stress. It will be seen that on this basis the lowest factor of safety for any beam which is represented in this paper would be about 2.5. It is probable that with accepted working stresses in the reinforcement the factor of safety based upon tension in the reinforcement would frequently be not greater than this. For the majority of the points shown in this diagram the factor of safety based upon the compression using a working stress in the concrete of 45 per cent of the cylinder strength would be much greater

*Conclusion* A recommendation of the use of 45 per cent of the compressive strength of the concrete as a working stress will be characterized by many as a very radical proposal. If the method of specification and that of inspection hitherto prevalent is to be continued, the authors will agree that such a working stress is too high. They believe that the proper form of specification would specify a minimum strength to be attained rather than given proportions between cement and aggregate. Correspondingly a proper method of inspection would determine by means of tests in the field whether the specified strength was being attained. Such methods have already been proposed *. Extensive recent investigations of the laws of the strength of concrete have shown some progress toward the solution of this problem. With such specifications and with adequate inspection the indications of the data available are that 45 per cent of the actual cylinder strength at an age of 28 days as a working stress in flexural compression is not more extreme than 32½ per cent of the cylinder strength with a rated strength of 2,000 lb per sq in for 1 2 4 concrete The St Louis tests reported in this paper give some indication of what strength may be expected from concrete as placed in general practice. All the beams of 1 2 4 concrete made by Company A failed by compression and consequently are reported in Table III. The average strength of the cylinders tested at 28 days was 1,372 lb per sq in. At 45 per cent of the actual cylinder strength the working stress allowed would be 628 lb per

---

* C M Chapman "A New Form of Specification for Concrete Aggregate Proceedings American Society for Testing Materials Vol XVI, Part II, page 180

sq. in., whereas by the Joint Committee Recommendations 650 lb. per sq. in. would be permitted. There is no reason for thinking that the contractor would have put any better concrete into a building than he put into these

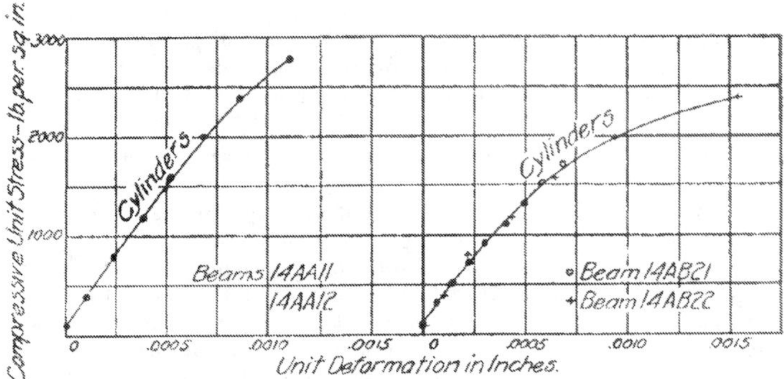



FIG. 10—STRESS-STRAIN CURVES FOR CONTROL CYLINDERS TESTED AT LEHIGH UNIVERSITY.

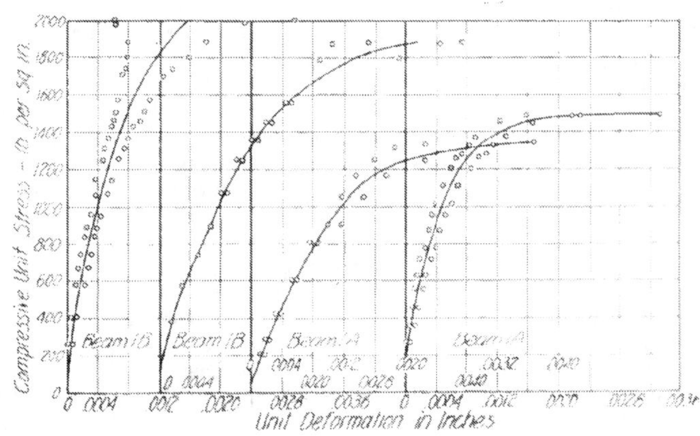



FIG. 11.—STRESS-STRAIN CURVES FOR CONTROL CYLINDERS OF BEAMS TESTED AT LAFAYETTE COLLEGE.

beams which were to be tested. Yet this need not be pointed out as an example of extremely poor work. In a building recently constructed by a contractor of highest standing and of national reputation, the average strength of the control cylinders of 1:2:4 concrete was 1,378 lb. per sq. in., while that of the 1:1½:3 concrete on the same job was 1,337 lb. per sq. in.

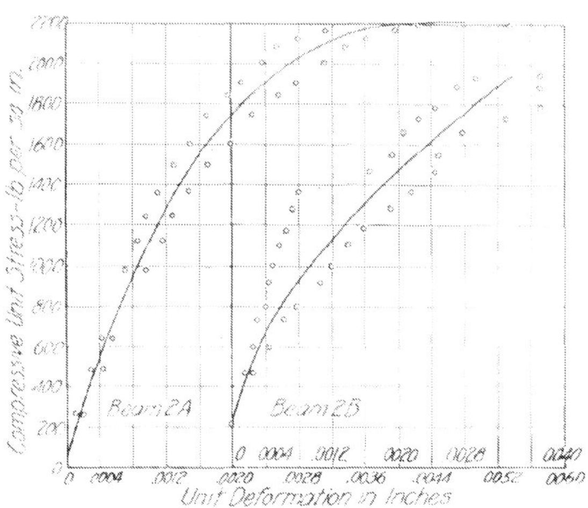


FIG. 12. —STRESS-STRAIN CURVES FOR CONTROL CYLINDERS
OF BEAMS TESTED AT LAFAYETTE COLLEGE.

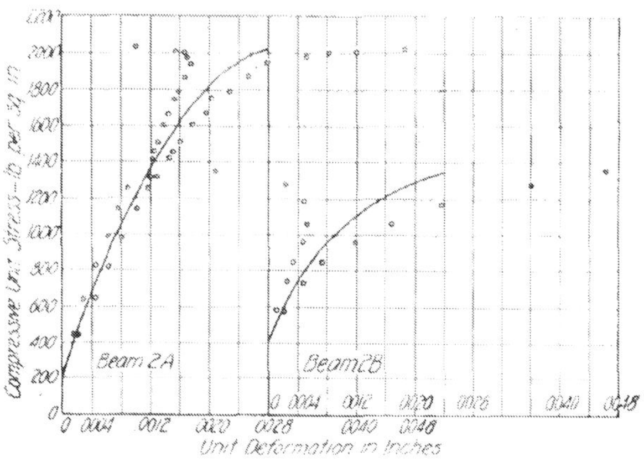


FIG. 13. —STRESS-STRAIN CURVES FOR CONTROL CYLINDERS OF
BEAMS TESTED AT LAFAYETTE COLLEGE.

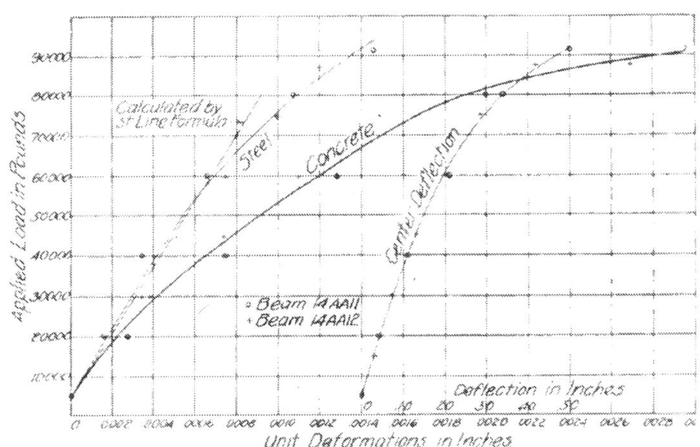


FIG. 14. LOAD-STRAIN CURVES FOR BEAMS 14AA11 AND 14AA12.

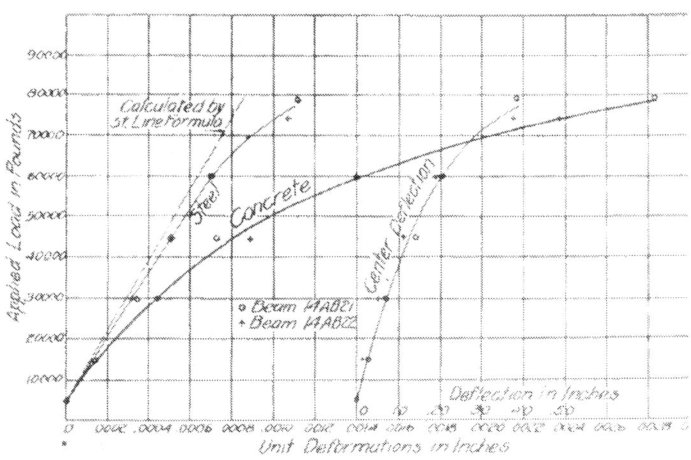


FIG. 15. LOAD-STRAIN CURVES FOR BEAMS 14AB21 AND 14AB22.

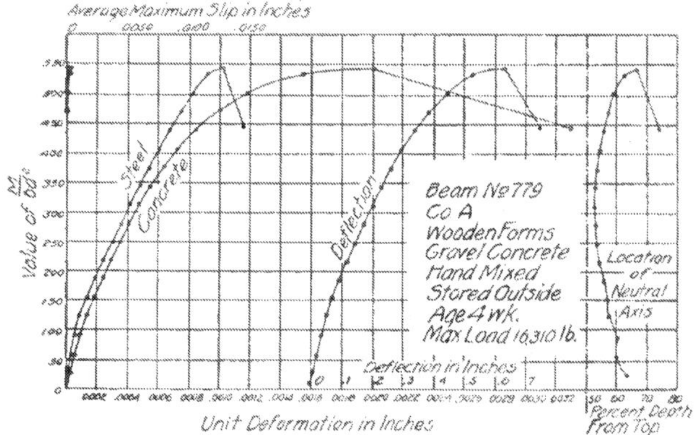


FIG. 16—TEST DATA FOR ST. LOUIS BEAM 779.

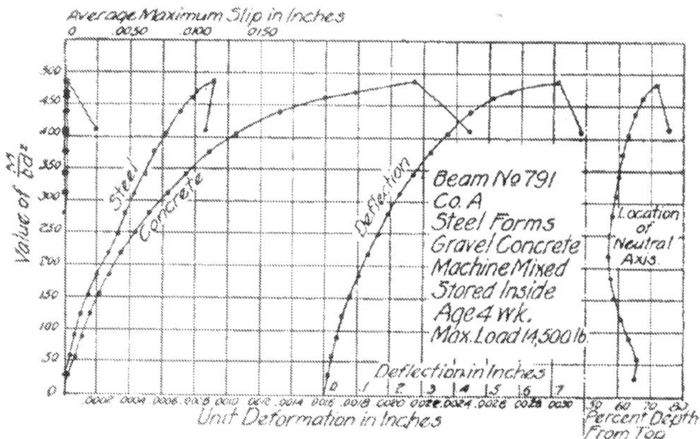


FIG. 17—TEST DATA FOR ST. LOUIS BEAM 791.

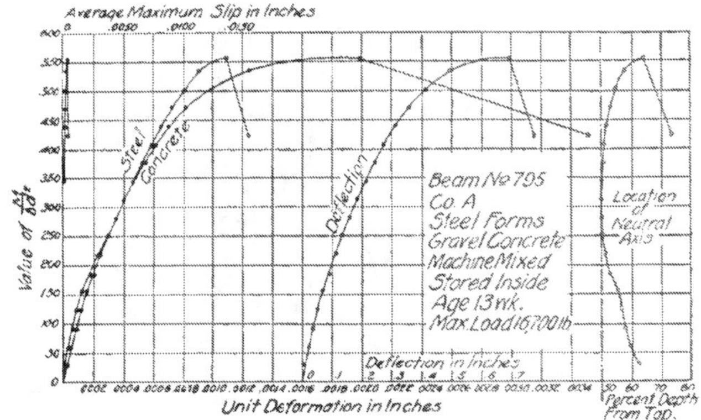


FIG. 18—TEST DATA FOR ST. LOUIS BEAM 795.

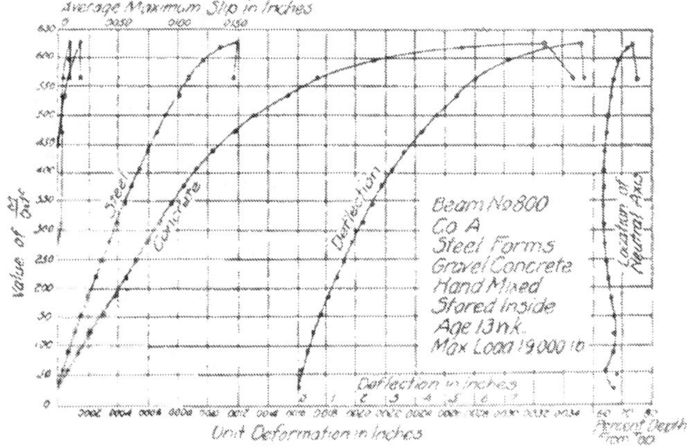


FIG. 19—TEST DATA FOR ST. LOUIS BEAM 800.

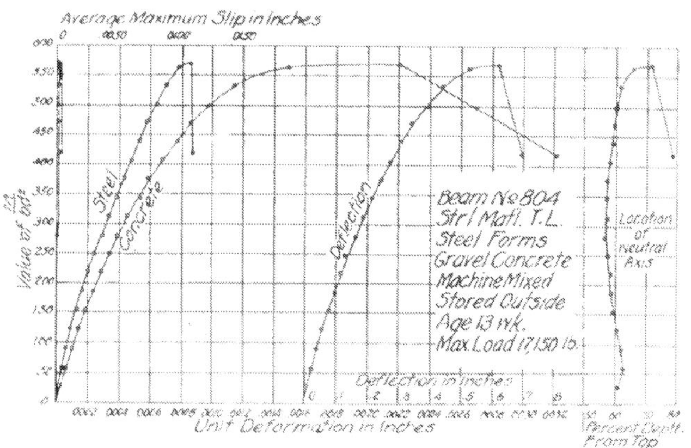


FIG. 20—TEST DATA FOR ST. LOUIS BEAM 804.

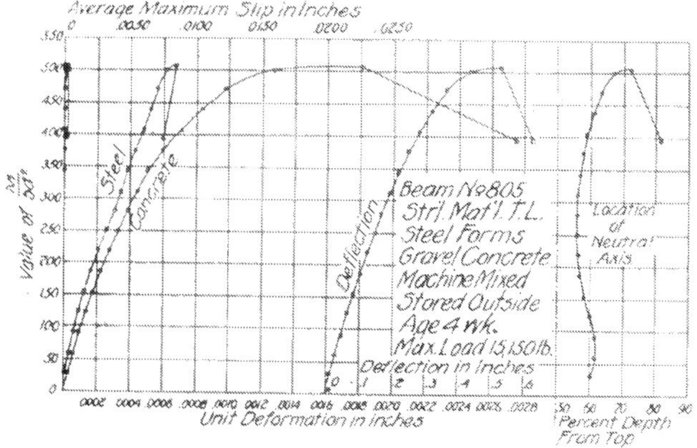


FIG. 21—TEST DATA FOR ST. LOUIS BEAM 805.

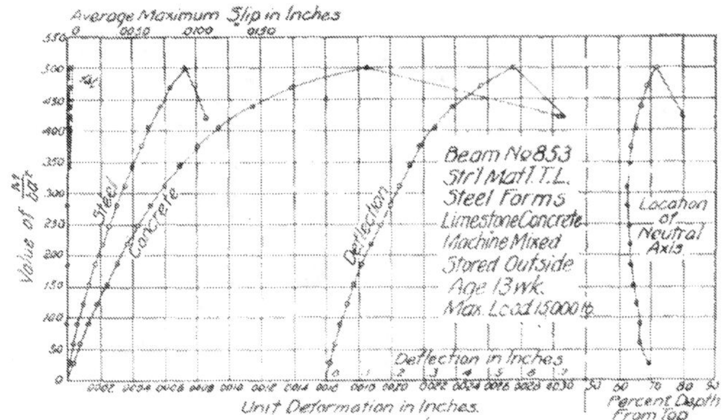



FIG. 22   TEST DATA FOR ST. LOUIS BEAM 853.

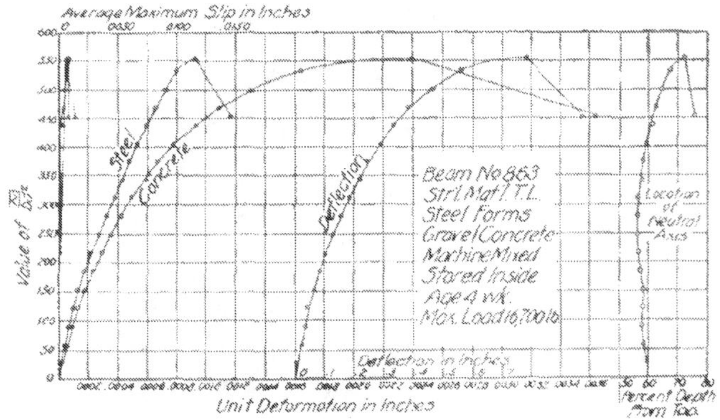



FIG. 23   TEST DATA FOR ST. LOUIS BEAM 863.

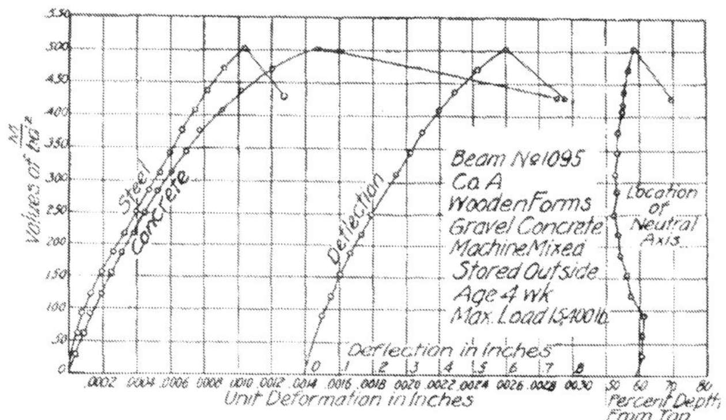


FIG. 24—TEST DATA FOR ST. LOUIS BEAM 1095.

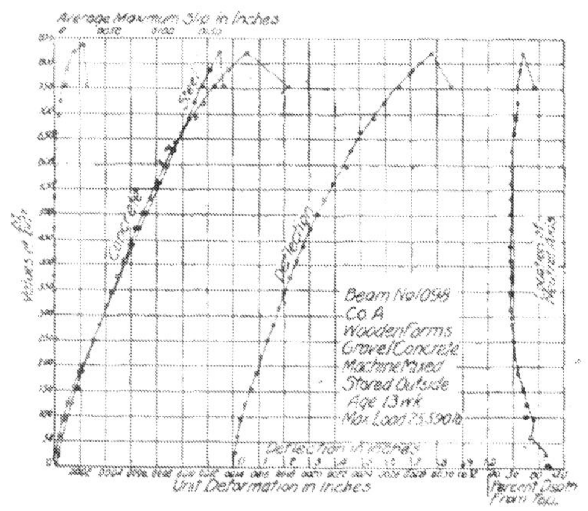


FIG. 25—TEST DATA FOR ST. LOUIS BEAM 1098.

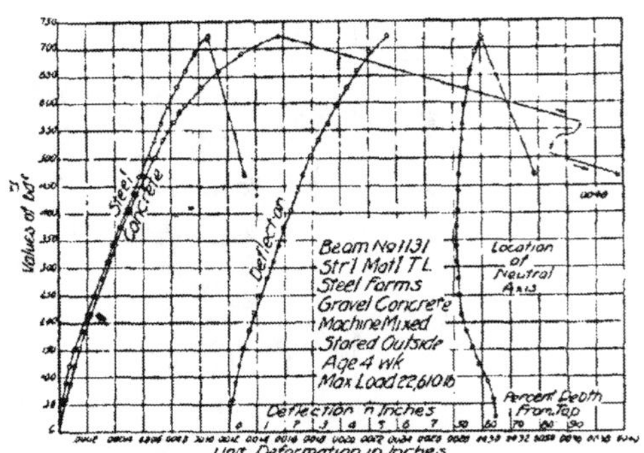



FIG 26—TEST DATA FOR ST LOUIS BEAM 1131

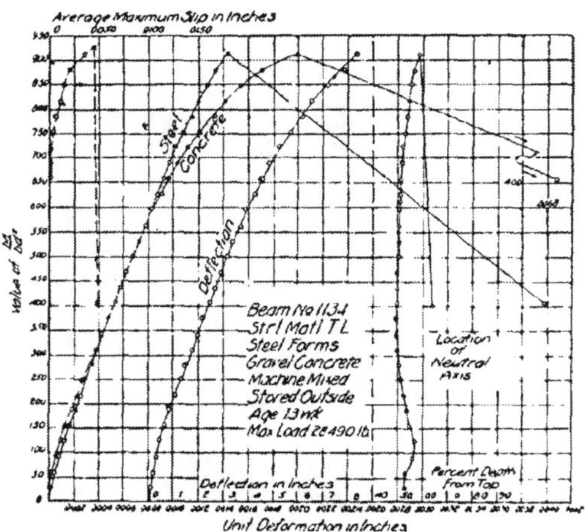



FIG 27—TEST DATA FOR ST LOUIS BEAM 1134

The 1 1½ 3 concrete would have been rated at 2 500 lb per sq in on the basis of the Joint Committee Report, and the working stress would have been 813 lb per sq in whereas using 45 per cent of the actual strength would have given only 620 lb per sq in The conclusion should not be drawn that the buildings so constructed are unsafe On the other hand, there is no indication that the concrete in the building referred to is not satisfactory, nor should it be concluded that the contractor profits from putting in concrete of a low strength It is often stated, and probably with justification that many other jobs show an excess of strength, which brings up the average to where it should be

With known costs for concrete and for steel and with working stresses fixed with relation to the cylinder strength of the concrete there will be a certain strength of the concrete which will result in the most economical structure It should be the purpose of the design to determine what this economical strength is, the specifications for the concrete should specify that strength, rather than an arbitrary mix, and the inspection should be such as to insure that this strength is attained Of course, it is possible that all the saving may be swallowed up in increased inspection cost but with the present range of strengths for concretes of equal richness it appears that a considerable increase in the ratio which the working stress may bear to the cylinder strength accompanied by effective inspection, would generally prove economical and that in some cases it would result in a more satisfactory structure finally

DISCUSSION

Mr Edward Godfrey —It seemed to me there are values given in the tables that are quite a distance from the average value assumed Would your factor of safety not vary considerably if you took the low values instead of the average?

Mr R R Zipprodt —There was a considerable range of strengths of concrete in the various beams With the lower strength concrete, we found a higher factor of safety With the higher strength concrete, the factor of safety was decreased Does that answer your question?

Mr Godfrey —I do not know whether it does or not The last two diagrams represent the strength of the beams in bending

Mr. Zipprodt —Yes, sir.

Mr Godfrey —Then if you take that average and judge your factor of safety on that average, would it not be very far from a good factor of safety when you take the low strengths, supposing some of the beams would show that low strength in place of the average or the high strength?

Mr Slater —In the lower curve of Fig 9 are indicated the ratios of the cylinder strengths which could be used as working stresses with a factor of safety of 3 08, using the average curve above as representing the ultimate strength This curve is given only for information, and shows that in general a higher working stress than the proposed value of 45 per cent of the cylinder strength could be used with a good factor of safety

Mr Godfrey refers to the variability of individual values of the concrete strength from the average curve and the resulting variation in the factor of safety One of the important purposes in using a factor of safety is to care for just such variations as those in the strength of the concrete and it is not to be supposed that for the lowest strength the factor of safety is as high as the nominal value However, using the ratios shown by the curved line as working stresses the lowest factor of safety would be for the point plotted at a concrete strength of 500 lb per sq in For this case the working stress would be about 78 per cent of the cylinder strength and the factor of safety would be 2 05 All but five of the beams represented in the diagram would show a factor of safety of 2 05, if designed on the same basis

Mr Godfrey —Then you design the beams as you go along and test the concrete how would you make the design before you know what the concrete is going to show in the cylinder?

Mr Slater —We are not proposing a method of inspection The question as to how that may be done is raised in the conclusion, there we state that if a satisfactory method of inspection can be provided by

( 147 )

which you can insure that you will get concrete of a strength not less than a certain amount, then the recommendation proposed will be safe. There have been two or three papers today in which questions of that kind have been brought up, as to whether we can be sure of strength greater than a certain amount  Whether it can be done is still open to question

MR GODFREY —In my opinion, good cement and lots of cement and the regular standard mix of ingredients is the thing that will insure satisfactory concrete, all things considered  Mixing concrete with brains instead of cement is precarious  Brains are very expensive when it comes to hiring them from 7 o'clock in the morning till 6 o'clock at night and maybe all night, as we would have to do if we kept an inspector, an expert inspector on every job all the time they were pouring concrete. Then there is much that seems to me to be retroaction  We do not know the strength of our concrete beams until the test comes out in 28 days  We might make a guess in 7 days, but the beams are hardened and placed and it is too late then to make any change, and it is my belief that we ought to stick right down to the standard ratios between cement and sand and gravel or broken stones, because cement is the safest thing to base our factor of safety on

MR STAILR —May I ask if Mr Godfrey means that he would dispense with brains on the job and would use cement instead and would stick to 1 2 4 concrete, or 1 1 2 concrete and specify on the basis of an arbitrary mix rather than make use of any recent information?

MR GODFREY —On the whole, I would stick to the present method There are occasions where large quantities of concrete can be made under supervision, where we have hundreds of thousands of yards to make on a large job, but there are so many other jobs where it would not be practical to change the mix and to introduce all this artist stuff, as it has been called, I believe, in this convention, in the mixing of the concrete  The large bulk of the work done in the country is in many jobs where we could not employ an expert inspector every hour that the work is being done

MR SANFORD E THOMPSON —The working stress of concrete used in beams at the present time, in many cases, is 50 per cent higher than the working stress in direct compression, and for the very reasons which are brought out in this paper, namely, that bending stresses act differently from direct stress  It must be remembered, further, that the factor of the safety of the steel referred to by the author is based on the *yield point* of the steel, the factor of safety of the concrete, as I understand is based on the other hand, on the *ultimate strength* of the concrete, now, whereas concrete does not have a very definite yield point, there is actually a yield point which is much below the ultimate strength, and furthermore, with repeated loading of the concrete above this yield point, the concrete will eventually fail  For this reason a factor of safety of 4 in concrete is but little more conservative than a factor of 4 based on the ultimate strength of the steel.  Another point that must be taken into consideration from the standpoint of practice is the fact that concrete laid by present-day methods is rarely up to the standard strength  The wet, sloppy, chuted concrete customarily laid in building construction, for example, usually has only about two-thirds the strength of 28 days that is assumed in designing the structure, in other words 1 2 4 concrete is apt to test about 1,400 lb per sq in instead of 2,000 lb

Prof A N Talbot —This matter is one in which I have been inter ested for many years  in fact, one of the standing problems given by me in research is to hunt up the results of all tests of beams which can be found in which the failure of the beam is in compression of the concrete  It has always been interesting to me to see how few such tests were avail able, even with beams having a large percentage of reinforcement  Most of those that can be found are from the tests of the Structural Materials Laboratory at St Louis, referred to, and those are with very high reinforcement

It is easy to see why the strength of the beam in compression should be greater than that of the column or compression test piece  The com pression test piece fails at a unit deformation or unit strain about 0 0011 to 0 0014 in per inch  a very narrow range, regardless almost of the quality of the concrete  It is pretty definitely settled that for specimens of that kind the question of deformation is the critical matter in the failure of the material rather than the matter of the stress which comes upon it  In the beam however, the extreme fiber may reach this deforma tion, and not break because it is held in place by the fibers below, and those fibers are held in turn by the fibers below them

In the experiments of the University of Illinois published a number of years ago, there were deformations in beams failing in compression reaching from 0 0020 to 0 0028 in, twice the ultimate deformation that would be found in the concrete in compression, this did give an added ultimate strength to the beam tested under those conditions  Evidently that does give an additional strength, an additional factor of safety  but in all discussion which I have heard when this matter of the utilization of the added strength was considered in determining what unit stress to use as a working stress, the argument has been put forward by those who hold for the lower stresses that while that might be available for a single load tested to failure by increasing the load, yet for a continued load, and especially for a load having many applications, failure would be reached long before that deformation could be obtained  In fact as has been referred to by Mr Thompson many feel that a value of not more than three-quarters—some have put it two-thirds or even one-half—of the ultimate strength of the concrete  there is a point at which the beam strength will end if the loading is to be repeated many times

I remember the tests which were made by Prof Van Ornum, at Washington University many years ago in which failure came from a repetition of these deformations  The mere fact that these beams and others have held without compression failure should not be taken as an indication that that stress should be used in the same way as the yield point of steel is used as a basis of the critical value upon which the working stress may depend

The point brought out by Mr Zipprodt concerning whether we might utilize this because of the conditions of the workmanship is one well worth considering   I think that we will all agree that as time goes on the art of concrete construction ought to improve through better knowledge of the conditions which have to be controlled in making proper concrete, through more experience in knowing whether the concrete is being properly handled so that we shall not need as large a so called factor of safety, that is, so large a range between the working stress and the stress which we know the beam may stand under the best conditions   Whether that time has come, or whether this value which has been proposed, of 45 per cent of the cylinder strength is a proper one seems to be a question which depends upon whether we have come to the time when we can depend on the strength of these beams being made in the same way that the laboratory beams are made   I think I should feel if I were myself doing a job with skilled labor and with plenty of care given to it, that I should be willing to use much higher working stresses than I should assume would be proper in a city under what might be indifferent construction and sometimes very poor construction   That, it seems to me, ought to be taken into consideration.

Mr W. A. Slater—There have been several points brought out that would be very interesting to discuss, but there are two of them that I think are rather important   I agree to the things which Prof Talbot has said, and I wish to point out that the proposal of 45 per cent does not contemplate any increase in working stresses over the stresses which now are generally used, because with the proposal is coupled the condition that we get the strength on which the working stress is based   The amount which the strength of the concrete that we now get falls below the strength on which we base our working stresses is so great that 45 per cent of the actual cylinder strength would be no greater than $32\frac{1}{2}$ per cent of the assumed strength rating 1 2 4 concrete at 2 000 lb per sq in

The other point is in regard to repeated stresses   We do not have any final information on that, and the questions which both Mr Thompson and Prof Talbot have raised are pertinent to this discussion, but there are two things which throw some light on the subject   The reason why we may generally regard the ultimate strength of a beam which fails in tension as the load at which the steel passes the yield point strength of the steel is that with steel of an ordinary grade it is not generally possible to load the beam fast enough, after the yield point of the steel is reached, to follow it down as it deflects   In other words even for the first application of the load, the maximum load is likely to come at the point at which the yield point of the steel is reached.   That is not true as regards the compression in the concrete, for the reason that not so large a deformation is required to produce failure   It is not certain that we can use the ultimate strength of the beam under a single application of load as a criterion for its ultimate strength under repeated load  but as to actual tests of the beam for repeated loads  we have some information which is interesting, though not conclusive   Four or five beams have been tested at the Bureau of Standards within the past two years under repeated loads  None have failed by compression in the concrete   It is true that none had stresses in the concrete which approach the ultimate strength of the concrete, but all did fail by tension in the steel and in some cases when the stress in the steel was no higher in proportion to its yield point than was the stress in the concrete in proportion to its ultimate strength   All of these beams failed at much lower unit deformations in the steel than would be required for tension failure under the first application of load  Just as Prof Talbot points out would be likely to be the case for compres sion in the concrete if we repeated the load often enough to get com pression failure

# THE ECONOMIC POSSIBILITIES OF LIGHTWEIGHT AGGREGATE IN BUILDING CONSTRUCTION *

By A. W. Stephens †

For the construction of reinforced concrete ships it was desirable to develop a concrete of minimum weight and maximum strength. This was accomplished by the use of a special fine ground portland cement and an aggregate which has been described in the technical press as "an artificially burned clay or shale uniformly filled with small non-connecting cells." This concrete weighed about 115 lb. per cu. ft., the mixture being one part cement, two-thirds part fine aggregate, and one and one-third parts coarse aggregate.

The material required for one cubic yard of 1-2/3 1-1/3 concrete was approximately 3.25 bbl. cement, 0.32 cu. yd. of fine aggregate and 0.64 cu. yd. of coarse aggregate. The average ultimate compressive strength of this concrete at the age of 28 days was about 4400 lb. per sq. in.

This lightweight aggregate is produced by a special process, and at present has a market price in excess of that of sand, gravel and trap rock.

The successful use of lightweight concrete in the construction of ships has caused the question to arise as to the economic possibilities of light weight aggregate for concrete used in the construction of buildings, and a study of the question is the purpose of this paper.

For the purpose of studying the saving in materials in building construction and the consequent advantage in the use of lightweight aggregate it will be assumed that it is possible to produce concrete weighing 144, 135, 126, 114 or 99 lb. per cu. ft. respectively, by varying the kind of aggregate used. It will also be assumed that the ultimate compressive strength at the age of 28 days is 2000 lb. per sq. in. making possible the use of an extreme allowable compressive fiber stress of 650 lb. per sq. in. with corresponding values for shear, etc.

The use of these concretes will first be considered for a typical bay 16 ft. 8 in. wide x 20 ft. long so located in a building that its slabs, beams and girders are continuous. The slab is assumed of a minimum thickness of 4 in. the 20 ft. long beams spaced about 5 ft. 6 in. on center are assumed as 1 ft. 8 in. total depth and the girders are assumed as 1 ft. 10 in. total depth.

For live-loads of 200 and 150 lb. the beams will be 8 in. wide and the girders 12 in. wide. For live loads of 100, 75 and 50 lb. per sq. ft. the beams will be 6 in. wide and the girders 9 in. wide.

The depth of beams and girders is governed by the span and to some

---

* Paper presented to the 15th Convention at Atlantic City June, 1919
† Chief Engineer Turner Construction Co., New York City

extent by the allowable shear value, and the width is governed principally by the amount of fireproofing required for the steel reinforcement

The amount of concrete per square foot of floor for live loads of 200 and 150 lb is 0 565 cu ft and for live-loads of 100 75 and 50 lb per sq ft is 0 505 cu ft

The saving in weight of steel reinforcement per square foot in the floor construction by the use of lightweight concrete in place of concrete weighing 144 lb per cu ft is approximately the same for live loads of 50, 75, 100, 150 and 200 lb per sq ft, and is as follows  For concrete weighing 135 lb per cu ft the saving per sq ft is 0 06 lb ; for concrete weighing 126 lb per cu ft, 0 11 lb  for concrete weighing 114 lb per cu ft, 0 19 lb, and for concrete weighing 99 lb per cu ft, 0 28 lb  The quantities are based on the assumption that the reinforcing steel in the floor members will be of exact areas as required by the computations. although it is not practicable to obtain this result in actual construction

In addition to the saving in steel reinforcement there is a saving in concrete in the columns due to the reduced weight of the floor construction. To determine this saving a six-story building will be assumed, each story height being 12 ft  The allowable compression on the concrete in the columns is assumed at 500 lb per sq in

The saving in concrete averages approximately 0 8 cu ft per story for 135 lb concrete  1 7 cu ft per story for 126 lb concrete  2 7 cu ft per story for 114 lb concrete, 4 2 cu ft per story for 99 lb concrete Expressed in terms of cubic feet of concrete per square foot of floor this saving is as follows  For concrete weighing 135 lb per cu ft, 0 0026 cu ft ; for concrete weighing 126 lb per cu ft, 0 0055 cu ft , for concrete weighing 114 lb per cu ft, 0 009 cu ft , for concrete weighing 99 lb per cu ft, 0 0128 cu ft.

In considering the saving in concrete and steel reinforcement given above, it should be noted that the slight saving in concrete in the footings has not been included  In order to determine in this case when it is more economical to use lightweight concrete than concrete weighing 144 lb per cu ft it would be assumed that concrete weighing 144 lb per cu ft costs $8.10 per cu yd, and that steel reinforcement costs 4c per lb in place  On this basis it will be more economical to use lightweight concrete when it costs less per cubic yard than the units covering this case in Table I

In the case of a 20 ft square bay of flat slab construction a similar investigation shows that it will be more economical to use the light weight construction when it costs less per cubic yard than the units given in Table I for this case

In order to determine the advantages in the use of lightweight concretes, having high compressive values, it will be assumed that it is possible to produce a lightweight concrete weighing 135 lb per cu ft with an ultimate compressive value of 2500 lb per sq in  permitting the use of an extreme allowable fiber stress in compression of 800 lb per sq in with corresponding values in shear, etc., a 126 lb concrete with an extreme allowable fiber stress in compression of 1100 lb per sq in, a 114 lb concrete with an extreme allowable fiber stress in compression of 1400 lb per sq in, and a 99 lb concrete with an extreme allowable fiber stress in compression of 1500 lb per sq in

On the above basis and assuming the cost of steel reinforcement and concrete as before it is found that for a continuous slab supported on two sides on beams that the use of lightweight concrete will be more economical than 144 lb concrete when it costs less per cubic yard than the units given for this case in Table II   The units as given take into consideration the saving in concrete in columns as in the first case

### TABLE I —COST PER CUBIC YARD OF CONCRETE

| Weight per cu ft in lb | | 144 | 135 | 126 | 114 | 99 |
|---|---|---|---|---|---|---|
| 16 ft 8 in x 20 ft bay beam and girder construction   Live-load per sq ft , 50 75, 100 150, 200 lb | | $8 10 | $8 25 | $8 10 | $8 60 | $8 90 |
| | Live-load per sq ft in lb | | | | | |
| 20 ft square bay flat-slab construction | 50 | 8 10 | 8 25 | 8 40 | 8 60 | 8 90 |
| | 75 | 8.10 | 8.25 | 8 40 | 8.60 | 8 85 |
| | 100 | 8 10 | 8 25 | 8 40 | 8 85 | 9 10 |
| | 150 | 8 10 | 8 30 | 8 50 | 8.70 | 9 20 |
| | 200 | 8 10 | 8 50 | 8 65 | 8 95 | 9 20 |

NOTE — Extreme compressive fiber stress value 650 lb per sq in

In the case of the beam and girder construction, with a bay 16 ft 8 in x 20 ft  the lightweight concrete having the high stress values for live-loads of 50, 75, 100, 150 and 200 lb per sq ft will be more economical than 144 lb concrete when it costs less per cubic yard than the units given for this case in Table II

For flat-slab construction, 20 ft  square bay with lightweight concrete of high stress values  it is found that the lightweight concrete is more economical than 144 lb concrete when for the several live load the cost per cubic yard is less than the units given for the cases as noted in Table II

No attempt has been made in this investigation to develop new types of building construction to which the use of lightweight concrete might be especially adapted

These studies serve to indicate the conditions to be met in the use of lightweight aggregate if lightweight concrete is to compete with that commonly used in building construction.

TABLE 11 —COST PER CUBIC YARD OF CONCRETE

| Weight per cu ft and extreme fiber stress value in compression | | 144 lb per cu ft 650 lb | 135 lb per cu ft 800 lb | 126 lb per cu ft 1100 lb | 114 lb per cu ft 1400 lb | 99 lb per cu ft 1500 lb |
|---|---|---|---|---|---|---|
| Continuous slab between two beams for live-loads 50 75, 100, 150, 200 lb per sq ft | | $8 10 | $8 50 | $9 10 | $9 50 | $9 80 |
| 16 ft 8 in x 20 ft bay, beam and girder construction Live-loads 50 75 100 150, 200 lb | | 8 10 | 8 50 | 9 10 | 9 55 | 9 80 |
| 20 ft square bay flatslab construction | Live-load per sq ft in lb 50 | 8 10 | 8 25 | 8 40 | 8 60 | 8 90 |
| | 75 | 8 10 | 8 25 | 8 40 | 8 60 | 8 85 |
| | 100 | 8 10 | 8 50 | 8 60 | 8 80 | 9 10 |
| | 150 | 8 10 | 8 70 | 9 15 | 9 45 | 9 70 |
| | 200 | 8 10 | 9 05 | 10 00 | 10 20 | 10 50 |

Committee Reports Presented to the
Sixteenth Annual Convention
American Concrete Institute

# REPORT OF COMMITTEE ON BUILDING BLOCKS AND CEMENT PRODUCTS

The Committee on Building Blocks and Cement Products has to offer for the consideration of the Institute the following resolution

*Whereas* There is evidenced in building codes and insurance rates a discrimination against building blocks as building units, and,

*Whereas* Such discrimination is based on poor blocks improperly made, and.

*Whereas* The majority of concrete products manufacturers are making high grade building units; and,

*Whereas* It is impracticable to have tests made on the products of all the manufacturers at the Underwriters' Laboratories,

*Be it Resolved*

(1) That tests by the Underwriters' Laboratories on standard panels of representative concrete building units are sufficient to demonstrate the fire-resistive qualities of properly made units of the various types and to form a basis for fair and equitable rates of insurance

(2) That the proper interests of the community and of the insurance company would be amply safeguarded by the adoption of equitable building codes, regulations and specifications so as to obtain concrete building units of requisite quality which would conform in large part to the specifications of the Institute

(3) That discriminatory rates on the part of the insurance companies would work an unjust hardship on the communities who would thereby be deprived of valuable and meritorious building units, and that a hardship would also be imposed on a large and growing portion of the concrete building industry which is producing a high class product

(4) That the Institute authorize this committee to enlist the coöperation of associations, corporations firms and individuals in furnishing materials and funds for conducting such tests, with the understanding that this committee has the privilege of using results of such tests in its reports to the Institute

(5) That the Institute appropriate a sum of money to form part of a fund for conducting tests and to determine fully the properties of concrete building units

The committee has agreed to proceed immediately to draft a new specification and building regulations for concrete building units, and this work can very well be carried on in conjunction with any work on tests as provided in the above resolution

ROBERT F HAVLIK, *Chairman*
W R HARRIS, *Secretary*

[By action of the convention Resolutions 1, 2 and 3 were referred to the Executive Committee and Resolutions 4 and 5 to the Committee on Resolutions  The latter committee later brought in the following resolution  which was adopted by the convention

*Whereas* There is a tendency of building codes and insurance rates to discriminate against cement building blocks, brick and hollow tile as building units, and,

"*Whereas* Tests by the United States Geological Survey, the Underwriters' Laboratories and others on standard panels representative of these building units are sufficient to demonstrate the fire resistive qualities of properly made units of various types

*Therefore be it Resolved* That the proper interests of the community and of the insurance company would be amply safeguarded by the adoption of equitable building codes regulations and specifications that will permit the economical use of these building units of requisite quality conforming to the recommendations of the American Concrete Institute thereby relieving a large and growing portion of the concrete products building industry which is producing a high-grade building material, of a hardship that is now imposed upon it

"ERNEST ASHTON
"S H HOLLISTER
"WALLACE R HARRIS
'HARVEY WHIPPLE
'FRANK C WIGHT
"RICHARD L HUMPHREY, *Chairman*"

EDITOR ]

# REPORT OF THE COMMITTEE ON NOMENCLATURE

The Committee on Nomenclature presented to the 1919 convention a
report consisting mainly of definitions and standard forms for the use of
the Institute in publishing the Proceedings  These were printed in the
Proceedings, vol XV, 1919, p 373  Having been before the Institute the
requisite number of days, these definitions and forms are submitted to the
convention to be passed to letter ballots as standard of the Institute

W  A  SLATER, Chairman

[The convention voted to submit the definitions and forms to letter
ballot  The Institute voted April 17, 1920, to adopt them as standard
—EDITOR ]

# REPORT OF SPECIAL COMMITTEE ON CONCRETE SHIPS AND BARGES

The original concrete ship program of the Emergency Fleet Corporation called for the construction of thirty-eight 7500-ton vessels, three 3500-ton vessels and one 3000-ton vessel, making a total of forty-two vessels. Immediately after the armistice, this program was reduced to eight 7500-ton tankers, two 7500-ton cargo vessels, three 3500-ton cargo vessels and one 3000-ton cargo vessel, or a total of fourteen vessels. In October, 1919, the two 7500-ton cargo vessels were canceled, leaving twelve vessels to be completed.

At this date all of the four small cargo vessels are in service. They are the "Atlantus," 3000 tons dead weight, and the "Polias," "Cape Fear" and "Sapona," each of 3500 tons dead weight. Of the 7500-ton tankers, three have been launched, the "Palo Alto," at San Francisco, and the "Selma" and "Latham," at Mobile. The remaining five tankers are in various stages of completion. It is expected that all will be launched before April 1, and all will be in commission before June 1.

In addition to these vessels twenty-one 500-ton canal barges were built by the Railroad Administration under the supervision of the Emergency Fleet Corporation. All of these barges are in service with the exception of one which was sunk in the Hudson River in the early part of December.

## CONSTRUCTION PROBLEMS

In general, it may be said that in carrying out the concrete ship program, no construction problems have been encountered that have not been successfully met. The original design of the 7500-ton tankers has been modified to some extent, owing to the discovery of undesirable high stresses in some of the members under test and service conditions. While the revisions contemplated involved concrete construction seldom, if ever, before attempted, it is believed that the changes will remedy the undesirable conditions. The experience of the vessels in service thus far indicates that, so far as the cargo vessels are concerned, there is ample structural strength, and, of course, the barge is a much simpler problem.

## TIME OF CONSTRUCTION

The hope that reinforced concrete would provide a material from which hulls could be built with much greater speed than is possible in the case of steel has not been realized. The average time of constructing the concrete hull has been seven months. Outfitting and equipping the hull have taken on an average between three and four months. Undoubtedly with the experience gained, this time could be materially bettered on future work.

## Seaworthiness

The experience with the ships in service thus far indicates that they are good sea boats. In every case of which there is record, these ships have behaved admirably in heavy weather and have won considerable praise from officers and crews. There is generally very much less vibration in concrete ships than in corresponding steel ships. There is also a very considerable increase in the period of roll which is quite desirable. The increase in the period of roll is undoubtedly due to the fact that these vessels have a relatively large moment of inertia around a longitudinal axis even when loaded with cargo. This is due to the mass of the concrete shell which is considerably greater than the mass of the shell in a steel ship. In none of the vessels in service has any leakage whatever been reported. A few shear cracks are noticeable in the shell and bulkheads in all the ships in service, but these cracks are unimportant and have no apparent effect upon the structural strength of the ship.

One characteristic of the concrete vessels built by the Emergency Fleet Corporation should be noted in this connection. Experience seems to indicate that these vessels are unable to successfully withstand severe concentrated blows on the shell without the shattering of the concrete. Impact which, in the case of the steel ship would probably only cause indentation to the plates, in the case of the concrete ship is apt to cause a shattering of the concrete over the area adjacent to the point of impact. A number of instances of injury of this kind have been observed, particularly in the case of the barges constructed for the Railroad Administration. In the case of nearly every barge the shell has been injured in one way or another, requiring repairs to the concrete. It has been found, however, that repairs are relatively simple and can be effected with little loss of time and at almost negligible cost. The barges in question have very little protection in the form of fenders. It is believed that where adequate fenders are provided, so that there is chance for the absorption of the work of a blow by means of some resilient material, such as an oak fender, this objectionable feature of the concrete barge may be obviated. Fenders on large ships have been found to be objectionable and are not being provided.

## Efficiency

The figures noted above for the dead weight capacity of the several ships constructed by the Emergency Fleet Corporation are the nominal dead-weight capacities contemplated by the design. In no case has the nominal dead weight capacity of the ship been realized. The average dead-weight capacity of the 7500-ton tankers will be in the neighborhood of 6800 tons. In the case of the "Atlantus," nominally having a capacity of 3000 tons, the actual dead weight capacity is 2542 tons, the "Cape Fear" and "Sapona," nominally 3500 tons have dead weight capacities of 3078 tons, the "Polias," nominally 3500 tons, built of heavy gravel concrete, has a dead weight capacity of 2460 tons. It was expected that the ratio of dead weight capacity to displacement would run from 0 55 to 0 60  The actual ratio of dead-weight displacement will not average but little more than 0 50

In making a comparison between the relative carrying capacities of steel and concrete ships, one important consideration should be kept in mind.  Taking into consideration a steel ship and concrete ship, each having the same dead-weight capacities, the concrete ship—because of the greater weight of the ship itself—must have greater dimensions than the steel ship and, in consequence, must have greater hold spaces  For heavy weight cargoes, such as steel, coal or oil, in which the dead weight capacity is reached before the hold spaces are filled, it is apparent that steel has an advantage over concrete as a material of construction, assuming that the construction and operating costs are equal  For bulky cargoes such as ordinary package goods, cotton, fruit, or other materials for which the space required exceeds about 70 cu ft to the ton, the concrete ship will actually carry more dead weight than the steel ship for the reason that the actual hold spaces of the steel ship will be filled before her dead weight capacity is reached

### Costs

The cost of the small cargo vessels, leaving out of consideration the "Atlantus," which was the first vessel built varies from $210 to $300 per dead-weight ton  The cost of the 7500 ton tankers will vary between $200 and $250 per dead-weight ton  These figures are based upon the nominal dead-weight carrying capacity rather than the actual  These costs naturally include certain experimental work and other expenditures which could be reduced on future work so that the above experience is not a sufficient basis on which to forecast the cost of concrete vessels under peace conditions and skillful management

### Conclusion

No definite conclusions should be drawn as yet from the experience with these vessels  It should be borne in mind that all of the vessels were under construction at approximately the same time and that there was little chance to profit by experience  When it is remembered that these were the first vessels ever attempted of this size, the showing is not discouraging  The only general conclusion that may be drawn from the experience of the ships constructed under the direction of the Emergency Fleet Corporation seems to be that it is possible to construct ships of concrete in about the same time and for approximately the same cost as the corresponding steel ships  This indicates that, after there has been more experience in the art it will be possible to reduce both the cost and the time for construction  There remains also the question of length of life of concrete ships  Only time can safely answer this question, although it should be stated that the brief experience of the "Faith" and the Emer gency Fleet vessels has disclosed no serious inherent weakness to shorten the life of the concrete ship

Barges and canal boats, in order to have a commercial future, must apparently overcome two objections—first, a reduction in cost as compared with wood and this may come through experience in design and construction, and, second, the development of a method to offset the damage sustained to the hull from slight collisions with tugs, other boats or in docking   We are appending a letter from James Bentley, dated Feb 11, 1920, which is of unusual interest.

This committee recommends that the Institute shall continue a committee to follow the development of the concrete vessel reporting annually

H. C. TURNER *Chairman*

---

SIR

It seems to have been definitely proved that concrete ships can be built can go to sea and behave in bad weather as well as a steel ship, but as we cannot discount the effect of time we are still in doubt as to their commercial success

There is no doubt in our minds that the Isherwood type rather than the multiple frame type is the best adapted to concrete construction, and wherever possible long sweep curves should give place to straight lines in steel design   This also applies to the hull form as it has been our experience that it is almost impossible to reuse interior hull forms from that part of the ship that has complicated warped surfaces Were it possible to use small gravel instead of the sharp edged clay aggregate that we are using a great deal of expense could be saved in the item of patching, as it is impossible to so place our present concrete that a perfect job is obtained where a large number of bars are in close proximity as they retard the flow of the concrete so that no amount of vibrating will cause all voids to be filled

We have demonstrated that the concrete ship can be built by labor entirely unfamiliar with ship construction and then at a price lower than the steel ship the plant for which work does not require the heavy tools and hence large item of expense that the steel yard necessitates

Experience in ordinary concrete work is of little value as so much more care and greater accuracy has to be demanded of the workmen that their previous slip shod methods all have to be unlearned   The formwork can be executed by ordinary form carpenters used to reinforced building work, but should be carefully planned out in advance in the draughting room and built in the carpenter shop so that quantity methods may be used.

I will confine myself to the construction features from a contractor's point of view, and what little I know about the operation of these ships

YARD EQUIPMENT.—This question is open to a good deal of discussion   In the yard we operated at Jacksonville we had large guy derricks mounted on towers so that the base of the derrick was level with the highest part of the ship   The booms covered the entire ships   In our judgment two gantry cranes traveling the length of the ship would probably have been as good or better   The derricks were not entirely satisfactory   The balance of the equipment consisted of a very well equipped carpenter shop, a mold loft industrial railways throughout the yard to transport the materials a well equipped steel shed with trolley carriers for handling the steel and power and hand benders   Also a hot bending plant and furnace for heating the large sized rods   There was the usual equipment of concrete mixers hoisting towers etc. The air plant for use in supplying air to the hammers, was quite large   We had altogether about 100 hammers for rapping the forms   In equipping a yard for building large concrete ships, great care must be taken to get the supports under the ways heavy enough   These should be much heavier than for an ordinary steel or wooden ship, as it is necessary to hold the ship absolutely rigid while it is being constructed, as if the supports should deflect the least particle a crack might appear in the work that has first been poured after the load of the upper work is applied

METHODS OF CONSTRUCTION.—The ships which we are building are 7500 ton oil tankers   This was a change from the original ships which were to have been 7500 ton cargo ships   Owing to the lack of previous knowledge and to the various changes made necessary to meet all the inspection rules enormous changes had to be made in the design as the work went along  This necessarily slowed up the work very much  As fast as the designs were received the work was laid out in a mold loft the same as any ship  Templates were made of every frame and from these the forms were accurately built in the carpenter shop  These were built in panel form so that they could be used over again  It was the intention when the work was started that eight ships should be built  When the armistice was signed, however the work was cut down to two ships  The molds were built with the intention of using them over again on the other six ships  After the outside forms had been erected the shell steel was then placed and later the frame steel and then the inside forms for the frames and shell  Owing to the necessity of keeping down the weight of the ship and the large amount of reinforcing in the concrete, this steelwork and formwork had to be done with the greatest accuracy—not more than 1/16 in variation could be allowed from the theoretical placing of the steel  This required great accuracy in bending  For the larger members we therefore used the hot method, that is we heated the bars at the points that were to be bent at to a cherry red, then dragged them out on a cast iron checkerboard platform and bent them to templates  The result was very satisfactory and not at all expensive  After the shell and frame steel and forms were placed this portion was concreted  Great difficulty was encountered in getting the concrete into place as the aggregate used was so light that it did not flow at all steadily and the large quantity of steel tended to retard it very much  The flow of the concrete was assisted by rapping the forms with light pneumatic hammers  The results obtained by this method were really quite remarkable, although even with the greatest care some bad work was obtained  We found however, that this high grade concrete could be readily patched and did not act exactly the same as ordinary concrete when applied as a patch

OPERATION OF CONCRETE SHIPS —We have watched the operation of these ships very closely  We find that there is a great prejudice against them  It is very difficult to secure crews for them and the shippers dislike to ship their goods in them  The cost of operation apparently does not differ greatly from that of steel or wood  They are very dry—they do not leak any perceptible amount—they are, however, very susceptible to injury by collision  Every time a tug bumps into them they are apt to damage the upper works  This damage however, is not at all serious and can be easily repaired  In no case have we heard of one of the frames being damaged — it is simply the skin between the frames that is punctured—generally a hole about 3 x 4 ft, which can be repaired by any sailor if he has the proper materials on board  They have a quanity of steadiness at sea that is quite remarkable  We give you below an extract from the log of the "Cape Fear" on her trip from Jacksonville to New York Harbor, which covers this point

"We run into a gale from N E with a velocity of around 65 miles per hour on December 10th which lasted until December 12th  During this gale there was a high sea running and I must say I never in all my sea going saw a ship act as graceful and well as the Cape Fear  At times large seas came at her looking as if they would come aboard and the ship would rise every time, proving she has a great amount of buoyancy  I tried her in the trough and she rolled very easy  On December 14th we had a moderate wind and sea from S W  The ship acted all right with a following sea but I don't think she will act as well before it as she will running into as the stern appears to me to be a little fine

The same kind of report has been made by many other Captains on their trips  We also give a report of the Captain that brought the 'Cape Fear' from Wilmington N C, to Jacksonville, when she was brought over to be outfitted

'My experience on the cement ship Cape Fear I feel it my duty to say something of our most delightful trip on that beautiful ship  We left Wilmington, N C  August 26th with a very neat and powerful iron tug belonging to Government and as she crossed the bar raising her beautiful bow high up as it to give farewell bow to her name sake wee disperpaied down the cost and there never was a more gracefull ship has never been seen  I myself has bin going to sea this 40 years and abcerlutely I would rather take my chances on one of concrate  Well now wee sighted Jacksonville bar  I believe it is 24 miles up river but never the less wee were soon at the city when the tug droped us comeing up our starboard side and noticed she was comeing head on wide open think she was going to sink us I steped back and my god what a ram and I sware I never felt it  I was standing directly over it and I was sure wee were ruined that was some lick and I tell right here if it had bin in steal or woden ship I am sure it would sunk her but it did not hurt us much they tell mee it can bee repaired at a very little cost or delay and I do know any sort of ship sure would have to go on the dock the Government has goten the wrong idear that cement ships are a fallure and you will find very shortly they will have to use them or other countrys will bee far ahead of them  I can not write like I can talk or I could tell you lots more never the less if you want to know any thing more I would like to talk with you                                    Archiebald Marine "

The concrete ship draws slightly more water than a steel ship, but not as much as a wooden ship of the same carrying capacity  For space cargoes the concrete ship undoubtedly has advantages as she has a greater internal measurement as the concrete framing does not take up as much space as the steel framing  For such cargoes as cotton, coffee  packing house products, harvesting machinery, canned goods, etc , the concrete ships will undoubtedly prove very efficient  For dead weight cargoes, such as iron ore, steel billets  and others of this character, they are not as good as the steel ships  They can be built for considerably less than the steel ships and undoubtedly their maintenance will be less

FUTURE OF THE CONCRETE SHIP.—In our judgment the concrete ship is not going to be popular until after the ships that are now built and being built are in operation for some time and then worth proven  They are going through a period of probation, and their future will depend on the results obtained in the operation of these present ships  None of the oil tankers have been put into commission at this date  Their success remains to be proven  If they are as successful as we hope, after two or three years trial, there should be a big field for them  However the design will have to be simplified and improved  One of the points most dwelt on by those who have studied this problem is the elimination of the frames  If a design could be worked out on a flat slab principle without increasing the weight this would be a big step forward  To date this has not been possible, but undoubtedly will come with experience

Toledo  Ohio, Feb 11, 1920

(Signed)  JAMES BENTLEY

In the report submitted to the Institute at Atlantic City in June, 1919, the committee mentioned a series of wear tests of mixtures commonly employed in floor construction to be carried out at the Structural Materials Research Laboratory, Lewis Institute, Chicago, the results of which would provide much useful data. An outline attached to the present

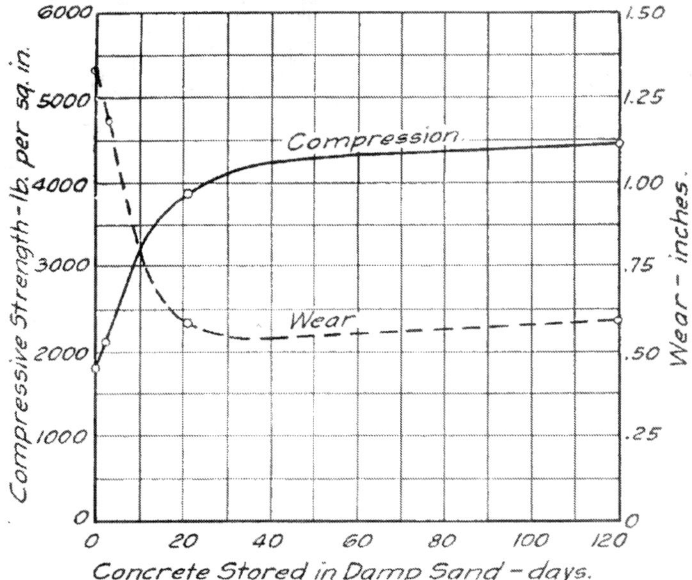



report indicates the scope of this investigation and the various factors that are being studied as affecting resistance to wear. The tests are well under way, but it is not possible to report results at this meeting.

Results of tests made in a previous investigation at Lewis Institute are shown by the accompanying chart (from Bulletin No. 2, "Effect of Curing Conditions on the Wear and Strength of Concrete," Structural Materials Research Laboratory), and are applicable to the construction of

## WEAR TESTS OF CONCRETE FLOOR MIXTURES

Structural Materials Research Laboratory Lewis Institute, Chicago

### Outline of Tests
(5th Revision Jan 9, 1920)

Wear tests of 8x8x5-in blocks

Compression tests of 6x12-in cylinders

Hand-mixed concrete

Cement a mixture of 5 brands purchased in the Chicago market

Concrete for each specimen to be proportioned and mixed separately

Make slump test for plasticity of concrete on all cylinders

Test at age of 3 months

Wear blocks to be made in sets of 10 and cylinders in sets of 1 one-half of all each number on two different days, unless otherwise noted

Wear tests made in Talbot-Jones rattler

| Group | Mix by Volume | Aggregate | | | Relative Consistency | Curing Condition Days Stored in | | Number of Tests | |
|---|---|---|---|---|---|---|---|---|---|
| | | Kind | Size | F M | | Damp Sand | Air of Laboratory | Wear | Compression |
| 1 | 1:4<br>1:3<br>1:2½<br>1:2<br>1:1½<br>1:1 | Elgin sand and pebbles | 0-11<br>0-8<br>0-4<br>0-2<br>0-3<br>0-1½ | 2 20<br>2 70<br>3 00<br>4 00<br>5 00<br>5 75 | 1 10 | 11 | 76 | 360 | 111 |
| 2 | 1:3<br>1:2½<br>1:2<br>1:1½ | Lake sand<br>Elgin sand | 0-11<br>0-28 | 1 60<br>1 40 | 1 10 | 11 | 76 | 100 | 40 |
| 3[1] | 1:1<br>1:3<br>1:2½<br>1:2 | Elgin sand and pebbles<br>Chicago crushed limestone | 0-1₂ | 3 00<br>4 00<br>5 00<br>5 50<br>5 75<br>6 00<br>6 25 | 1 10 | 11 | 76 | 810 | 224 |
| 4[2] | 1:3<br>1:2½<br>1:2 | Elgin sand and pebbles | 0-¾ | 1 00 | 0 90<br>0 95<br>1 00<br>1 05<br>1 10<br>1 25<br>1 50 | 11 | 76 | 180 | 84 |
| 5[3] | 1:3<br>1:2½<br>1:2 | Limestone screenings (Chicago)<br>Limestone screenings (Wisconsin)<br>Granite screenings<br>Copperstone screenings<br>Slag screenings<br>Chatts screenings<br>Precious metal slag<br>Marble screenings<br>Disintegrated sandstone | 0-2<br>0-8<br>0-4<br>0-4<br>0-8<br>0-½<br>0-4<br>0-4<br>0-4 | 3 60<br>4 31<br>3 20<br>3 74<br>3 84<br>5 11<br>4 55<br>2 45<br>2 27 | 1 10 | 14 | 76 | 270 | 108 |

[1] Duplicate Elgin sand and pebbles for wear tests only for standard charge of slot

[2] Make 6 additional sets for test at 28 days for study of rattler charge

[3] Make blocks in 2 courses: bottom 3 inches, from Elgin aggregate and top 2 inches, from aggregates noted

| Group | Mix by Volume | Aggregate | | | Relative Consistency | Curing Condition Days Stored in | | Number of Tests | |
|---|---|---|---|---|---|---|---|---|---|
| | | Kind | Size | F M | | Damp Sand | Air of Laboratory | Wear | Compression |
| 6 | 1 : 3, 1 : 2½, 1 : 2 | Elgin sand and pebbles | 0–2 | 4.00 | 1.10 | 1 | 89 | 429 | 168 |
| | | | | | | 2 | 88 | | |
| | | | | | | 3 | 87 | | |
| | | | | | | 7 | 83 | | |
| | | | | | | 14 | 76 | | |
| | | | | | | 28 | 62 | | |
| | | | | | | 12 | 18 | | |
| | | | | | | 56 | 34 | | |
| | | | | | | 70 | 20 | | |
| | | | | | | 77 | 13 | | |
| | | | | | | 84 | 6 | | |
| | | | | | | 87 | 3 | | |
| | | | | | | 88 | 2 | | |
| | | | | | | 89 | 1 | | |
| 7 | 1 : 3 | Elgin sand and pebbles | 0–2 | 4.00 | 1.10 | | 0 | 320 | 128 |
| | | | | | | | 7 | | |
| | | | | | | 14 | 14 | | |
| | | | | | | 28 | 21 | | |
| | | | | | | 60 | 28 | | |
| | | | | | | 90 | (1) | | |
| | | | | | | | 3 mo[2] | | |
| | | | | | | | 9 mo[2] | | |
| 8 | | Absorption Tests of Concrete<br>  Retain all wear blocks in this series for absorption tests in water at room temperature<br>    Continue to 28 days<br>Miscellaneous Tests of Aggregates<br>  Sieve analysis<br>  Unit weight<br>  Absorption after 3 hours immersion | | | | | | | |

[1] Days necessary to make age at test 60 days
[2] 1 or 90 days storage in damp sand

one course sidewalks and floors. The present floor specifications of the Institute call for protection of the surface "for at least ten days" by an earth or sand covering kept wet.

The probable effect of proper protection upon a floor surface of this type is graphically illustrated by the chart. The tests from which the curves were obtained were all made at the end of 120 days on four series of samples, the first was stored in air 120 days, the second in damp sand 3 days and in air 117 days, the third in damp sand 21 days and in air 99 days, and the fourth in damp sand 120 days. The concrete was equivalent to a 1 : 1½ : 3 mixture.

The results show that an increase of over 75 per cent in compressive strength and a reduction of over 40 per cent in amount of wear or an equivalent increase in resistance to wear is obtained by ten days' protection with damp sand during the early period of hardening, also that an increase in compressive strength is accompanied by a corresponding increase in resistance to wear.

When it is considered that a floor in a building is seldom thoroughly wetted after the moisture present in the concrete at the time of construction has dried out, the need for proper and adequate protection of the floor surface during an early hardening is at once apparent. It is almost invariable practice in the construction of concrete roads and street pavements to protect the surface during early hardening by an earth covering. A concrete factory floor, particularly one subjected to heavy trucking, is an indoor pavement, and should have the same kind of protection if the owner wishes to obtain full returns on the money invested in the materials and labor utilized in the construction of the floor.

Since the meeting in June the revised standard specifications for sidewalks and for floors have been accepted through letter ballot. The committee has no changes to suggest at present in these specifications, but results of the wear tests now under way at the Structural Materials Research Laboratory will undoubtedly afford a basis for improvement of the specifications in the sections relating to the construction of the wearing surfaces of two course sidewalks and floors.

J. E. FREEMAN,

*Chairman*

DISCUSSION

Mr K H Talbor—In curing floors the practice in some places has been to use sawdust in preference to sand, simply because of its ease in handling and its cleanness  There has been some objection to the use of sawdust  I wonder if Mr Freeman would not give us his experience in that connection?

Mr J E Freeman—I have nothing to say in connection with actual experience with sawdust material as to covering for floors, except that it has been reported in a number of cases that certain classes of sawdust placed on the finished floor have had an adverse effect upon the green concrete interfering with the obtaining of the proper strength and wearing qualities  In view of that fact the committee felt some hesitancy about making a general recommendation with regard to the use of sawdust

Mr Louis R Cobb—I would like to ask if there has been much trouble from discoloration of the floor slabs by the use of either sand or sawdust as a covering?

Mr E D Boyer—There is always the danger in wood or sawdust from tannic acid and consequent staining of the surface of the floor ; that is the reason we hesitated about recommending the use of sawdust.  It is no doubt cheaper than sand, but sand is a better material

Mr P M Brunfr—I have used considerable sawdust, having laid the floors in about twelve or fifteen telegraphic stations here in Chicago, and we bought our sawdust wherever we could get it  I do not know from what lumber the sawdust was obtained, but we have not had a single instance of sawdust discoloring our work  At the same time I know that if you lay some kind of lumber on a cement floor while it is damp or wet the boards will stain the floor, due to some material in the lumber  I only want to say that we have used sawdust on over 200,000 ft of work and never had any complaint

Mr W. F. Tubesing—I find that one of the worst features of using sand is that on big work where a story is placed every six days, shores have to be put on top of the floor almost two or three hours after the finish is placed  The sawdust retains moisture longer than sand  Further more, the droppings of cement mortar, which cannot be avoided, come through, and in the case of sand form a hard surface which is hard to separate when you want to clean the floor  The sawdust seems to break up loosely so that I think on big work I would prefer to use sawdust in place of sand

Mr D A Abrams—I think there is no question that sawdust has a good many attractive features for floor covering  I do believe, however,

( 171 )

that it should be used with considerable caution  A year and a half or so
ago I had a report on the floor of a very important building, a laboratory
building not many miles from Chicago, a building that cost several hundred thousand dollars   The floors were found to be in very bad condition
A short time after the building was opened, investigation showed that the
floors had been covered with sawdust, and every indication pointed to
the fact that the soluble acids in the sawdust had attacked the fresh
concrete and pitted the surface and given a very inferior wearing surface
The experience in this particular case with sawdust was very important,
and it seems that considerable care should be used in the selection of saw
dust for floor covering

## REPORT OF SPECIAL COMMITTEE ON UNITS OF DESIGN

The tendency of modern factory construction is toward simplicity
In the earlier days of structural steel, each rolling mill had its own rolls,
which varied in small details from those of every other mill and which
covered an enormous gamut of sizes

Designing engineers, in striving for economy as they thought, called
for sizes varying by a few pounds weight for each slight variation of load
to be carried, with the result

> (1) That the engineering cost was more expensive than neces
> sary
>
> (2) The tonnage output of the rolling mill was reduced
> owing to the innumerable changes in rolls required
>
> (3) The work of the fabricating shop, together with the
> opportunity for error was greatly increased owing to the possi
> bility of mistaking one section for another, which differed only
> in minor degree

It was, of course, difficult to get material from several different mills
and use it interchangeably, because of the lack of standardization    It
soon became apparent that the multiplicity of shapes and weights put a
tax on the use of structural steel that was unnecessary and undesirable
As a result, the decision to roll only certain shapes and weights was
reached and designers were compelled to adapt these shapes and weights
to their use

Needless to say, a good deal of agitation and misgiving was occa
sioned  but today we know that the change has been justified, that the
smaller number of sections to be obtained are nevertheless sufficient for
any case that may arise, and that economy has gone hand in hand with
change   The standardization of structural steel is but one example
Mention might be made of steel sash and other items used in the con
struction of buildings.

The lack of standardization with its attendant bothers is clearly
shown in the products of the various brick yards, hardly any two of
which produce brick of a size and color so nearly alike as to enable them
to be used interchangeably with the bricks from another yard   In a time
like the present, where there is a decided shortage of brick, this condition
is an unmitigated hardship

Today we are facing an unprecedented demand for new buildings on
the one hand, and a shortage of materials and labor  a condition of con
gestion and embargoes on the railroads, and an unrest in the labor field
that is reflected in a lessened output per man for the hours worked   It is
perhaps due to the shorter hours that there seems also to be a falling off
in efficiency over that which obtained before 1916

This can be accounted for at least partially if it is remembered that even before the war the workmen did not hit their full stride the moment the whistle blew, neither did they work at full speed up to the moment of closing at noon or night, but rather a period of one half to three quarters of an hour of gradually increasing effort in the morning and to a lesser degree at noon elapsed before the average gait was attained, and not less than fifteen minutes before the finish of the morning or afternoon shift a perceptible let-down took place as the men got ready to quit

This condition of an early finish and a slow start obtains today, but owing to the shorter day now prevalent, it means an actual decrease in the total output compared with the output of an equal number of hours for the longer day, although in each case comparing hour for hour the men may be working at exactly the same rate

The reduction of output is greatly aggravated by the actual shortage of skilled and unskilled labor   This deficiency is estimated by the brick masons' union to be not less than 10 000 men for their trade alone.  Such a lack of workmen in the face of a tremendous demand for workmen, both by builders and manufacturers, has a tendency to increase the drift from job to job with the resulting effect that new men must constantly be hired and educated for new duties

It is or should be quite apparent that, in a limited period of time, it is much harder to teach a man how to perform a number of different tasks and obtain satisfactory results each time than it would be to teach one thing, and by constant repetition to reach a high standard of efficiency

To illustrate this point, at a visit to one of the shipyards during the early part of 1918 inquiry was made in regard to the sources of labor and the adequacy of their training for intricate work of building ships   A man working in the copper shop was pointed out with the statement that his previous occupation was that of baker   The only duty of this man, insofar as the shipyard was concerned   was that of making ventilators   At first his performance on this by no means simple job was rather mediocre, but by constantly keeping him hammering out one kind of ventilator day after day a short time only passed before excellent work was turned out

It is quite possible to take men of average intelligence and make them good workmen at any one job in a very short time, providing they are kept at one job without variation   It is probable that the difficulty of obtaining satisfactory results advances in a much more rapid proportion than the number of tasks to be performed would indicate

At the present time, the bar mills are being forced to reduce the number of sizes and kinds of bars rolled   This is largely an economic condition   The men in the rolling mills are paid on a tonnage basis the overhead of the mill, too is charged against the tonnage output   The mills recognizing these facts are today rolling approximately two-thirds of their output in sizes above the three-quarter inch base size and one-third in sizes smaller than base

To take a typical case, one ton of ⅜-in round bars would equal 5320 lin ft whereas it would equal but 1330 ft of ¾ in round bars Unquestionably the cost of labor and overhead on the larger size must be much less per ton than that of the smaller

It is very probable that for the immediate future at least the intermediate 1/16-in sizes will be abandoned and designers of concrete structures will be forced to content themselves with sizes that advance by even ⅛ s

Citing again the steel sash shops as an example of the tendency toward standardization, just so long as the regular stock sash with flat heads and horizontal pivoted ventilators are ordered a reasonable time of delivery may be obtained If, however to satisfy a whim of the owner or engineer vertically pivoted ventilators are called for the whole operation of the shop is thrown out of gear The workmen in the sash mills are paid a regular rate plus a bonus for output Just as long as the work is standard and regular the men earn a bonus worth while Inject, however, something special, and the routine of the factory stops the men do not make their bonus with the result of a prompt disintegration of the morale and a great falling off of efficiency

Examples may be multiplied but this will perhaps suffice to indicate the desirability of standardization not only in rolling mills and factories, but in the closely allied industry the manufacture of buildings

Constant thought and attention must be given to the relative cost of labor and materials In 1916, on any average job, a division of the money spent in producing the structure would indicate that labor cost about 30 percent and materials purchased about 70 percent of the total Today the division would be approximately 40 percent for labor and 60 percent for materials and it is predicted that in the near future, owing to the rising price of labor, this division may be more nearly 50 50 As the labor cost increases, it becomes self evident that more and more material can be used if, thereby, labor can be reduced

To apply this line of reasoning directly to the individual parts of a concrete building is not simple It is very difficult to make it clearly obvious that where a number of beams in a building are of one size, although the loading may vary sufficiently to allow decreasing the depth or the width in some instances, nevertheless such change, while it would undoubtedly save material would probably make the saving at the expense of a considerable extra cost for labor and supervision

It is proposed by the committee to submit at the next meeting of the American Concrete Institute actual design and estimating data, illustrating the possibilities of a greater degree of unification. particularly relative to footings, columns and beams

In the meantime, a few specific instances of details that apparently economize but actually add to cost will be indicated

  (1) Blueprints for a building recently submitted showed a total of 54 footings These footings were in the form of truncated

pyramids with a square or rectangular base   Slight variations
in the size and shape of the base and of the top on which the
column rested resulted in 19 separate types of footings   Of this
number 14 occurred once, 2 occurred twice, 1 three times, 1
occurred five times, one twelve and 1 sixteen times

The footings as detailed doubtless saved some concrete over that
required by simple steps, but the saving was made at the cost of some
very fussy and expensive form work

(2) A second example which might be cited is the case of a
building with different story heights

While this may sometimes be necessary to tie into existing buildings,
variations of this sort require piecing out or cutting off all supporting
shores under the floor forms, as well as the column forms themselves, and
is an added expense

On another building of flat-slab design with circular interior columns,
the column caps were called for 6 ft 6 in in diameter   The standard head
made by the metal column mold companies is 6 ft in diameter.   This
head was therefore a special piece of equipment and cost considerably more
than the standard would   If the head had been made the standard 6 ft
diameter, and ½ in extra concrete added to the depth of the plinth the
shearing value of the concrete would have been the same and the total
volume of concrete used would have been no greater and a saving would
have been made in cost

To touch on wall and interior columns in general it is undoubtedly
economical to keep the column size unchanged through at least two
stories, varying the column mix, and if necessary, having some excess
strength in the upper lift   This is particularly true where the columns
are square or rectangular and wooden forms are used

Still another point in connection with wall columns in flat-slab
buildings may be illustrated   In the earlier days of flat-slab construction
the use of drop panels was largely confined to the interior columns, the
wall beam usually was built entirely above the slab and a simple haunch
on the inside face of the wall column below the slab sufficed for all but
extraordinary demands   Today, designs frequently call for a plinth at the
wall column as well as at the interior

As this plinth extends either side of the column, it necessitates a small
drop beam the depth of the plinth being carried across the head of the
window   and in order to obtain sufficient strength   it is also necessary to
carry the beam above the slab   Probably it will not be disputed that this
is more expensive than a simple beam above the slab, and usually per-
forms no function which could not have been adequately arranged in a
simpler way

Another condition that occasionally arises, is that where it is specified that gravel can be used for aggregate in the floors, beams, etc., but that broken stone must be used for aggregate in the columns

In many parts of the country gravel is the only easily available supply, or it can be purchased more economically than broken stone.  Under these conditions gravel would naturally be desirable, but its use would mean getting aggregate from different stock piles and routing each batch of concrete on the floor so that no gravel concrete was placed in a column

The roof of a building also requires careful attention.  It is desirable that the regular floor forms be used with as little variation as possible The story height should be the same as that of the floors below  The ceiling should remain flat, and it is a question if it is necessary to pitch the upper surface, provided a good job is made of the roofing.

Summarizing briefly

Footings —Where the sides of footings are sloped the number of forms to be made should be reduced to a minimum by utilizing the same sloped form for footings even when the area of the base courses below the sloped portion are different sizes  In many cases a stepped-up footing without steel will prove more economical than reinforced concrete footings Care should be taken in the use of plain concrete not to exceed a reasonable unit in tension

Columns —In order to effect economies in the formwork it will often be found desirable to maintain the same cross section of column through several stories  In the case of interior columns where metal forms are used it is important that that portion of the metal form which adjoins the floor construction shall be uniform in the several stories to avoid the changing of the floor forms  When metal forms are used for interior columns the reduction in the size of column, if made at all, should be made in every other story  The vertical steel reinforcement should be made up of as large bars as are consistent to good practice in order that the handling expense may be reduced to a minimum.

Beams and Girders —In determining the depth of beams and girders of floors a careful study should be made to determine the depth which will give the minimum total cost for the reinforcing steel and concrete combined  This should be considered, although very often the minimum depth to be used for a certain span or the criterion of shear will govern the depth actually determined upon

In general, the forms for roof construction should be the same as those for the floors in order to avoid the expense of re making the forms It is very seldom possible to re make the forms and save enough concrete to make it worth while  Every effort should be made to so plan the construction that forms can be used from floor to floor

Story Heights —From the standpoint of economy it is desirable that the story heights be such that it will not be necessary to lengthen out the column forms to provide for the upper stories

STEEL REINFORCEMENT.—In order to avoid excess of labor costs in the field it is desirable to reduce the number of lengths and sizes of reinforcing bars to a minimum, even if in so doing a slight excess in steel reinforcement is sometimes necessitated. In this connection the number of bars used in any member should be reduced to a minimum, provided all the requirements for bond, etc., are taken care of. A minimum number of stirrups of maximum size should be provided to reduce labor cost.

A. B. MacMillan, Chairman

Mr H C Turner—We have here a presentation of the problems of the contractor from the business man's viewpoint  I think that very often engineers designing work give too great consideration to the theoretical problems of design instead of the practical problems  In this respect I think contracting differs from manufacturing today  I know that many manufacturing concerns are meeting the high cost of labor by a more thorough study of machines and manufacturing processes, and in some cases manufacturers are actually producing their products at a cost not so very much above the cost before the war  This report, I think, tends to point the way for contractors, that is, we must give study to the design so that we may minimize work in the engineering office as well as the work of the purchasing department and work in the field.

Mr W. F. Tubesing—The last couple of years we have gone a step further than is suggested in the report  We have tried to make columns conform to a certain width so that we could expand or contract the column by merely taking off the cleats  Also for beams we use standard panels which will make the average beam 16½ in deep and will make the average girder about 22½ in deep  That is the greatest depth that can be gotten out of a certain number of forms with 6 in boards nailed together.  We have found that by so doing we have been saving on the lumber cost and also on the steel ratio

Mr L C Wason—On some buildings where truncated, cone-shaped footings have been used, and where engineers specified forms for that shape, we have been careful to mix the concrete plastic, that is, just stiff enough so that it would not slump down and then to build the footing without any formwork whatever, probably using 10 to 15 percent more concrete than the theoretical design shown on the plans  In making up this several times, there is a saving of all formwork and the advantage of getting a strong, durable footing

Mr Cloyd M Chapman—In the report there is an allusion to the possibility of leaving the roof slabs flat on both the under surface and the upper or waterproof surface  I would just like to ask whether the committee or anyone present has anything to say in regard to the use of cinder concrete or the building up of crickets or ditch surfacing on top of a flat roof  I have seen some difficulties with roofs attributed to the use of cinder concrete as a means of giving a pitch to a flat roof

Mr W. F Tubesing—I can cite two cases where the pitch produced from the cinder concrete in three years forced the wall out 6 in  There must have been some leak along the flashing where the water got back of the wall. Those walls had to be taken down and rebuilt at great expense

MR. A. W. STEPHENS.—We have had the same experience mentioned, that is, the tendency of the parapet walls to be pushed out by the expansion of the cinder concrete. We believe it to be due to expansion of the concrete rather than an intrusion of water and in much of our later work, where we are using cinder concrete, we are providing an expansion joint in the cinder concrete beneath the waterproofing, using some plastic material to fill the space. We have not interpreted our trouble as being the leakage of water through the waterproofing itself. I might add that there is a danger in the use of cinder concrete, in that if it becomes saturated with water before the roofing is put on, there may be trouble for some time, due to the leakage of the water which is contained in the cinder concrete through the roof slab. I remember one case where a barrel was kept in the top story for over a year catching that water as it dropped

# REPORT OF COMMITTEE ON REINFORCED-CONCRETE HIGHWAY BRIDGES AND CULVERTS.

An outline is attached hereto of the subjects that have come to mind at this time offering a beginning in the work of the committee  This outline was submitted to the members of the committee and is presented here as a progress report of the committee to the Institute

## RECOMMENDED PRACTICE

ARCHITECTURE —Concrete lends itself to a most graceful and admirable form of architecture with special characteristic potentialities in concrete bridge development wherein an unlimited field is offered.  It can hardly be refuted that this feature has been sorely neglected in our American bridge practice, the whole of which has been so recently and voluminously developed   There is a need of paramount importance, for a more thorough consideration of this opportunity as offered to all phases of bridge design

Bridge Engineer Torkelson, of Wisconsin, strikes the keynote as follows  "When it is considered that concrete bridge work is designed for permanence, the question of proper appearance is a very important one  We can stand for an ugly piece of work if it is going to be removed in a few years  but when it is to be permanent, we cannot stand for anything except the best   Our experience is that when taxpayers get a taste of work that is good, not only from a standpoint of utility but appearance as well, they are enthusiastic about it and more than willing to pay the cost'

CONSTRUCTION JOINTS —The question of construction joints is one of the most important considerations in concrete bridge design   Very often it is necessary to waive seemingly economic considerations in design in order to provide the proper construction joint   No bridge plan is complete without showing the location of every possible construction joint involving the daily capacity of an average mixing plant, so that the contractor will know the intention of the design beforehand and be prepared to regulate his work accordingly.  Recommendations should be made dealing with construction joints of large and small arches built on either a normal or skew span  for horizontal joints in mass work  for joints in rectangular and T-beams, in slabs, etc

Where a pier or retaining wall is of such height necessitating horizontal construction joints  the rusticated or grooved joint has been used to good advantage in preclusion of the otherwise irregular, unsightly joints

The lengths of the reinforcing rods should be so determined that only a sufficient amount for the proper bonding should project beyond the construction joint   The Chairman has a photograph showing rods at least 35 ft in length supported vertically above the top or skewback of a pier in arch construction

CURBS—What height and protection? It seems that extremely low curbs should be avoided on bridges. The high cost prevents a vehicle mounting the sidewalk and crashing through the railing.

CLEARANCES—The standard vertical and lateral clearance for steam and electric railways should be given in our report. These are practically uniform for all roads.

DEVICES—It might be advisable to give some space to devices that have proved their worth in simplifying construction, such as form ties, spacers, bar cradles and hangers, wire mesh, etc. Devices in construction will be discussed under that topic.

DRAINAGE OF FLOORS—As a matter of fact expansion joints, drainage, waterproofing and construction joints are so correlated that all must be considered jointly in a successful design of a floor system. Water must be carried off the floor in as many places and as quickly as is possible.

Avoid placing downspouts in concrete sections without due regard for expansion of metal drain pipes.

Avoid placing outlet of drain where the drip will pour over concrete surface or overhead where icicle formation will endanger life. Copper baskets filled with rock salt and placed at the top of a down spout has been found to be effective in preventing the formation of icicles and freezing up of pipes.

The drainage of abutments and retaining walls by French drains and weep holes should be considered.

EXPANSION JOINTS—Expansion joints in concrete construction are as absolutely necessary as they are in steel construction. How far apart can they be placed to work effectively in the various types of concrete design, in floors over arches, spandrel walls over arches, in T beam or rectangular beam or slab construction, in flat slabs, in retaining walls, abutments etc.? What are the respective merits and defects of the various types of expansion joints, viz. sliding, rocker and cantilever joints? For the sliding joints, steel, copper and bronze plates and asphaltic membrane have been used with varying degrees of effectiveness. A complete break in a structure by an arrangement of a double row of columns, depending upon the flexure in the column to take up the movement due to temperature changes, has proved effective.

Sliding joints, in the chairman's opinion are to be discouraged on account of their uncertainty. Due to unforeseen slight settlement or irregular construction, a friction on the sliding joint may be developed which has greater resistance than the vertical section of a particular member in shear, which results in an unsightly and dangerous crack near the expansion joint.

In spandrel floors over arches a vertical joint in the floor slab formed by cantilevering slab from spandrel or cross walls has proved very effective since by this arrangement the vertical movement of the floor due to rise and fall of the arch ring and the horizontal movement in the floor system itself are well taken care of.

Electrolysis—What precaution should be taken in reinforced concrete bridge construction to guard against this possible destructive action?

Fill over Arches—For arches and culverts placed under deep fill, what precaution should be taken to prevent overflow of embankment over head walls and wing walls? The slope of embankment used in the determination of the length of barrel should vary for different heights of fill using same material in embankment

How should a deep fill be made over an arch?

Foundations—Classify the various soils and give their bearing power Advise precaution in using these figures recommending actual tests of soil for particular bridge. A thorough classification is necessary for use in estimating purposes when time is not available for an actual test of the soil

Preliminary Study and Investigation of Bridge Site—What should be included in the survey what soundings and investigation of waterway, etc? Recommendations of former committees have covered these considerations very well

Paving—Requirements in design to cover the various classes of paving

Plans—What details are required?

Reinforcing Steel—Specifications? Bending diagrams and thorough list of all bars should be shown on plans What is best form of stirrups? What protection of stubs exposed through winter weather? What should be the minimum spacing of bars in beams?

Types of Bridges—Classify bridges and give type best suited for various general conditions of span, length width foundations, etc

Waterproofing—Waterproofing systems can be divided into two classes (a) Membrane and (b) integral (a) Three materials generally used are the felts, papers and cloth or combination of these materials (b) Numerous integral methods of questionable value, are on the market These are not applicable to any degree in waterproofing bridge floors susceptible to cracks

A waterproofing membrane should be protected and made more durable by covering it with asphaltic mastic, a layer of brick or a 2 in layer of concrete Asphalts or other bituminous pavements should not be laid directly on the membrane

Piers and Abutments—What protection in streams to guard against scouring action of water?

Piers in roadways. Are they a menace or a help in safeguarding traffic?

### Assumptions in Design

Arches—What range of temperature should be considered in the various climatic zones? Does the present accepted formula give values in excess of those that actually exist? Bulletin 30 by C S Nichols and C B McCullough of Iowa State College covers the first effort known to the chairman in determination of the actual temperature changes and effect

It seems that this work could easily be carried on to check and enlarge upon results already obtained

TABLE OF WEIGHTS OF MATERIALS —Required a table giving the weights of all materials used in design

LOAD ASSUMPTIONS —Review highway loadings, trucks and traction engines, also electric traction loading, enlarging upon the table of 1919 committee report   Classify electric traction loading by weight in increments of 5 tons for both city and interurban cars, giving spacing of wheels and truck centers   Determine what laws have been passed by all state legislatures in regulating or limiting the weights of vehicles

LOAD DISTRIBUTION —What distribution of concentrated loads should be made over simple rectangular slabs, over a series of T beams over slabs superimposed on steel I-beams over arches distributed through various depths of fills, and on floor slab and girders of a through-girder bridge? In the 1919 report of this committee, these various considerations were given thought for the first time   The recommendations therein are by no means conclusive   The subject is, therefore, open to wide discussion and further investigation

IMPACT —How should allowance be made for this factor?  By recommending a loading in excess of an actual loading or by using actual loading and adding a factor depending upon length of span or dead load or otherwise?

DESIGN OF SLAB OF T-BEAMS —The committee should specify differences in design of a floor system of the slab and beam type wherein the dimensions of the one for flange and stem do not exceed present recommendations as to the effective width of compressed area  and the other, in which the span of slab exceeds width of compressed area   In the former very little steel is required in the flange and no provision seems necessary for the negative moment in the slab over the stem   In the latter it seems reasonable to take care of a negative moment in the slab or flange   This was covered in 1919 report with reference only to the first condition

EARTH PRESSURES —The Chairman understands that the Bureau of Public Roads has made some tests in determination of earth pressures against retaining walls   Much data on this important subject is needed Means should be taken to collect whatever data is available and to enlarge upon the tests   The subject could profitable be investigated as a graduate thesis and the chairman therefore suggests an effort to interest the various technical schools to this end

DESIGNS OF FORMS —What pressure should be assumed in design of forms?  What unit stresses in the timber?

FAULTY DESIGN —It might be advisable to tabulate some of the mistakes that have been made repeatedly   For example  (a) Timber grillage, supporting masonry piers or abutments, out of the water   (b) Tendency to use empirical formulas in design of walls and abutments   (c) Avoid side difference in sections of wing walls and abutments at junction of the two (d) Foundations above first line   (e) Lack of proper drainage of retaining walls and abutments, etc

## SPECIFICATIONS

A complete specification covering the selection of material and regulation of work seems necessary.  There are certain precautions that must be taken in all forms of concrete bridge work that are not properly covered by other committees of the Institute   The specifications should be complete in every detail even though it is necessary to repeat some of the work of other committees

## METHODS OF CONSTRUCTION

ARCH CONSTRUCTION—Describe the various types of arch centering methods of constructing arches by voussoirs, method of constructing skew arches.

REMOVAL OF FORMS—More thorough recommendations are needed governing the removal of forms for variable temperatures   It seems that a more scientific analysis leading to definite regulations could be developed governing this important consideration   There is some good data pertaining to this subject, the most important of which is a paper presented by Prof A B McDaniel printed in the 1916 Proceedings of the Institute

CHUTING CONCRETE—This method of depositing concrete has developed so rapidly and with such presumable success that many abuses of the system exist   The committee should ferret out these abuses and incorporate warnings precluding same in proposed new specifications

A B COHEN Chairman

# REPORT OF COMMITTEE ON FIREPROOFING

In the report of this Committee for 1919, certain recommendations were made, relating to engineering practice for reinforced concrete columns where four hour fire protection is required. In the interval since that report was prepared, a considerable number of fire tests of concrete columns have been made by the Bureau of Standards at Pittsburgh. These results are to be found in a report * entitled Fire Tests of Concrete Columns, that has been submitted to the Institute for presentation at the 1920 meeting, and which contains data which seem to justify the recommendation of one additional aggregate and of one additional expedient for the prevention of spalling.

As will be seen from that report and the previous reports of the fire tests of concrete columns made at Pittsburgh, extensive spalling has invariably taken place in the fire tests of hooped columns from highly silicious gravels, made in the usual way. Most of the columns tested have had a thickness of 1½ in. of protective concrete over the steel. Two columns, Nos. 79 and 80, from Pittsburgh gravel, with 2½ in. of protective concrete (see Table) gave results that were distinctly better than those with protective concrete only 1½ in. thick, Nos. 73 74 and others, and yet so poor in comparison to those shown by columns from more favorable aggregates, with 1½ in. of protective concrete, that the expedient of securing better protection in the case of columns from highly silicious gravel, by providing an unusual thickness of protective concrete, does not seem worthy of recommendation. On the other hand, the two columns from Pittsburgh gravel, Nos 77 and 78, with a thickness of 1½ in. of protective concrete reinforced by a light grade of expanded metal, of large mesh, to prevent the loss of protective concrete by spalling gave fairly satisfactory results. While the results of the test of these columns were not as good as those columns from limestone trap rock and blast furnace slag aggregates, the loss of strength in the four-hour fire test as determined by loading to failure in the furnace while the column was still hot, was less than 60% in both cases, which presents a strong contrast to the results from columns from the same aggregate Pittsburgh gravel without reinforcement in the protective concrete, which failed under the working load before the four-hour fire test was completed.

Columns from Pittsburgh gravel, Nos 82 and 83, with 2½ in. of protective concrete with the light expanded metal reinforcement in the outer concrete to prevent the loss of protective concrete by spalling could not be loaded to failure in the furnace, at the end of the four-hour fire test, due to the fact that their strength exceeded the load limit of the furnace equipment, which is equivalent to a stress of approximately 3480 pounds

* Printed on p. 20 of this volume

pei square inch on the effective area of these columns When tested cold, after fire test, in a testing machine of high capacity, these columns showed an ultimate strength only slightly lower than that of a similar column, No 84, which had not been subjected to fire test  Judging from these results, it would appear that if the protective concrete of columns from highly silicious gravel aggregates were reinforced with expanded metal so as to prevent loss of protective concrete by spalling, they would be sufficiently protected by the thicknesses of protective concrete recommended for different conditions in the last report of this committee  The expedient of providing such reinforcement in the protective concrete of columns made from highly silicious gravels is accordingly included among the recommendations for columns

DATA FROM TESTS OF ROUND HOOPED COLUMNS OF FIFTEEN-INCH EFFECTIVE DIAMETER

| Aggregate | Column No | Thickness of Protective Concrete, in | Time of Failure under Working Load | | Max Stress Tested Cold without Fire Test, lb per sq in | Max Stress at End of 4-hour Fire Test, lb per sq in | Max Stress Tested Cold having been Loaded to 3480 lb per sq in at End of 4-or Fire Test |
|---|---|---|---|---|---|---|---|
| | | | Hrs | Min | | | |
| | 73 | 1½ | 3 | 50 | | | |
| | 74 | 1½ | 3 | 20 | | | |
| | 75 | 1½ | | | 4 880 | | |
| | *77 | 1½ | | | | 1,995 | |
| | *78 | 1½ | | | | 2,120 | |
| Pittsburgh gravel | 79 | 2½ | | | | 1,495 | |
| Pittsburgh sand | 80 | 2½ | | | | 1 640 | |
| | 81 | 2½ | | | 5,590 | | |
| | *82 | 2½ | | | | | 5,115 |
| | *83 | 2½ | | | | | 4 950 |
| | *84 | 2½ | | | 5,155 | | |
| High limestone gravel | 85 | 1½ | | | | | 4 440 |
| High limestone sand | 86 | 1½ | | | | | 5 240 |
| | 87 | 1½ | | | 5 620 | | |

* Those columns which had expanded metal in the protective concrete are indicated by an asterisk

Two gravel concrete columns, Nos 85 and 86, in which the aggregate was low in quartz content, have been fire tested  Approximately ninety per cent of the gravel was made up of limestone pebbles and there was a high percentage of limestone in the sand  The columns had 1½ in of protective concrete with no expanded metal  These columns showed no tendency to spall in the fire test and gave comparatively good results in other respects  Neither of them failed under the maximum furnace load when tested hot at the end of the four-hour fire test  When tested cold, after the fire test the ultimate strength was found, in both cases, to be more than 75 per cent of that of a similar column No 87, which had not been submitted to fire test  These results indicate that gravels and sands that are very high in limestone content are suitable for use in fire-resistive concrete  It is probable that all gravels that are low in quartz may prove, on investigation, to be free from the spalling tendency. How high a pro portion of quartz can be included in gravels without the resulting concretes spalling under fire test conditions cannot be determined from the tests thus far made. The evidence now available appears to be sufficient, however, to justify the recommendation, which is to be found in a later para graph of this report, that gravels high in limestone content be given a preference, for fire resistive concrete, over highly silicious gravels

The recommendations made in the report of this committee for 1919, amended to conform to the evidence presented in the foregoing discussion, may be stated as follows

1 That in concrete columns where four-hour protection is required, protective material not less than 2 in in thickness shall be provided over the steel In columns in which a high percentage of steel is used, increasing the importance of affording it ample protection the thickness of protective material shall be 2½ in for four-hour protection, and special care shall be given to the accurate placing of the steel in the forms, to avoid inadequate protection on any side

2 That for fire-resistive construction, limestone, trap rock, blast furnace slag, well burned clay and gravels composed largely of limestone pebbles be given a preference over highly silicious gravels

3 That where highly silicious gravel aggregate is to be used, in columns without hooping, and with no special safeguards round columns be given a preference over rectangular ones

4 That where highly silicious gravel aggregate is to be used, all columns, but especially rectangular columns and round columns with spiral reinforcement, be safeguarded by means of one of the following expedients

(a) Placing expanded metal or other high weight large mesh reinforcement in the outer concrete to prevent the loss of protective concrete by spalling

(b) Giving columns additional protection of approximately 1 in of cement plaster, either on metal lath or reinforced with light expanded metal or other suitable material

W A Hull *Chairman.*

## REPORT OF COMMITTEE ON REINFORCED CONCRETE
### STORAGE TANKS

The committee has held several meetings at which a tentative recommended practice for fuel oil storage tank construction was discussed. A number of important changes have been made in the preliminary draft as prepared prior to the meetings and the revised recommendations will be placed in proper form to be included in the "Proceedings" of this convention as information accompanying this progress report.

These tentative recommendations concern only reinforced-concrete tanks for fuel oil storage and do not cover the construction of large concrete-lined earthen reservoirs, since that is really a separate subject.

Your committee feels that a joint conference with the National Fire Protection Association's Committee on Inflammable Liquids is highly desirable as a means of formulating a joint report on the subject of concrete tanks for fuel oil storage which will be acceptable both from the standpoint of construction and fire protection. The committee requests therefore that it be empowered to invite the N. F. P. A. committee to such a conference and select from our committee representatives to meet with similar representatives from the N. F. P. A. committee in joint conference to prepare such a report. It is felt that such a joint committee having the sanction of both organizations, could prepare a report which would have more weight than if the Institute were to prepare an individual report, since many of the factors entering into the construction of a concrete oil storage tank are directly connected with the subject of fire protection.

Supplementing this progress report the committee submits as information data on the general subject of fuel oil and concrete tanks for fuel oil storages.

### DATA ON FUEL OIL TANKS

The advantage of fuel oil over bituminous coal for power production, combined with the insecurity felt by manufacturers and other users of fuel in the labor situation, as related to coal production, has stimulated the use of fuel oil to such an extent that many large installations of oil burning apparatus have been made, and its continued and increasing use is anticipated.

As fuel oil presents a definite fire hazard if not properly controlled, the best method of storing and handling it is now being studied by national organizations, and by municipal districts having interests to protect.

### PHYSICAL PROPERTIES OF FUEL OIL

In answer to the question that sometimes arises, "What is a fuel oil?" these quotations are given from a paper presented by Ernest H. Peabody, of the Babcock and Wilcox Co., at the International Engineering Congress, San Francisco, 1915.

( 189 )

### WHAT IS FUEL OIL?

The origin of petroleum can hardly be considered an important matter to prospective users of fuel oil   The question whether it is animal, vegetable or mineral or all three (which seems likely), organic or inorganic, belongs rather to the province of the geologist to decipher   Those interested may refer to the scientific papers on this topic, published in the Transactions of the American Institute of Mining Engineers for 1914, and I understand also that a paper is to be presented at the Fourth International Petroleum Congress at San Francisco 1915, by Dr David T Day, of the U S Bureau of Mines, which will settle the controversy—probably   But the available supply of oil and prospects of its continuance are of prime importance to the vessel owner who contemplates using oil as a fuel

Let us consider them   In the first place  What is fuel oil?  We are told that petroleum consists of very many combinations of carbon and hydrogen and hydro carbons which, while they may be entirely simple to the chemist   seem extremely complicated and abstruse to the lay mind, as for example  Propane ($CH_2CH_2CH_2$) or Dimethylpropylmethane ($C_3H_2$) $CH$ ($CH_2CH_2CH_3$), or Hentriacontane ($C_{32}H_{66}$)

How much of this intricate product may we expect to be turned over for use as fuel oil?  I have asked Dr Day to answer this question, and am indebted to him for the following statement

"From the standpoint of the petroleum trade  fuel oil, in general, includes all oils which are not saleable for some other special purpose at a higher price than that which prevails for oils to be sold for fuel oils, or to be burned under boilers   From the trade point of view, it also includes special distillates burned for power purposes  such as gasolene  naphtha, motor spirits, and various kerosene distillates   The actual amount of oil devoted to fuel purposes varies continually with the condition of the production of crude petroleum   During the time of flush production such as has existed in the Oklahoma fields during the past year, due to the extraordinary production in the Cushing field, a great deal of crude petroleum is sold as fuel oil on account of the necessity of disposing of it when no better market is available   The use of such oil is not advisable for fuel purposes not only because it contains valuable gasolene and kerosene, but these contents so lower the flashing point of the fuel oil as to make it open to the objections to gasolene stored in a a confined space, as on a battleship, where the vapor is liable to produce explosions on contact with air

"Until the last twelve month  much of the production of California crude oil was sold for fuel purposes, practically as it came from the well   Within the last year, however, the practice of topping off the valuable gasolene and kerosene in a comparatively small proportion of California oils has so increased that not more than 25% of the fuel oil of California is now crude oil   In states other than California and Oklahoma, and to a slight extent Texas  fuel oils consist chiefly of the least valuable distillates and some residium   The distillates of such low value as to be sold for fuel oil are usually the products distilling off after kerosene, and those too heavy for burning in lamps and also too thin to be used as lubricating oils   Such oils generally have the name of gas oils, and are more valuable for use as gas oils than for fuel purposes, but the market for gas oils is easily over-supplied, and the surplus goes for fuel oil

"The annual production of petroleum in the United States is about * 266 000 000 bbl in round numbers  of which at least 100,000,000 bbl is consumed as fuel   This proportion will hold fairly well for the petroleum production of the world  that is about 2/5 of the world s production may be considered 'fuel oil'   In regions such as the East Indies, the petroleum is to a large extent too valuable for use of residium and even crude oil for fuel purposes is very general, and exceeds the average proportion "

It may be of interest, perhaps, to make further abstracts from Mr Peabody's paper concerning physical properties of fuel oil

The heat value of fuel oil varies between about 16 000 and 20,000 B T U per lb, 18 000 to 19,000 being the common values

### HEAT VALUE FUEL OIL

| Source | Specific Gravity av | B T U per lb av |
|---|---|---|
| California  6 fields | 958 | 18 270 |
| Texas, 3 fields | 921 | 19,024 |
| Pennsylvania  1 field | 886 | 19 210 |
| Mexico  2 fields | 951 | 18 196 |

In a paper published in the Journal of the American Chemical Society, October 1908, Sherman and Kropff give the following formula for oils above 15° Beaume

B T U  per pound  equals 18 650 plus 40 (Beaume—10)

* The 1919 report of the Geological Survey shows a production of 376,000 bbl

## Viscosity

Viscosity may be described as the resistance to internal movement or the internal friction of a liquid

## Flash Point

The "flash point" of oil is the temperature at which inflammable gas or vapor is given off   It is determined simply by heating the oil and as the temperature rises testing it with a spark or flame until the vapor is distilled off and ignites and the flash is noticed.

## Density of Oil—Specific Gravity

The Beaume hydrometer scale for liquids lighter than water is generally used, 10° Beaume being equal to the specific gravity of water

The United States Bureau of Standards has adopted the following formula for converting readings on the Beaume scale, lighter than water, to terms of specific gravity

Specific gravity at 60° F  equals 140/130 *plus B*

## Specific Heat of Oil

The specific heat of oil varies with its composition   It will be greater the richer the oil is in hydrogen, and lower in proporton to a greater carbon content

The following figures are reproduced from Holde's work on 'Examination of Hydro carbon Oil

| Crude Oils From— | S G | S H |
|---|---|---|
| Japan | 862 | 453 |
| Pennsylvania    .. | 810 | 500 |
| Russia | 908 | 435 |
| California | 960 | 398 |
| Bu-tenari | 842 | 462 |

## Coefficient of Expansion of Oil

It may be considered that at ordinary temperatures crude petroleum expands under the influence of heat approximately five ten thousandths (0 0005) of its volume for each degree F (0 009) per degree C   This coefficient decreases for the heavier oils, being a fraction of the specific gravity

Subsequent to the presentation of this paper  a valuable treatise reporting the investigations of the Bureau of Mines on the coefficient of expansion of California crude oils and distillates was presented at the first annual meeting of the American Society, at San Francisco, by Mr A S Crossfield   The conclusions arrived at are as follows

' 1   The value of the coefficient new used in California practice approximates 0 0009 per 1° C  (0 0005) per 1° F   From the results of this investigation it is apparent that this value is considerably too high  and that the correct value more nearly approaches 0 00072 per 1° C  (0 004 per 1° F )

"2   The value of the coefficient for crude oils and distillates within the ranges of temperatures used  is a straight line function of the temperature and increases with an increase in temperature

"3   The value of the coefficient for crude oils within the ranges of specific gravity used, is a straight line function of the specific gravity   The value for distillates deviates somewhat from a straight line '

## Precautions Against Danger

The time is long past when the use of fuel oil on shipboard is opposed on account of insurmountable danger   Oil has the distinct advantage over coal that it is not subject to spontaneous combustion, and many fires that have occurred in ships bunkers at sea would not have been possible with oil

Certain precautions, however  must be taken, such as suitable arrangements of vent pipes  protection of bunker bulkheads if exposed to heat  and particularly the use of an oil with a reasonable high flash point   The United States Navy  in cooperation with the Bureau of Mines, has investigated the matter of the probable explosion of gases in storage tanks, and it was found that no inflammable gases were formed in any amount in the storage tanks or bunkers until the oil was heated to the flash, i e, that the representative oils tested contained no dissolved gas or vapor sufficient to form an explosive mixture at temperatures below the flash point   The largest percentage of vapor in the atmosphere of fuel oil tanks of various battle

ships tested was 0 04%, whereas about 0 9% is required to form an explosive mixture
It was also found that any oil in the bunker tank had to be heated to within 60° F of
the flash point before even a faint "glow" or partial burning was obtained on introducing a naked flame into the tank

A possible danger evidently exists of heating heavy oils obove the flash
point when heating coils are introduced into the tank for facilitating
pumping, unless suitable precautions are taken

### STORAGE LOSSES SHOULD BE REDUCED

In the vicinity of the source of the oil, the usual method of storage
has been by the construction of large reservoirs, some simply excavated in
the earth, others with the earth excavation concrete lined, without roof,
and others provided with light roofs to retard evaporation

In this method of storage, particularly with unlined and roofless reservoirs, there is considerable loss of oil, and the extent thereof is illustrated
by the following quotations from Bulletin 155, Bureau of Mines, on "Oil
Storage Tanks and Reservoirs ' It is therefore recommended that all large
storage basins or reservoirs at the source of supply as well as the outlet
be concrete lined to limit seepage and concrete roofed for permanency, and
to reduce evaporation losses to a minimum.

#### LOSSES IN STORAGE BY SEEPAGE

Oil losses by seepage from steel tanks and from well constructed concrete lined
reservoirs can be considered practically nil   From unlined earthen reservoirs how
ever, seepage losses may be very large   It is difficult to determine just what these
losses are for the reason that most of such reservoirs, as previously stated are used
as emergency containers  the oil put into them coming unmeasured from flowing
wells   However, there is a record of a 500 000 bbl unlined reservoir in the Kerr
River field, California, that had to be abandoned on account of the excessive seepage
losses   Although the reservoir was in use only a short time, pits dug subsequently
in the bottom disclose that the oil had already penetrated for a depth of more than
20 ft

#### LOSSES BY EVAPORATION

If we knew definitely the volume of useful hydro-carbon products that vanish
into 'thin air" from the wells, the transportation systems  the storage farms and the
refineries of the United States in a single year's time, we might well be staggered by
the size of the figures   To form some realization of the gigantic proportions one
needs only to stand in the vicinity of a flowing well newly brought in and witness
the volume of gases rising like exaggerated heat waves from the well itself, from the
flow tanks in which the oil is collected, from the sump into which it has overflowed
and from every surface exposed to the atmosphere   The greatest unmeasured loss,
of course, takes place in the vicinity of the well   Nevertheless, this loss continues in
a large measure, especially as regards light oils, through the gathering systems,
the transportation systems  and the receiving tanks of the refineries  and even from
oil of low gravity there is a continual stream of the light hydro carbons escaping from
its surface so long as it remains in storage

These quotations are given for the purpose of impressing the reader
with the economical necessity of using a container for the oil that will limit
to the greatest extent the losses from both seepage and evaporation, especially after the oil has been marketed, transported for hundreds of thousands
of miles, and thus given a definite commercial value far in excess of its
value in original storage

### Reduction of Fire Hazard

Furthermore in built up sections, and particularly in cities there is the advisability of providing a container which will be the least hazard to surrounding buildings from the viewpoint of the fire insurance underwriters and by officials of commonwealths or municipalities.

### Concrete Tanks for Fuel Oil Storage

Steel tanks have generally been used for oil storage after the oil has been transported from the oil fields by the producing companies as they are usually built above ground, without the necessity of complying with underwriters' rules or as in the past with municipal regulations.

There is no question but that a steel tank whose height is not limited by the lift of an oil pump and which is not protected by dikes can be built cheaper than concrete under usual conditions. But when the insurance underwriters and municipalities safeguard oil storage by requiring under ground construction near buildings, surround steel tanks by concrete dikes if above ground, where rules and necessity require protection of steel if underground, and where a gravity flow of oil is prohibited, thus making a further requirement that they shall be underground a reversal of conditions results to the advantage of reinforced concrete.

There has been a general impression that concrete is not proof against seepage of oil through it and especially under hydrostatic pressure. This impression is perhaps to a great degree warranted in the construction of tanks with high walls where the concrete work has not been continuous. But for tanks to hold fuel oil where the flow of oil by gravity is prohibited, and where the depth of the tank is limited to 15 ft., this being about the maximum height heavy fuel oil can be lifted by an ordinary oil pump, reinforced concrete has proved a satisfactory and dependable material if scientifically handled.

Deep tanks whose walls are too high for ordinary continuous depositing of concrete require special study and consideration, but for shallow tanks, either above or below ground, reinforced concrete has advantages over steel, and a few of these are named for illustration.

Concrete tanks well designed and built require no rust protection either when built above or below ground nor maintenance repairs such as calking or painting. Underground concrete tanks are not subject to electrolysis, such tanks readily resist hydrostatic pressure from ground water as well as earth pressures. The tanks can be easily adapted to any unusual shape required by a particular location. The low conductivity of the material insulates the oil against temperature changes thus retarding evaporation in summer and making it easier to handle the oil in winter weather. The materials for the construction of reinforced concrete tanks are to a great extent obtained locally, thus eliminating many delays arising from ship ment of the materials from a distance and enabling quick construction of the tank.

To obtain the full value of the advantages of reinforced concrete the completed tank must hold fuel oil without leakage or material seepage after completion  If work is done in a haphazard unscientific manner the results are generally poor.  To obtain satisfactory results, reinforced concrete tanks must be designed correctly, with due regard to both internal and external stresses and conditions, by competent and experienced engineers, and when built the materials of construction must be correctly proportioned, mixed and placed by competent contractors, and under skilled inspection

When these necessities have been provided for, reinforced-concrete tanks will contain fuel oil of a density up to 35° Beaumé, and probably higher without seepage

In answer to a letter written to a large consumer of fuel oil in reference to three 220,000 gal. concrete tanks which have been in use for a year, and which are built mostly above ground, this reply was received

> Oils of both the paraffine and asphaltic bases are used depending upon the contract, with the result that there is at all times a mixed oil in the tanks  Tests were made during the months of May June, July and August of this year on the pipe line, with the result that the degrees Beaume range from 28° minimum to 33 5° maximum at 60° F  The average was close to 30° Beaume  As far as we have been able to determine the tanks show no leakage, and are perfectly satisfactory for these oils

The oil used by this company was for annealing purposes and was of a higher specific gravity than the oils generally used under boilers, the specific gravity of the Mexican oils being in the vicinity of 12° Beaumé

It may seem, perhaps as it an unwarranted departure had been made from the subject matter of this report  There is, however, a general demand for information about fuel oils, and those who are interested in fuel oil containers should know  in a general way at least  the physical characteristics of the oil.

It has been suggested by insurance underwriters that fuel oil to be stored in concrete tanks be limited to a maximum gravity of 20° Beaumé  But as mixed oils up to 35° Baume, of varying viscosities, have already been stored satisfactorily in concrete, in not one case only but in many, and as it is not necessary to heat the lighter oils for pumping, thus lowering the viscosity, it is recommended that the limit for such storage be 35° Beaumé, until subsequent experience warrants a change of this limit

## GENERAL CONSTRUCTION REQUIREMENTS

Tanks should be located so as to decrease the fire hazard to a minimum The design, location and equipment of fuel oil tanks must be considered from several viewpoints  that of the owner, the insurance underwriters, the municipality in which they are to be built, the oil burner and equipment company making the mechanical installation  and of the engineer having charge of the design of the complete layout

The owner selects a site, preferably for economic use of grounds for handling of the fuel oil  If tanks are to be buried, he determines what load the roof shall carry   He also determines the capacity of the tank or tanks to insure storage of sufficient oil for consumption over a specified period of time

The insurance underwriters take into consideration the fire hazard presented by each individual installation and advise the owner as to the capacity allowed under the conditions proposed also as to the acceptabil ity to them of the proposed pumping and piping layout   They also require certain safety appliances which perhaps have or may not have been embodied in the plans of the equipment company

The commonwealth or municipality or metropolitan district may or may not have regulations governing the storage of fuel oil   If there are such regulations, the approval of the officials in charge must be obtained, and when obtained it sometimes becomes necessary to obtain building permits from the proper authorities

The oil burner and equipment company usually designs the supply and feed piping, the pumps, the safety appliances, determines their location and the location of the fittings in contact with the tank, installs heating coils for raising the temperature of the oil for pumping where required, and in general does all of the detail work pertaining to the mechanical installation of the system

A competent experienced designing and constructing concrete engineer, satisfactory to or representing the owners should be responsible for the design of the concrete tank, should inspect the construction of it, especially during the placing of the concrete, and should have the authority to harmonize the different interests.

Concreting in tanks should be limited to three continuous operations in placing, that is, (a) the floor and footings (b) wall (c) columns, if any, (d) roof

The capacity limit under ordinary conditions that is, for the con tractor who does not handle large work, is about 200 000 gal   If larger tanks are contemplated, special care should be taken to provide construc tional facilities to carry out the work as hereinafter recommended   An argument in favor of tanks of moderate size is that in case of accident or fire a lesser amount of oil would be involved

Care should be taken in the design to provide for all external and internal stresses, namely hydrostatic pressure of contents external hydro static pressure from ground upon the floor and walls, earth pressure on walls live and dead-load on roof

In continuous or restrained members positive and negative bending moments should be given equal consideration   Temperature reinforcement should be figured and placed in walls and floor independent of other rein forcement   The maximum range in temperature should be predetermined as a basis for calculation

While the hydrostatic pressure of water in soils is about 50 per cent of the full hydrostatic pressure it is recommended that not less than $62\frac{1}{2}$ lb per sq ft for the full head of water be assumed and allow the difference as a factor of safety for unforeseen conditions

Steel in tension whether in circumferential tension or in tension due to negative bending moments on the face of rectangular tank walls exposed to the oil to resist oil pressure should be designed for a safe working stress of 10,000 lb per sq in for all work above ground and 12 000 lb per sq in for underground work   In other cases the working stress in the steel may be taken at 16 000 lb per sq in   In circumferential walls, the thickness of the concrete should be based upon a maximum tensile strength in the concrete of 150 lb per sq in  but a minimum thickness of 8 in at the top and 10 in at the bottom is recommended for walls to give space for spading

Vent pipes are to be placed to conform with underwriters or fire insurance requirements and municipal regulations   At least two man holes should be provided for each tank 20 ft in diameter and over and one manhole for tanks of lesser diameter   The multiplicity of manholes is recommended so that oil vapors or gases may be more quickly diffused when the tank is opened up prior to being cleaned out and other work being done within

Fittings for pipe connections as required should be placed where shown on the plans and attachments to hold heating coils also placed where indicated

As previously emphasized, the services of competent engineers and engineering contractors experienced in this work are required in making the design and specifications and in superintending the construction in order to carry out the foregoing recommendations

Attached hereto is a tentative recommended practice for the construction of fuel oil storage tanks covering the selection of materials the proportioning, mixing and placing of the concrete, its protection during hardening and other features of importance   Such a recommended practice is intended to serve as a guide to engineers and others in preparing specifications governing any particular piece of work

## TENTATIVE RECOMMENDED PRACTICE FOR THE CONSTRUCTION OF CONCRETE FUEL OIL STORAGE TANKS

### MATERIALS

CEMENT.—The cement should meet the requirements of the current standard specifications for portland cement adopted by the American Society for Testing Materials and this Institute (Standard No 1). It should be stored in a weathertight structure with the floor raised not less than 1 ft from the ground. Cement that has hardened or partially set should not be used.

AGGREGATES.—Before delivery on the job the contractor should submit to the engineer a 50 lb sample of each of the aggregates proposed for use. These samples should be tested and if found to pass the requirements of the specifications, similar material should be considered as acceptable for the work. In no case should aggregates containing frost or lumps or frozen material be used.

FINE AGGREGATE.—(a) Fine aggregate should consist of natural sand or screenings from hard tough crushed rock or pebbles consisting of quartz grains or other hard material clean and free from any surface film or coating and graded from fine to coarse particles passing when dry a sieve having four meshes per linear inch. Fine aggregate should not contain injurious vegetable or other organic matter as indicated by the Colorimetric Test, nor more than 7 per cent by volume of clay or loam. Field tests may be made by the engineer on fine aggregate as delivered at any time during the progress of the work. If there is more than 7 per cent of clay or loam by volume in one hour's settlement after shaking in an excess of water the material represented by the sample should be rejected.

(b) Briefly, the Colorimetric Test may be applied in the field as follows. Fill a 12 oz graduated prescription bottle to the 4½ oz mark with the sand to be tested. Add a 3 per cent solution of sodium hydroxide until the volume of sand and solution, after shaking amounts to 7 oz. Shake thoroughly and let stand for 24 hours. The sample should then show a practically colorless solution or at most a solution not darker than straw color.

COARSE AGGREGATE.—Coarse aggregate should consist of clean hard tough crushed rock or pebbles graded in size, free from vegetable or other organic matter, and should contain no soft flat or elongated particles. The size of the coarse aggregate should range from 1 in down not more than 5 per cent passing a screen having four meshes per linear inch and no intermediate sizes should be removed.

MIXED AGGREGATE.—Crusher run stone bank run gravel or mixtures of fine and coarse aggregates prepared before delivery on the work should not be used because the ratio of fine to coarse material varies so widely as to lead to concrete mixtures of greatly varying proportions.

WATER.—The water should be free from oil, acid and injurious amounts of vegetable matter, alkali or other salts.

REINFORCEMENT.—The reinforcing metal should meet the requirements of the current standard specifications for billet steel reinforcement of the American Society for Testing Materials, excepting that cold twisted square bars should not be employed in the construction. Reinforcing should be free from excessive rust, scale, paint or coatings of any character which would tend to reduce or destroy the bond.

## PROPORTIONS

UNIT OF MEASURE.—The unit of measure should be the cubic foot. Ninety-four lb. (one sack or one-fourth barrel) of cement should be assumed as one cubic foot.

PROPORTIONS.—The concrete should be mixed in the proportions by volume of 1 sack of portland cement, 1½ cubic feet of fine aggregate and three cubic feet of coarse aggregate.

MEASURING.—The method of measuring the materials for the concrete, including water, should be one which will insure separate and uniform proportions of each of the materials at all times.

## MIXING

MACHINE MIXING.—(a) All concrete should be mixed by machine (except when under special conditions the engineer permits otherwise) in a batch mixer of an approved type equipped with suitable charging hopper, water storage and a water measuring device which can be locked.

(b) The ingredients of the concrete should be mixed to the required consistency and the mixing continued not less than one and one-half minutes after all materials are in the mixer and before any part of the batch is discharged. The mixer should be completely emptied before receiving materials for the succeeding batch. The volume of the mixed material used per batch should not exceed the manufacturer's rated capacity of the drum.

(c) The mixing plant should be of sufficient capacity and power to carry out each prearranged operation without danger of delay during the process.

CONSISTENCY.—The quantity of water used in mixing should be the least that will produce a plastic or workable mixture which can be worked into the forms and around the reinforcement. Under no circumstances should the consistency of the concrete be such as to permit a separation of the coarse aggregate from the mortar in handling. An excess of water should not be permitted as it seriously affects the strength of the concrete and any batch containing such an excess should be rejected.

RETEMPERING.—The retempering of mortar or concrete which has partially hardened, that is, remixing with or without additional materials or water, will not be permitted.

## Reinforcement

PLACING —Reinforcing steel should be cleaned of all mill and rust scales before being placed in the forms   All reinforcement should be bent or curved true to templates  placed in its proper position as required by the plans and securely wired or fastened in place  well in advance of the concreting   Reinforcement should be inspected and approved by the engineer before any concrete is deposited

SPLICING —Wherever it is necessary to splice the reinforcement  no lap splice should be less than forty diameters   No two laps of adjacent rods should be directly opposite each other in circular walls

## Depositing

GENERAL —(a)   Before beginning a run of concrete all hardened concrete or foreign material should be completely removed from the inner surfaces of all conveying equipments

(b)   Before depositing any concrete  all debris should be removed from the space to be occupied by the concrete, all steel reinforcing should be secured in its proper location  all forms should be thoroughly wetted except in freezing weather unless they have been previously oiled  and all formwork and steel reinforcing should be inspected and approved by the engineer

HANDLING —Concrete should be handled from the mixer to the place of final deposit as rapidly as possible and by methods of transporting which would prevent the separation of the ingredients   The concrete should be deposited directly into the forms as nearly as possible in its final position so as to avoid rehandling   The piling up of concrete material in the forms in such a manner as to permit the escape of mortar from the coarser aggregate should not be permitted   Under no circumstances should concrete that has partially set be deposited in the work

DEPOSITING —(a)   Where continuous placing of concrete in floor and walls is impracticable  the operations should be in the following order

1    The concrete of footings and floor
2    The concrete of walls
3    The concrete of columns  if any
4    The concrete of the roof

(b)   No break in time of over forty five minutes should occur during any one operation except between columns and supported roof slabs  where six hours should elapse to permit the settlement of concrete in the columns   In placing concrete in floors  it should not be allowed to set up on exposed vertical faces where work is temporarily discontinued   Column footings should be placed monolithically with floor and the floor reinforcement so designed as to distribute the column load over a sufficient area

(c)   In walls the concrete should be placed in layers of not over 12 in  for the entire wall so that a monolithic structure will result   The concrete should be thoroughly worked around the reinforcing material so as to completely surround and embed the same

(d) If the placing of concrete is unavoidably interrupted by accident or otherwise the previous surface should be roughened and washed clean with a hose, a mixture of 1 1 mortar slushed on uniformly before further concreting is done and the new concrete deposited immediately thereafter

(e) When deposited in the forms concrete should be thoroughly spaded against the inner and outer faces of the forms so that it will densely compact and force out the trapped air and work back the coarser particles from the face of the forms  More and better work can be accomplished by using light wooden sticks one by two inches planed smooth with sheet steel blade at lower end rather than with heavy spades  Enough laborers should be employed spading *continuously* to obtain satisfactory results

DEPOSITING CONCRETE DURING FREEZING WEATHER— (a) During freezing weather, the stone sand or water or all three materials should be heated so that the concrete mixture will have a temperature of at least 60° F  After concrete is deposited precaution should be taken to prevent freezing for at least forty eight hours  Concreting should not be begun when the temperature is below 15° F

(b) The tank should not be placed in service until after the engineer in charge of the work is assured that the concrete has gained sufficient strength to resist all involved stresses

## FINISHING

The floor and roof should be brought to grade with a straight edge or strikeboard finished with a wood float and troweled to a smooth surface as soon as possible after the concrete is deposited  Voids in walls if any should be filled with a 1 1½ mortar as soon as the forms are removed

## FORMS

MATERIAL—The forms should be of good material planed to a uniform thickness and width tongued and grooved for walls, strongly made and located or held in place by exterior bracing or on the outside of circular walls by circumferential bands so that no distortion allowing displacement of concrete is possible

WORKMANSHIP—Joints in forms should be tight so that no mortar will escape  If forms are to be reused, they should be thoroughly cleaned a slush mixture of one half petrolatum and one half kerosene makes a good mixture for oiling forms  The use of bolts or wires through the concrete should be prohibited

REMOVAL—The forms should not be removed until the concrete has sufficiently hardened so that no deflection or damage will result  In warm weather column and wall forms should remain undisturbed for at least forty eight hours, and roof forms at least seven days  In cold weather no predetermined rules can be made

Sliding Forms.—Contractors equipped to handle the work with sliding forms may be permitted to do so provided the forms are left at one level until the concrete which will be exposed on raising them has hardened sufficiently to sustain the weight of the concrete above.

## Details of Construction

Joints.—Unless the roof is insulated against temperature changes by sufficient earth cover or the reinforcing in walls and roof is designed to take care of temperature stresses likely to occur, an expansion joint should be provided between the tops of walls and the bottom of roof slabs so that any expansion of the roof due to temperature will not transmit bending moment into the walls.

(b) In roof slabs where temporary stops are necessary they should be made on the plane of least shear, that is, at the middle of beams or slabs.

(c) If walls and floor are not deposited in one operation an approved joint or dam should be provided between the floor and walls. It can be made as follows: (1) Provide a recess in the floor to engage the wall and insert a galvanized iron strip about 8 in. wide with joints soldered and riveted so as to form a continuous band on one side of the recess, or (2) place a 10 in. strip of deformed sheet metal 1 in. back from the inside form and engaging both floor and wall, and after wall form is removed the 1 in. recess is to be plastered with a 1-1½ mortar to make a 6 in. covered base.

Treatment of Concrete Surface.—As some owners will insist on a guarantee of oiltightness for a term of years, and as contractors who figure work on a contract basis in competition will not usually guarantee work designed by others it may be found desirable to use on oilproof skin coating regardless of the density of the oil to be stored, applied by a reliable contractor who guarantees his work.

Backfilling.—Backfilling should not be done around the walls nor deposited on the roof until in the opinion of the engineer in charge it can be safely done.

Venting of Tanks.—(a) An independent permanently open galvanized iron vent terminating outside of building shall be provided for every tank.

(b) Vent openings should be screened (30 by 30 nickel mesh or its equivalent) and shall be of sufficient area to permit proper inflow of liquid during the filling operation and in no case less than 2 in. in diameter. Vent pipes shall be provided with weatherproof hoods and terminate 12 ft. above the top of fill pipe, or, if tight connection is made in filling line, to a point 1 ft. above the level of the top of the highest reservoir from which the tanks may be filled and never within less than 3 ft. measured horizontally and vertically from any window or other building opening.

Tanks of 500 gal. capacity or less may be provided with a combination fill and vent fitting so arranged that fill pipe cannot be opened without opening the vent pipe.

(c)  Where a battery of tanks is installed, a vent pipe may connect to a main header, but individual vent pipes shall be screened between tank and header  The header outlet shall conform to the foregoing requirements

FILLING PIPE—End of filling pipe in tank shall be turned up so as to form a trap or seal, and when installed in the vicinity of any door or other building, opening shall be as remote therefrom as possible so as to prevent liability of flow of oil through building openings  terminal shall be outside of building in a tight, incombustible box or casting  so designed as to make access difficult by unauthorized persons.

MANHOLE—Manhole covers shall be securely fastened in order to make access difficult by unauthorized persons  No manhole should be used for filling purposes

TEST WELL OR GAGING DEVICE—A test well or gaging device may be installed provided it is so designed as to prevent the escape of oil or vapor within the building at any time  The top of the well should be sealed and, where located outside of a building  kept locked when not in use  Where indicating devices are used, they should be connected to substantial fittings that will minimize the exposure of oil  No device should be used the breakage of which will allow the escape of oil

PIPEFITTINGS—If pipes pass through the walls they should be flanged sections with a space of about $1\frac{1}{2}$ in  left between the flange and the concrete on each side of the wall  this space should be calked later with litharge and glycerine or other approved oilproof material  It is advisable also to have a ring projecting about 2 in  around the pipe sleeve which engages the concrete

CARE OF SURFACE WATER—(a)  In many cases it becomes necessary to construct reinforced concrete tanks in localities near tidewater  rivers, streams or water basins where water pressure may be derived through porous soils  Care should be taken to keep this water pressure from fresh concrete until it has attained sufficient strength to fully resist the assumed hydrostatic pressure

(b)  One or more sumps should be provided and the floor should be underdrained so that water will flow freely to the sump  Suitable pumping facilities should be provided so that water can be pumped continuously  A flange pipe projecting just above the floor may be built into the concrete and the top of the pipe covered with a cap to be bolted or screwed down when pumping is no longer considered necessary

(c)  It is becomes necessary to sheetpile or shore the tanks  the shores should be so designed that they will not pass through the walls and thus leave openings that it would be necessary to fill later

CLEANING OUT TANKS  WARNING—It is dangerous to life to enter fuel oil tanks soon after they are opened  There is danger of suffocation from oil fumes on account of the absence of sufficient oxygen  Therefore it should be required that all manhole covers be left off  to admit complete diffusion before workmen enter, and to accelerate this diffusion the use of a compressed air line is advised

PROGRESS REPORT OF SPECIAL COMMITTEE ON CONTRACTOR'S
PLANT FOR REINFORCED CONCRETE CONSTRUCTION

The work to be covered by this Committee is of such great extent
and the time available before the convention of this year so limited, that
it was thought advisable to report to the Institute what progress had
been made on this work with a suggestion that if the Board of Direction
so desire the Committee would be pleased to continue their work during
the coming year and submit to the Institute a more comprehensive report
and recommendations for the convention of 1921.

All members of the Committee have made and are continuing to make
careful studies from an analytical standpoint of the various representative
jobs now under way or completed in order to procure actual information
as to the efficiency of the various layouts of plant used on those operations
These studies have put at the disposal of the Committee a great deal of
information which is going to need careful consideration if the proper
interpretation is to be made of the data at hand, so that useful recom
mendations may be made in regard to future installations of plant

So far it has been possible to arrange in more or less concise form
the information procured from one piece of work, namely the new buildings being constructed at the present time for the United States Aluminum
Company at Edgewater, New Jersey  It was thought that the analysis
of these data although not complete, would be of interest to those at this
year's convention and therefore the study of that job from the standpoint
of plant layout is included in this report  At the present time, the
members of the Committee are making an investigation of at least a dozen
other typical pieces of work and with the time available before the
convention of next year it is hoped this and other information can be so
tabulated and compared that definite conclusions may be arrived at as to
the relative economy of different methods of operation

One of the first problems of importance which faces the superintendent
of construction work is the study of his requirements as to the operating
plant and the arrangement of this plant so that the work may be carried
on in an economical manner both as to cost and time  This is true of
any kind of construction work but the problem is a more difficult one
when concrete is to be the medium of construction, because, due probably
to the enormous growth of the concrete industry within a comparatively
few years, we find that there is far less of a standard established in the
design and arrangement of construction equipment for concrete work than
for structural steel, brick and other forms of construction which have
been in vogue for a longer period of time

There are many elements which must be given careful consideration
if a wise decision is to be made in regard to the plant layout and when it

is realized that practically all of the unit costs made on a job are affected by the success of the plant operation the necessity is evident for a careful study by a person of mature judgment and experience

The principal reasons, of course, for the use of modern equipment are first—the conservation of labor during the period of construction, and second—the expedition with which the work may be carried on  Here, then, we have the first problem of determining how much we can afford to expend on plant with its installation and operation so shadow all of the savings which its use might reasonably be expected to make in labor costs during the operation of the job  A study of the plant installation on a number of recent construction jobs of varying magnitude shows such a great variation in this relation between cost of plant and the savings derived therefrom that it is evident that engineers and contractors have not in many cases given this matter sufficient consideration

At the present time a suitable plant is more necessary than ever before if the work is to be carried on successfully  The extremely high rates now paid to labor and the scarcity of men make labor-saving devices of far greater relative value than heretofore  and mean that a larger appropriation for machinery and its installation now represents a good investment

Special conditions often arise which greatly affect the amount of plant decided upon with good judgment for a special piece of work.  When the relation of the labor market and the time allowed for the work is studied, it may be found that the shortage of labor is so marked that practically every possible labor-saving device is essential in order to conserve the efforts of the small crew available so that the work may be completed on time

A large job which is to be built in fast time often presents a special problem in the question of receiving materials  Large quantities of sand, stone and cement which it is necessary to concentrate at the various mixing plants would often cause great congestion around the job and it is necessary to make very considerable expenditures for plant and auxiliary structures to expedite the receiving of these materials so that the progress of the work may not be impeded

In considering the layout of plant for concrete construction work it is probably wise to limit our study to typical work, because if we were to include such projects as large dams, bridges, special foundations and extensive tunnel work, we would find the majority of the items of plant quite similar to those on ordinary work—probably operating in a different relation to each other due to conditions  We would find, however, many special means of transportation such as cable ways, cranes or compressed air for carrying concrete and other materials, and the result of such an investigation would leave us with a decision as to what would only be suitable for some single piece of work, and not with definite recommendations as to what represents a suitable plant layout for typical construction work in concrete, about which the majority of our members are interested  If, therefore, we limit our investigation to the wide field of concrete con struction work which might be grouped under the general head of buildings which would be intended to include warehouses, factories, office buildings, houses, piers etc, we would have information which should be of specific value for this great field of work   This information would also be of considerable use in the study of plant for special structures in concrete, for it would be easy of adaptation to their specific requirements.

A study of a typical piece of concrete construction work shows that there are a considerable number of divisions of the work, each quite different from the other   The use of suitable plant enters into each of these to a greater or less degree, and, therefore, in order to make a more intelligent study of the plant necessary for a certain piece of work, it would probably be well to separate the operation into its principal component parts   In this way, we may see what is necessary for each part or what combination of plant will probably handle the whole

These various divisions might be considered as follows   Concrete, Reinforcing Steel, Lumber and Form Work  Brick, Tile, etc.

The machinery which is necessary for handling the materials entering into concrete from the time they are brought to the job until they are placed in the forms as mixed concrete represents the great majority of plant necessary in concrete construction work, and will be considered first in the order in which the various operations take place on these materials

(*a*)   Receiving Materials —The materials to be considered under this head are cement, sand, gravel, stone or other aggregate  and the operation consists of unloading these materials from barges, railroad cars, trucks or other means of conveyance in which they have been brought to the site of the work, and the transportation of these materials from their unloading points to the mixing plant

(*b*)   Mixing —The materials here considered are the same as above, in addition to water, the transportation and handling of which is such a simple task that no special plant other than pipes or possibly pumps and storage tanks are usually necessary   The operation on these materials consists of charging the same in proper proportions into the mixer from the point where they have been deposited by the receiving department, and the mixing of the same

(*c*)   Hoisting.—Here we have to handle the mixed concrete, and this operation, which is necessary on practically every piece of work, might really be considered as the first part of the operation of placing, but inasmuch as there are so many different systems of placing concrete and so few of hoisting  this operation would better be considered separately

(*d*)   Placing —Here we find as many different systems employed as in receiving materials  and this operation needs careful study so that a proper decision may be reached as to what methods the job best adapts itself to

Practically all concrete work is now reinforced with steel, and in considering the economical handling of steel reinforcement probably more good judgment is necessary in the location and arrangement of the unloading point, storage and fabricating yard and arrangements for hoisting than in the selection or effort to use too much equipment in connection with this work. The operations on reinforcing steel are about as follows:

Unloading, Transportation to steel yard for storage, Bending and fabricating, Transportation to hoist, Hoisting, Distribution on work

Next to the materials entering into the concrete the lumber for forms represents the bulkiest item which is to be received and handled. Here, as in the case of reinforcing steel, more is usually accomplished in the way of economy by carefully planning the relation of the lumber and form making yard to the place where the forms are to be used than by any attempt to use a great amount of machinery in connection with this work.

The items of brick, tile, etc., usually enter into concrete construction work to such a degree that some additional plant is generally found economical for their use.

### SELECTION OF PLANT FOR HANDLING CONCRETE

Each job needs individual study and it is useless to expect that definite recommendations can be made as to plant layout that would be equally useful on two different pieces of work without adaptation to the exact conditions of each.

It is possible however, by a careful study of the work that has been done for the determination of the most successfully operating plants, to make definite recommendations as to how the problem should be approached so that the procedure may be uniform for all work.

In a general way, an increase in the outlay for plant and its installation causes a decrease in the daily operating cost of the work, and the problem before us is to find the economical relation between the money invested in plant installation and the amount saved thereby.

In comparing the usual layouts which seem practical from a study of the work to be done we find the following general items entering into the cost of the work. These items, when distributed over the amount of work to be done, give us the unit cost of the same.

1. Cost of plant chargeable to job (material only)
2. Cost of installing and taking down (labor only)
3. Cost of maintenance (labor and material)
4. Cost of operation (labor and material)

*Item 1* represents the difference between the purchase price of the machinery and materials and the salvage value of the same at the end of the job.

*Item 2* is the labor cost of installing and taking down the plant and auxiliary structures.

*Item 3* is the value of labor and materials used to maintain the plant.

*Item 4* would be the labor and material costs of operating the plant, including the cost of labor actually employed in receiving materials and placing concrete as well as that used in operating the plant.

The combination of these four general items, which gives a minimum total represents what will probably turn out to be the most suitable layout for the job in question, unless special conditions have to be given undue consideration.

In order to arrive at a correct cost for these four items, careful estimates must be made. An intimate knowledge of the machinery and equipment at our disposal, and its performance or production is essential, as otherwise the estimate of the cost of maintenance and operation will be at fault.

In order to see how this method of analysis works out in a definite case, we will use for an example the plant layout for the buildings now being constructed for the United States Aluminum Company at Edgewater, New Jersey.

The study of plant for this work presented the problems usually met on a job of this size, and in addition, because of its location and the arrangement of the work, several unusual features had to be given consideration before final decision was reached as to what seemed to represent the best plant layout for these buildings.

The accompanying sketch shows in a general way the location and extent of the work to be done. Buildings 1 and 2 represent seven additional stories on top of three-story concrete buildings previously built by the owners, making these buildings when complete ten stories in height. Buildings 4, 6 and 8 are nine stories in height, the first story being omitted due to the sharp rise in the ground towards the foot of the Palisades to the west. This brings all of these buildings to a uniform roof level. Building No 5 is a two-story and mezzanine, connecting building No 6 with the building now in place to the south.

All told, there was slightly more than thirty thousand yards of concrete to be placed in these buildings and at the time that the plant for receiving, mixing and placing the concrete materials was considered it seemed safe to assume that, due to conditions of the sand and gravel market, it would be necessary to receive sand and gravel or stone separately, making roughly 45,000 yards of coarse and fine aggregate to be received and transported to the mixing plants. It was afterwards found possible to supply this work with a suitable mixture of sand and gravel, which materially reduced the extent of the receiving and handling but did not change except in detail the arrangements which had already been made in regard to plant layout.

There was also to be considered in connection with the plant for receiving materials an item of about 50,000 barrels of cement, but when it was found that cement delivered by lighter cost about 10 cents a barrel more than by railroad, it was agreed that the work of receiving cement must be considered separately from the sand and gravel which was to be transported from Long Island Sound by scows.

When the extent and arrangement of the work to be done was considered, it was tentatively decided that two one-yard mixers would be used, and the location of these two mixing plants was in general agreed upon from the basis principally of convenience and minimum travel for mixed concrete. With this much decided upon a careful study was made of the problem of getting the sand and gravel from the scows to the mixers for the least cost. Receiving materials for concrete on this job presented a special problem, and therefore, in the analysis which follows will be considered separately.

It seemed logical to use the Owners' pier as a place for unloading the scows, as no useful public dock was available within a convenient distance of the job. This dock had been previously constructed in light manner by the owners for their use in receiving materials and supplies from boats.

An inspection of the plan shows that the buildings are separated from the Hudson River by River Road, the main north and south highway subjected to very heavy traffic, and by some freight tracks of the New York, Susquehanna & Western Railroad. The relative levels of the railroad tracks and River Road made a roadway out onto the pier impossible, even without considering the objection of the railroad officials to a grade crossing.

Therefore, the various alternates which seemed in any way reasonable were about as follows:

A—Unload scows at nearest public dock available by motor truck and transport material directly to mixing plants by truck and then elevate the materials by bucket conveyor or derrick drag line, etc.

B—Unload scows at Owners' pier into motor trucks and bring the loaded trucks to the mixing plants over an elevated structure giving sufficient head-room clearance at railroad tracks and River Road, and elevating the materials at mixing plants as before.

C—Unload scows at Owners' dock directly into a hopper over a belt conveyor run at a proper elevation to give required clearance at railroad and River Road, and also land the materials in an elevated position at the mixing plants.

A careful study of any other possible schemes convinced us that the choice would lie amongst one of these three, and it was then for us to determine which was the most economical for the service rendered.

The costs involved in alternate "A" per yard, based on handling 30,000 yards, was as follows:

| | | |
|---|---|---|
| 1 | Dock charges | $0 02 |
| 2 | Unloading | 30 |
| 3 | Transporting | 60 |
| 4 | Elevating . | 12 |
| 5. | Plant cost | 30 |
| 6 | Maintenance | 05 |

$1 39 × 30 000 = $41,700

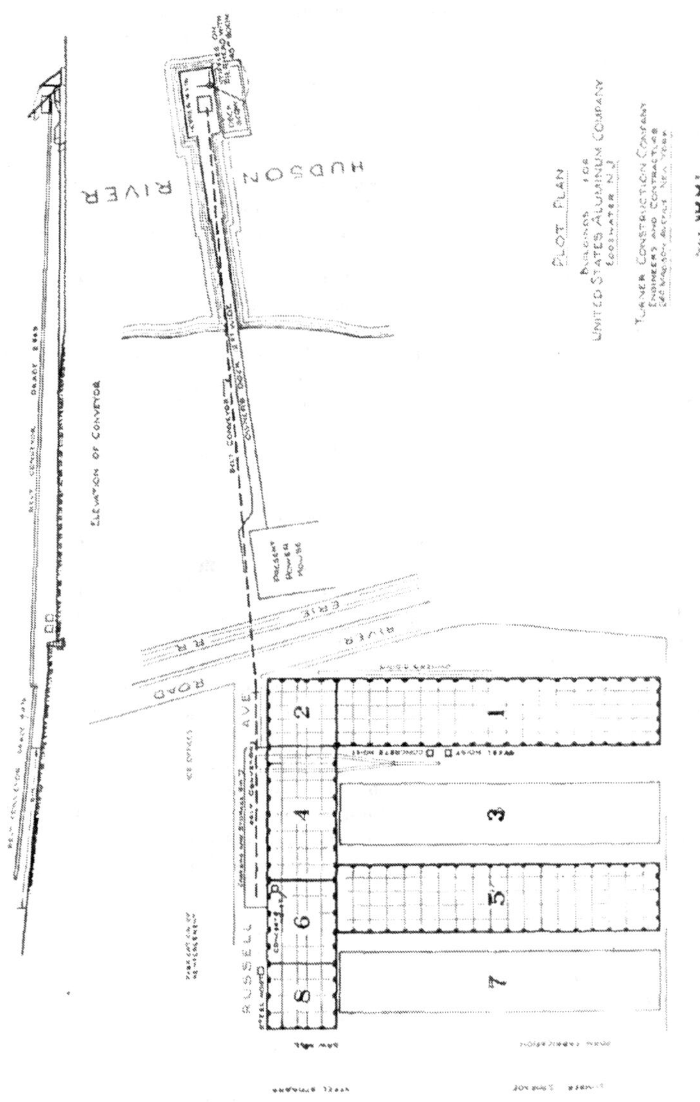

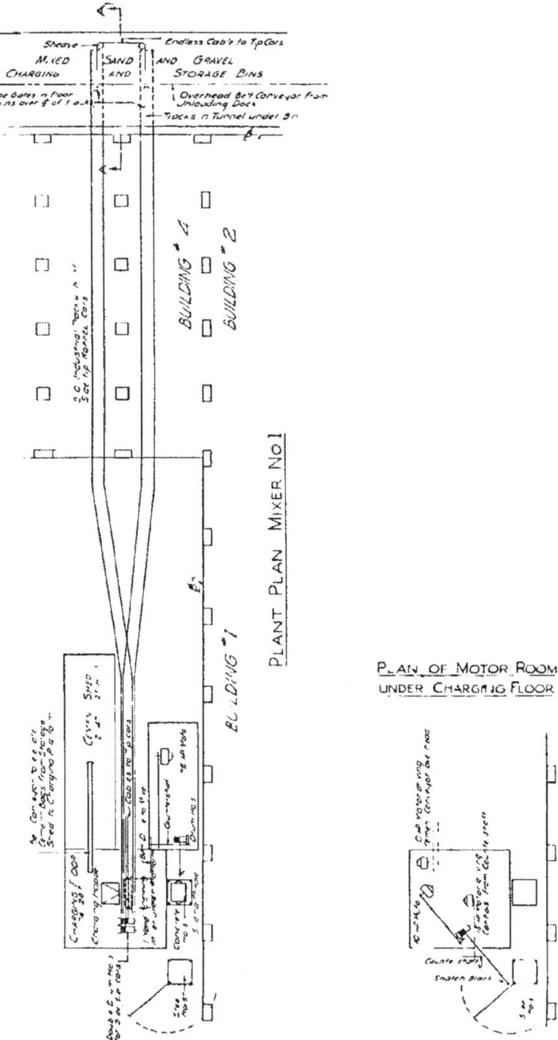
Sheave
Endless Cab's to Tip Cars
MIXED
SAND
AND GRAVEL
CHARGING
AND
STORAGE BINS
Stone Gates in Floor
of Bins over ¢ of Track
Overhead Belt Conveyor from
Unloading Dock
Tracks in Tunnel under Bin
BUILDING #4
BUILDING #2
BUILDING #1
PLANT PLAN MIXER No 1

PLAN OF MOTOR ROOM
UNDER CHARGING FLOOR
Counter Shaft
Snatch Block

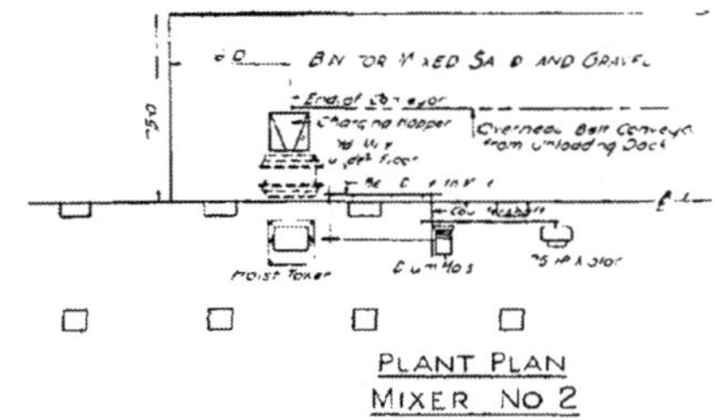


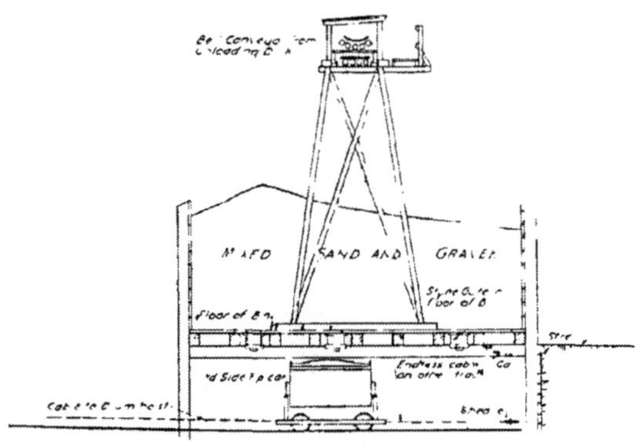


PLANT PLANS AND DETAILS

BUILDINGS FOR
UNITED STATES ALUMINUM COMPANY
EDGEWATER N J

TURNER CONSTRUCTION COMPANY
ENGINEERS AND CONTRACTORS
244 MADISON AVENUE NEW YORK

SCALE

*Item 1* is the actual charge made by the owners of the dock for the privilege of using their property

*Item 2* is the best bid received from various stevedores for unloading materials into motor trucks and includes the furnishing of all necessary equipment and therefore there is no charge from this work entering into plant cost

*Item 3* is the best bid received from various stevedores and trucking companies for transporting the materials from the dock and dumping the same at the mixing plants. This figure includes the furnishing of all necessary equipment and operating force, and so no charge for this work enters into the plant account

*Item 4* is the operating cost of elevating the materials at the mixers, such as power, maintenance of plant, and labor, but does not include the material and labor cost of installing bucket elevators, which charge appears under Item 5

*Item 5* represents the cost of all material and labor entering into the installation of elevator bins, roadway from Russell Avenue to Plant No. 1, etc less value of materials that can be salvaged at end of job

*Item 6* represents the cost of labor and material entering into the maintenance of all plant as described under Item 5

An analysis of "B" gave the following results

| | | |
|---|---|---|
| 1 | Dock maintenance | $0 01 |
| 2 | Unloading | 30 |
| 3 | Transporting | 50 |
| 4. | Elevating | 09 |
| 5 | Plant cost | 60 |
| 6 | Maintenance | 05 |

$1 55 or $46 500

*Item 1* covers the cost of maintenance of the Owners' dock so that same may be left at the completion of the work in practically the same condition in which it was turned over to us

*Item 2* is the same as Item 2 of alternate "A" Considerable saving could probably have been made in this item by installation of our own derrick as was finally done as described in Item 2, alternate "C," which increased the plant cost but reduced the unloading cost by half

*Item 3* covers the same work as Item 3 in alternate "A" but is less because of the considerably shorter haul

*Item 4* covers the same work as Item 4, alternate "A," although the plant is somewhat different. A bucket elevator and bin would be used at Plant No 2, whereas at Plant No. 1 the trucks would be dumped from the trestle over a tunnel wherein tip cars would be loaded by gravity and hauled to mixers, the cost of installation and operation being about the same as for a bucket conveyor, but the plant cost is materially decreased because the cost of the tunnel is considerably less than the bin which is necessary at Plant No 1 under alternate "A."

*Item 5* This item runs very high, due to the excessive cost of labor and materials entering into the construction of the trestle, the other items being less than under alternate "A"

*Item 6* covers same work as Item 6, alternate 'A'

The estimated costs involved under alternate 'C" are given below This is the alternate that was adopted, and the actual costs have checked up fairly well with the estimate

| 1. | Dock maintenance | $0 01 |
| 2 | Unloading | 17 |
| 3 | Transporting | 20 |
| 4 | Elevating | 09 |
| 5 | Plant . | 48 |
| 6 | Maintenance | 07 |
| | | $1 02 or $30,600 |

The belt conveyor had a number of advantages which were not considered when its selection was made simply on the basis of cost Its operation has been so satisfactory that we would probably be influenced in its favor on future installations when it only showed an equality in cost with other means of handling materials. Its ability to operate in any kind of weather, its mechanical simplicity with resulting small maintenance charges, and its relatively large salvage value at the end of the work are some of its best points

The layout of the conveyor as finally made does not present any unusual features except that due to its size and the consequent amount of power taken to drive it Some thought was necessary in the design of the driving mechanism

At the dock end of the conveyor a hopper of about 18 yards' capacity was constructed and the sand and gravel was deposited directly into this hopper by the clam shell bucket which unloads the scows The mixture of sand and gravel is distributed evenly on the belt from this hopper through an ordinary stone gate This belt is of rubber 24 in wide of six ply construction and is installed in two parts—the first part running from the hopper at the dock to the drive tower just west of River Road, a distance of about 680 ft , the second part runs from this drive tower to the storage pile at mixer No 2, a distance of about 250 ft —all told about 2,000 ft. of belt is used Both of the belts are driven at a speed of about 350 ft per minute by a 50 H P electric motor in the drive tower About 35 H P is used by the long belt and 15 H P for the short belt From this arrangement it will be seen that the long belt drives from the head and a short belt from the tail In order to avoid the bother of constant tightening of the long belt, a compound drive is used so that a belt pull of over 3,000 pounds might be imparted to the belt and yet let its return side run in an entirely slack condition To accomplish this, two 24 in pulleys were geared together and so located that the belt had about 2 300 square inches of contact on these pulleys, which were faced with rubber belting to increase their resistance to slip  The short belt was driven by a live tail pulley and the head pulley was arranged with the usual takeup for slack

It was found necessary to change the alignment of the short belt by about 6½ degrees so that it would follow the direction of Russell Avenue  This was accomplished by the insertion of a special set of bevelled gears in the driving mechanism

The general arrangement of the installation of the conveyor is shown on the accompanying sketches  The usual trippers were not used in removing the sand and gravel from the belt for mixer No 1  instead adjustable plows were installed so that the materials might be scraped from the belt at any point along the storage pile, and while this method of removal probably consumes more power than the standard tripper, it represents a considerable economy in installation and has operated in a very successful manner

In order to transport the sand and gravel from the main belt to mixing plant No 1, an auxiliary belt was first considered, but when the cost of installation was estimated it was found considerably cheaper to use the two tip cars on an endless cable operated by double drum hoist  With this arrangement no storage bin was necessary over the mixer  These cars are loaded by gravity in small tunnels running under the storage pile as shown, and are then hauled to the mixer and dumped directly into the hopper, the gauging of materials being done by the gate man who loads the cars  The arrangement is such that one car is at the mixer while the other is being loaded in the tunnel

The cement for mixer No. 1 is unloaded from the cars on the Owners' siding alongside of building No. 1 directly into hand trucks and placed in cement storage house  It is brought up to the mixer platform as needed by an 8 in belt conveyor driven by a 10 H P motor  The cement for mixer No 2 is unloaded from cars on the same siding and trucked directly to the mixer platform where a small storage is maintained

The arrangement of the No 1 mixing and hoisting plant is more or less typical of the layout adopted by this company for a number of years  A 75 H P electric motor is used to drive both the mixer and the hoist  A heavy single drum hoist is connected by belt to this motor and an extra pulley on the drum countershaft in turn drives the mixer  The concrete bucket is hoisted on a double whip at a speed of about 250 feet per minute  It is estimated that about 45 H P is consumed by the hoist, while the mixer uses about 20 H P

The hoist is placed as close as possible to the hoist tower so that the hoisting engineer may have a clear view of operations  In order to make possible the extremely short cable lead from the drum to the tower a 22 in sheave sliding on a 2 15/16 in shaft is used instead of a snatch block at the base of the tower

A No 4 Ransome mixer with one yard capacity is used at this plant

It is equipped with charging hopper into which the tip cars discharge and into which the cement is dumped by hand from the bags delivered by conveyor to the mixer platform. The water is drawn from a gauging tank.

When the decision in regard to hoisting and placing of concrete was made the usual alternate schemes were considered and it was finally agreed to build a wood tower of proper size to take a one yard Lakewood bucket which was to dump into a hopper at each floor level. From these hoppers, each of which is equipped with two concrete gates, the concrete is distributed by two wheeled carts of 6 cubic feet capacity.

The decision to place concrete by means of carts was influenced by several factors. The shape of the building was such that all parts of it could not be covered with a spouting equipment without undue cost for installation and our inability to procure such equipment in the time allotted also affected the decision made.

The estimated unit costs of the four general items already described were as follows for Plant No. 1, which was expected to handle about 12 000 yards of concrete

| | | | | |
|---|---|---|---|---|
| 1 | Cost of plant chargeable to job | $0 40 | per | yard |
| 2 | Cost of installing and taking down | 52 | " | " |
| 3 | Cost of maintenance | 08 | " | " |
| 4 | Cost of operation | 1 48 | " | |
| 5 | Total cost of mixing, hoisting and placing | 2 48 | " | |
| 6 | Cost of receiving sand and gravel | 1 02 | " | |
| 7 | Cost of receiving cement | 12 | " | |
| | Total of all costs chargeable to concrete | $3 62 | " | |

While this plant has operated very successfully from a mechanical standpoint, yet the excessively high labor rates and the inefficiency somewhat higher than was anticipated. Plant No. 1 was completed and put into operation before Plant No. 2 was erected and a further study of the situation as regarded the scarcity and cost of labor, taken together with the greater yardage to be handled by No. 2 showed that it would be wise to make a larger expenditure for this plant in an effort to cut down the number of men necessary for operation and to decrease the cost of lumber and labor in installation.

This plant as finally constructed followed about the same arrangement of motor mixer, and hoist as No. 1. No tip cars however, are necessary, as the sand and gravel is deposited directly by the belt to a storage pile back of the mixer from which it is drawn by gravity into the hopper. It was decided also to use an Insley steel tower and bucket and the counterweight boom and chuting equipment for placing concrete. This plant has not been in operation for a long time but the indications already are that there is a considerable saving in the cost of placing concrete and the erection cost of steel tower was considerably less than the making and erecting the wood tower.

The estimated unit costs of the same four general items for Plant No 2, which is expected to handle about 18,000 yards of concrete, are as follows

| | | | | |
|---|---|---|---|---|
| 1 | Cost of plant chargeable to job | $0 38 | per | yard |
| 2 | Cost of installing and taking down | 47 | " | " |
| 3 | Cost of maintenance | .08 | " | ' |
| 4 | Cost of operation | 1 30 | " | " |
| 5 | Cost of mixing, hoisting and placing | 2 23 | " | ' |
| 6 | Cost of receiving sand and gravel | 1 02 | " | " |
| 7 | Cost of receiving cement | 15 | " | " |
| | Total of all costs chargeable to concrete | $3 40 | " | " |

From this it will be seen that the estimated average unit cost for the job of receiving mixing hoisting and placing of all materials for concrete amounts to about $3 49 per yard  The actual costs so far made on the work indicate that some saving is going to be made over the estimated costs

Plant other than already described for concrete consists of two wooden towers suitable for use as wheelbarrow elevators for hoisting brick and tile, and equipped with swing booms for hoisting reinforcement lumber forms, etc  For buildings 1 and 2 the tower is near the concrete hoist for Plant No 1, for remaining buildings tower is in Russell Avenue between buildings 6 and 8

All lumber and steel is received by rail on sidings along River Road from which it is hauled to job by motor truck and stored in a joint lumber and steel yard immediately west of Building 8  Spiral column reinforcement is stored and fabricated on Russell Avenue opposite Building 6  As the buildings are of flat slat type of construction this constitutes practically all of the yard work on reinforcement

The lumber yard contains wood mill with usual swing and rip saws boring machine and emery wheel for saw gumming  Owing to congested condition of site, forms were made up in lumber yard and hauled to building on trucks.

R C WILSON *Chairman*

## REPORT OF THE COMMITTEE ON CONCRETE INDUSTRIAL
## HOUSES *

The members of the Committee on Concrete Industrial Houses were
so engrossed in war work during 1918 that it was found undesirable to
present a report to the June 1919, Convention in Atlantic City. As no
report has been presented since June 1918, and as that report was pre
pared prior to Feb 1 1918 it seems desirable that references be made to
those industrial housing projects which have been consummated by the use
of concrete during 1918 in order that there may be a record of these in the
minutes of the Institute. Appended to this respect is a bibliography
covering not only the developments since 1917 but also those projects
undertaken earlier. Additions may be made from time to time so that
the minutes of the Institute will contain the history of concrete house
development. (See Appendix 1.)

Prior to 1918 experience in constructing concrete houses had demon
strated five general facts which have been substantiated during the past
two years. First the actual quantity of concrete per house is so small
that if the cost of placing in monolithic construction is to be kept between
reasonable limits, small equipment, light and easily moved must be
utilized. Second where a number of houses are to be built in close
proximity so that the cost of transferring forms and other plant from one
house to another and the rental cost of forms per house is low, monolithic
concrete systems using elaborate steel or wood forms are economical.
Third the use of small wall forms or wall machines placing small amounts
of concrete at one time makes possible the economical construction of
monolithic concrete houses in large or small groups or scattered lots.
Fourth the use of large precast units for walls floors stairs etc. in
inexpensive houses is only economical when buildings can be standardized
and when a large number of houses are to be built in one location and in
one operation. Fifth small precast units whether slabs or blocks have
the advantages of factory production methods and the use of little or no
special equipment in erection. They, therefore are available for the
construction of the larger percentage of houses whether these be located
on one piece of property or on scattered lots. In determining the type
of concrete construction to be adopted in the erection of an individual
project consideration must be given to the cost under local conditions
including not only cost of labor but also that of special equipment
required

The operation at MacDonald, Ohio, near Youngstown, where monolithic

---

*Appendices Nos 2 to 6, descriptive of various types of house construction are
abstracts of articles that have appeared in the technical press. They are therefore
not reported here, but they will be printed as part of the National Conferences on
Concrete House Construction, in which they were also presented in a report.—EDITOR

double wall houses are built (Appendix No 2), shows how the construction can be reduced to its lowest terms by the adoption of a small form so designed as to give an air-space between the two parts of the double wall The concrete wall gives a durable base for stucco which can be so placed as to insure a pleasing appearance This type of wall form can be used almost as economically on one house as on two hundred and fifty houses, except that the fixed charges such as for moving plant and rental of plant will be somewhat higher for the single house than where a number are built in one locality With a large undertaking it is necessary to put on sufficient equipment to complete the operation as rapidly as desired

The completion of the unit construction houses at East Youngstown Ohio (Appendix No 3), is of great interest as when the last report of this committee was made the contract had just been awarded and some work undertaken The successful completion of the undertaking at East Youngstown proves the adaptability of this method for industrial housing, and the homes built at Forest Hills L I show that it can be used where a high class suburban house is required

The monolithic construction as utilized in the construction of houses at Phillipsburg and Union, N. J (Appendix No 6) is of peculiar interest in illustrating the economy possible by carefully working out details of forms and falsework

A discussion of three types of equipment that have been devised for the economical placing of concrete in monolithic houses will not be out of place at this time During 1917 D S Humphrey of Cleveland developed a concrete conveyor for placing concrete walls and roofs on the summer cottages which he was building at Euclid Beach Park This consisted of a trough with semi-circular bottom up which traveled scrapers propelled by chains The material was discharged from the conveyor into a spout which swung freely allowing the concrete to be placed at any point in the wall or roof slab This machine was developed for one set of houses, but was used very successfully in the construction of the concrete houses built by the Hydraulic Pressed Steel Co Cleveland, Ohio, for their employees A single mast guyed in vertical position up which a concrete bucket runs is manufactured by the Insley Manufacturing Co at Indianapolis, Ind A light hopper at the proper height fits a spout through which the concrete is distributed to place The lightness of this equipment, its simplicity and low first cost recommend it for this use A light gasoline hoist and a small derrick placed on the wall form also have been used the concrete being dumped and lifted from the ground to the form above

Small precast units divide themselves into two classes, the precast slab held in place by precast and field units and concrete block (Appendix No 4)

The block may be divided into two general classes, one piece and two piece blocks The two piece construction is described in Appendix No 5 by George A Rose, in his description of the Halifax Nova Scotia, work Their experience showed concrete blocks offered many advantages where it is necessary to push a project through with speed. The unit is sufficiently small to allow the work to progress as rapidly as a mason can lay them in the wall, and by keeping overall dimensions in mind which will fit the block the architect can use his ingenuity to work interesting exteriors of different designs.

Criticism has been directed against concrete block due to its improper development in the early stages, yet it affords an excellent opportunity to utilize concrete economically for any design of dwellings. The development of the Hodges Stucco Machine which throws the stucco into place with sufficient force to practically insure proper bond has recently focused attention on the almost unlimited field for concrete block as a base for stucco. Practically the only criticism that has been directed against the use of concrete for the walls of dwelling houses, whether of monolithic, block or other unit construction, has pointed to monotonous surface effects probably due largely to the absence of color contrasts. This criticism has been successfully overcome by the employment of various colored surfaces the use of colored stuccos, concrete trimstone or color contrasting with the body of the wall, contrasting colors in roofs and care in painting window frames and other trim to procure "contrasting effects." Reference might also be made to the Donaldson systems of reinforced concrete built without forms. This combines a monolithic frame of columns, beams and floor slabs with a double stucco wall suspended from and supported on the wall girders and interior beams (Appendix No. 1). Reference might also be made to the Ballinger-Perrot system of stucco on concrete studs using cement gun equipment.

In closing, it is desirable to call attention to the need of proper planning, not only of the general layout of the project and the design of houses but also the methods of construction. The experience of the Carnegie Steel Co. is not different from that of any other individual manufacturer. They have all found it much more difficult to build 250 houses than to build one house. All have found that there are many details which must be standardized and carefully worked out simultaneously if the work is to be completed at reasonable cost. In the construction of groups of concrete houses as in similar work with houses of other materials it will be found that unless there is a systematic study made for the standardization of interior trim, doors, windows, stairs, etc., the cost of the house will exceed expectation.

Your committee recommends, first, that the name of the Committee on Concrete Industrial Houses be changed to the Committee on Concrete Houses, and second that the scope of the committee's work for the coming year be broadened to cooperate with the Committee on Treatment of Concrete Surfaces in a study of methods of applying stucco, to cooperate with other interested agencies in the perfection of building codes allowing the economical construction of concrete houses and to study methods to be recommended for protection against fire in buildings with concrete walls but somewhat combustible interiors.

*Appendix No 1*

## CONCRETE HOUSE CONSTRUCTION

### BIBLIOGRAPHICAL REFERENCES ON REPORT OF THE COMMITTEE ON CONCRETE INDUSTRIAL HOUSING


Five room stucco house, size 24 by 28 ft 6 in    Stone used in building porch, wall and chimney    Porch columns are built of wood with stucco finish    Floor of porch and steps are made of concrete    Illus
*Amer Carp and Builder*, Sept, 1916    B 21 to 49

Macomber, A K
Dwelling of unusual construction on ranch of Mr A K Macomber near Hollister, Calif    House is a Moorish type of architecture and a feature will be a patio in the center with a concrete swimming pool, 52 by 72 ft in size
*Architect and Engineer of California*, Aug, 1913    V 34 1 113

"A concrete house with double walls    Binghamton, N Y"    Striking example of hollow wall construction    various interesting details    some figures of cost    Illus    Plans
*Building Age*, Feb, 1915    V 37 2 63–65

Western type of two-family house    Striking exterior finished in rough stucco with roof covered with gray asbestos shingles    Exclusive of front and rear porches, the building is 56 feet long and approximately 25 feet wide    Illus
*Building Age* Feb, 1916    V 38 2 19–25

Hoag W G
How I built my ideal concrete house    A fireproof house designed by a layman who had well defined ideas of his own    Illus
*Building Age*, Feb, 1916, V 38 2 47–52

Fradden W E
Concrete cottages for working men    Two examples embodying compact arrangement of rooms with economy of construction    Illus    Plan
*Building Age*, April, 1917    V 38 4 203–04

Byers, C A
House of California mission type    Exterior walls are constructed of cement stucco over metal lath    Basement walls are of solid concrete 9 inches thick, and its concrete floor is surfaced with a ½-inch finish of cement    Illus    Plans    Diag
*Building Age* April, 1917    V 39 8 409–18

Stucco coated suburban residence of Mrs M Lawrence at Pelhamwood N Y    Foundation walls are composed of local stone laid up in lime and cement mortar    Cellar floor is composed of concrete    Illus    Plans
*Building Age*, May, 1917 V 39 5 227–34

"A concrete house for $1000 in South Orange and in Union, N J    Ingersoll System"    Monolithic concrete housing construction on wholesale basis    Illus    Plans
*Building Age*, June, 1918    V 7 302–04

Construction of concrete houses in Porto Rico    Concrete is the popular building material in Porto Rico    Houses designed and built to meet the requirements of the warm climate    Illus    Plans
*Building Age* Aug, 1918    V 40 8 396–400

Rhodes, F P
Details of construction of concrete houses
*The Canadian Builder and Carpenter*, April, 1914

Lay David
A concrete block house example of artistic effects on a fireproof dwelling built at moderate cost in a suburb of New York Illus
*Cement Age* June, 1906 V 3 1 36–37

Parsons, Frederick
Concrete cottage as the house beautiful
*Cement Age*, July, 1906 V 3 2 81–90

Moyer, Albert
An artistic true concrete residence Aggregate is exposed to give color and pleasing texture Illus
*Cement Age*, Jan, 1908 V 5 1 54–61

Cameron, De Lancey A
Concrete offers opportunity for varied designs in country house construction Illus
*Cement Age*, Dec, 1907 V 5 6 372–78

Turner C A P
Concrete building stone A cement product which is rapidly advancing in public favor Not a cheap process, but admirably adapted to high class work Illus
*Cement Age*, Jan, 1908 V 6 1 30–45

Larned, C E
The Edison concrete house conclusions of engineers concerning the practicability of the project Purpose of the inventor
*Cement Age*, March, 1908 V 6 3 268–78

Houses built of concrete Recent progress shows improvement in design and structural methods Examples of early work and modern concrete buildings Illus
*Cement Age* May, 1908 V 6 5 44–456

Designs for concrete houses with description and cost data Illus Plans tab
*Cement Age*, May, 1908 V 6 5 457 78

Dwelling of "metal lumber" and concrete constructed of Pergers metal lumber and cement plaster on expanded metal lath Illus
*Cement Age*, May 1908 V 6 5 484–87

Concrete houses on the Pabst estate in Waukesha County, Wisconsin Illus
*Cement Age* May, 1908, V 6 5 613–17

An economical and picturesque concrete house One of the striking examples of concrete now becoming quite numerous in Southern California, Illus
*Cement Age*, Nov, 1908 V 7 5 349 51

Wetzstein, Mentor
Fireproof stucco construction Concrete block stucco houses Illus
*Cement Age*, Feb, 1909, V 8 2 112 46

An interesting example of rock surface block Criticism of this type of block Illus
*Cement Age*, Feb, 1909 V 8 2 153–55

Houses of Pauly concrete hollow tile These tiles simple in design and methods of use Have several important advantages over the terra cotta tile Illus
*Cement Age*, Feb, 1909 V 8 2 159–62

Simple methods of house building truss metal lath used for reinforcing exterior walls as well as partitions Illus
*Cement Age*, April, 1909 V 8 4 287 89

Concrete "grafted" on an old farm house without its being disturbed Heavy columns decorated with tiles Whole effect as of the old world Illus
*Cement Age*, May, 1909 V 8 5 321–31

Prize plans for concrete houses    Universal Portland Cement Co offered
    prizes for designs which were submitted in a competition of the Chicago
    Architectural Club    Illus    Plans
    Cement Age, May, 1909    V 8 5-332-45

Residences of concrete, and interesting collection of illustrations of concrete
    houses of the reinforced block and stucco types
    Cement Age, May, 1909    V 8 5 344-53

Foster, F A
    The decoration and protection of cement surfaces    Illus
    Cement Age, May, 1909    V 8 5 366-70

A unique sanitary house    Designed by M D Merrill and model exhibited
    at the Congress on Tuberculosis, held in Washington. D C    Illus
    Cement Age, May 1909    V 8 5 371-75

Howes, Benjamin A
    Reinforced concrete houses, with special reference to architectural
    details    Illus
    Cement Age, March, 1910    V 10 s 185-91

Pittsburgh Architectural Club prize contest for concrete house plans.    Illus
    Plans
    Cement Age, May. 1910    V 10 5 284-300

Residence of P A Torres of the Atlas Portland Cement Co, built of Pauly
    hollow concrete tile    Illus
    Cement Age May, 1910    V 10 5 302-11

At Brentwood Md is designed on the lines of the model which received the
    first gold medal at the late International Congress on Tuberculosis
    Cement Age, May, 1910    V 10 5 312

Cement companies in the promotion of concrete dwelling construction    Illus
    Cement Age, May, 1910    V 10 5 316-22

Hering, Oswald C
    Two colonial houses in which French and Italian features have been
    harmoniously introduced to meet the demand of present day living
    Cement Age, May, 1910    V. 10 5 332-36

Wynkoop, John (Squires and Wynkoop)
    A concrete house    Description of the constructive features, including
    reinforcing, heating, ventilating and electric wiring plans
    Cement Age, Oct, 1910    V 11 4 200-05

Parry, O R
    Concrete house at Pine Beach, N J    Construction tower used to pour
    concrete by gravity.    The house is roofed with cement shingles and
    interior walls left untreated    Illus    Plans
    Cement Age, Feb, 1911    V 12 2 78-81

Construction of three reinforced-concrete houses    Specifications, drawing
    and photographs describe work plainly    cost data given
    Cement Age, May, 1911    V 12 5 229-37

Artistic and low-priced "poured" concrete homes in the "Concrete City" of
    Virginia Highlands, a suburb of Washington    Steel forms used for
    walls    Exterior is only brush coated    Illus    Diag    Plans
    Cement Age, May, 1911    V 12 5 242-45

H P Didricksen
    Concrete block residence construction    Properly made concrete blocks
    should offer every advantage known to any other building material
    and lack the disadvantages
    Cement Age, June, 1911    V 12 6-32 C

Concrete residence in a New England town, Fitchburg, Mass   Wall of rein-
      forced concrete with hollow tile furring   Illus.
   *Cement Age*, Aug , 1911

A reinforced concrete seashore house in Margate Park, N  J   Moravian
      Tiles set in the porch panels below the window   Columns given
      wash of pink
   *Cement Age*, Sept , 1911   V  13  3  98  101

Transforming a frame structure into one of concrete   Method described
   *Cement and Eng News*, July, 1910   V  22, p  290

Stucco residences in Denver of White Portland Cement   Illus
   *Cement and Eng News*, Feb , 1915   V  27  2  36–37

Hollow block residence with stucco exterior   Main part of house is 40 by
      40 feet with sun parlor 12 by 18 feet on east side and kitchen 12 by
      20 feet,  sleeping porch above on south side   Property of E  W
      Leplant   Illus
   *Cement and Eng News*, April, 1915   V  27  4  90

Residence of A  Bryan, showing high grade block construction   Illus
   *Cement and Eng News*, Dec , 1916   V  28  12  268

Illinois  Evanston, Chicago, Lincoln Park
      Brushed concrete surfaces   Residence at Evanston and lighting
      pillar and concrete bench at Lincoln Park
   *Cement and Eng News*, Feb , 1917   V  29  2  36–37

Webb  Warfield
      Building the stucco-coated house   Some reason why this form of
      construction should appeal to the present day home builder   Entrance
      to estate at Chestnut Hill Mass   Cement stucco house at Newton,
      Mass
   *Cement and Eng News*, Feb , 1917   V  29  2  39–40

Illinois  Oak Park
      Stonekote” stucco exteriors for residences
   *Cement and Eng News*, March, 1917   V  29  3  64

Description in detail of construction of concrete house at Hackensack, N  J ,
      by using the Herman J  Shubert forms and methods
   *Cement Era*, Dec , 1914   V  12, p  6

White, Charles, E  J
      Latest North Shore concrete home  Lake Forest, Ill   McLennann
      house is built of cement block   Hollow concrete blocks used for
      exterior walls, covered with portland cement plaster   17 rooms
      Illus   Diag   Plans
   *Cement Era*, Feb , 1915   V  13  2  14–16

In the Woods,” a concrete home in Chevy Chase, Md   New home of
      David Fairchild, a successful blending of Japanese simplicity, European
      permanence and American materials   House built of hollow tile
      covered with a cream-colored cement plaster   Illus
   *Cement Era*, April, 1915   V  13  4  48  49

The “Stewart House” at Waterloo, Iowa   All blocks for building made in
      two pieces, the separate pieces being held together by galvanized
      wall ties placed in the blocks as they were made   Novelty is combined
      garage and sleeping porch
   *Cement Era*, Dec , 1915   V  13  12  43

Africa  Tripoli, Barbary
      Concrete block residence of W  F  Riley   Blocks made by Ideal con-
      crete block machinery   Natives made blocks   Illus
   *Cement Era*, May, 1916   V  14  5  56

White, C. F.
> Will we build cement houses in 1917?  Description of cement plastered house with cast cement ornamental panels  and description of bungalow with exterior coating of cement plaster    Illus
> *Cement Era*, Jan, 1917   V 15 f 30 33

Cement stucco house fifty-six years old
> Residence of M  D  Botsford,  Sherburne  N  Y    Built in 1855  House is octagonal in plan, the exterior finish of the walls being stucco penciled off to represent stone
> *Cement World*, Sept, 1911   V 8 6 29

Concrete in South Africa
> Governor's residence at Salisbury in Rhodesia    Building is a single story structure, surrounded by a wide veranda    Is 140 feet long by 125 feet wide, with a detached kitchen block 100 by 30 feet
> *Cement World* Nov  1911   V 5 pp 8–21

Dignified and attractive house design    Prospective and floor plans for six-room residence
> *Cement World*, Feb, 1912   V 5, p 52

A Dutch colonial house design    Architectects prospective and dimensional floor plans for an attractive well arranged eight-room residence of cement stucco construction
> *Cement World*, April, 1912   V 5, p 51

" An artistic house near Washington, D C    Designed and built under the supervision of an amateur concrete worker
> *Cement World*, Sept, 1912   V 5, p 53

Suggestions for design in concrete and rough cast buildings based on a study of examples of old Dutch architecture in Cape Colony
> *Cement World*, May 1913   V 7 p 24

A modern residence embodying a combination of many unusual architectural features worked out with the aid of cement   Estate of E W Reynolds Pomona Valley, Calif
> *Cement World*, July, 1913   V 7, p 22

Examples of moderate cost private homes showing the architectural versatility of concrete
> *Cement World* July, 1913   V 7, p 35

A review of recent experiences in the erection of moderate priced concrete homes in Muskegee, Okla, Gary, Ind, Ludlow, Mass  Washington, D C, and Rochester, N Y
> *Cement World*, Oct, 1913   V 7, p 22

One of the earliest examples of concrete dwelling construction in Iowa
> *Cement World*, Feb, 1914   V 7, p 54

"Hand-Made Cement House"   Unique examples of residence construction for which concrete was chosen as the best available medium for expressing individuality
> *Cement World*, May, 1914   V 8, p 47

Stucco and brick veneer residence    Architect's scale drawing, showing layout of a substantial, well-planned ten-room residence
> *Cement World*, May, 1912   V 5 10 58

"The Concrete Estate"   Some interesting examples showing the possibilities of concrete for house and garden beautification
> *Cement World*, Nov  1912   V 5 22

Canadian block residence    Fenwick residence in Ontario    Panel-faced blocks used for main body of wall  rock-frame for corners and window trim and ashlar blocks for verandas    Foundations are solid poured concrete   Concrete block carriage shed and henhouse   Illus   Plans
> *Cement World* Jan, 1915   V 8 10 49 50

Wood, C M
    Complete concrete house   Opportunities for cement products men in
    the growth of the fireproof building idea   Illus
    *Cement World*, July, 1916   V 10 26 28

Medusa Waterproofing in facing of concrete blocks   Illus
    *Cement World*, Nov , 1916   V 10 8 82

Residence of concrete block   The concrete block industry has developed
    rapidly within the past year   Illus
    *Concrete*, Jan , 1905   V 3 1 15-16

Concrete block residence erected at Terre Haute Ind , in 1893   A good
    illustration of time element in that of concrete blocks   Illus
    *Concrete*, April 1905   V 3 4 21

Concrete residence at Syracuse, N Y   Shows exceptionally good artistic
    taste   Foundation and trimmings made by the Onondaga Latholite
    Co   Geo A Wright, Architect   Illus
    *Concrete*, Aug , 1905   V 4 3 13

Cement residences on the Pacific Slope   Past year has marked great activity
    in the use of portland cement in the Pacific Coast states   Illus
    *Concrete*, Oct , 1905   V 4 4 14-15

The building of the City Beautiful   Description of a concrete house, with
    illustrations
    *Concrete*, March, 1907   V 7, p 22

Design for a concrete house, two stories, to cost $1538   Plans and descrip-
    tion of house with cost data
    *Concrete* April, 1908   V 8, p 28

Swiss chalet constructed of hollow concrete building rock   Description of
    chalet, with photograph, plans and cost data
    *Concrete*, July, 1908   V 8 p 29

Illinois man's novel method of concrete construction rivals Edison's   Descrip-
    tion of construction of a concrete mess house by casting sides and then
    raising them into place
    *Concrete*, Sept , 1908   V 8, p 19

Engineer builds economical concrete house with simple equipment   Illus
    Diag   Plans   An illustration of what can be done with concrete by
    an individual not equipped with commercial forms   Cost data given
    *Concrete*, Jan 1916   V 8 1 3-5

Eight years of nature's work on concrete house at South Orange, N J
    Residence of Albert Meyer built in 1907 relatively old among concrete
    houses   Illus
    *Concrete*, Jan , 1916   V 8 1 8

Concrete boulders and casements, features of Waco house   Residence of
    L Williams   Walls of hollow monolithic concrete construction from
    basement to roof   They were constructed without frame with hollow
    wall machine   Illus   Plans   Tab
    *Concrete*, Jan , 1916   V 8 1 28

$2500 concrete wall cottage, near Middleburg, Pa   Thin very wet mix of
    concrete used large quantity of crushed field stone embedded in the
    mixture   Illus
    *Concrete*, Jan , 1916   V 8 1-12

An example of fireproof residence construction at Kansas City, Mo   Illus
    *Concrete*, Jan , 1916   V 8·1 14-16

Concrete house construction by new form system   Built by system which
    is invention of H J Shubert   Forms consist of two metal-lined wood
    sections secured to U-shaped unit frame which are in turn supported
    by scaffold and which grip wall to preserve alignment Illus Diag Plans
    *Concrete*, Jan , 1916   V 8 1 32-33

Ross, Glen M.
"A band-box two-family apartment to be built of concrete at Rochester, N Y." Walls, floors and roofs of concrete   Arrangement compact, with many unique features   Cost data given
*Concrete*, Feb , 1916   V 8 2 61

Dingman, Charles F
"Concrete house with tile-lined walls at Jersey City, N J" Well dampproof as well as a heat insulator   All the concrete work cast in place
*Concrete*, March, 1916   V 8 3.11C.

Baumgardner, Carl W
"A double-wall concrete house economically built in cold weather " Improvised heater for aggregates   Walls and partition constructed with hollow wall machine, doing away with wall forms   Cost data given   Illus   Plans
*Concrete*, March, 1916   V 8 3 111-13

' A concrete house with precast walls designed by Irving J Gill and erected at Hollywood, Calif " Walls cast in horizontal position and then raised with special equipment   Methods devised some years ago by Col Aiken, U S Army
*Concrete*, May, 1916   V 8 5 198-97

Experiments have shown that the temperature in summer in concrete houses is 10 to 15° lower than in frame houses and that fuel savings of as much as 20 per cent are often made in winter
*Concrete*, Oct , 1916   V 9 4 115

Bosworth, P H
Concrete homes in national defense   "The all-concrete residence the future home of the human race'   A home for defense in renascence of an old custom
*Concrete Age*, Oct , 1913   V 19 1 11

"Decorative possibilities of concrete in house building."   Illus
*Concrete Age*, Jan , 1914   P 18

The wide adaptability of reinforced concrete for residence construction, with reference to its fireproof qualities
*Concrete Age*, June, 1914   V 20, p 11

"Poured concrete houses in Australia "   Concrete poured in molds and used in house construction   Illus
*Concrete Age*, Sept , 1914   P 16

"Naval concrete construction "   Concrete house built in the manner of a frame house, all parts concrete
*Concrete Age*, Sept , 1914   P 28

Magnificent reinforced concrete ranch residence in Texas   Cost about $150,000   Property of Mrs Henrietta M King   Illus
*Concrete Age*, April, 1915   V 22 1 13

Cement in home building   what it has accomplished in the past and what it will accomplish in the future
*Concrete Age*, Sept , 1916   V 24:6 22-23

Illustrations of concrete homes with courts and pergolas
*Concrete Age*, Jan , 1917   V 25 4 38

Six-room dwelling house made of bales of cement-covered straw   House is 48 by 18 feet in size; cost $270
*Concrete Age*, Feb , 1917   V. 25 5-18

Residence of reinforced concrete for Mr J H W Hawkins, one of the leading architects, after his own design
*Concrete Age*, June, 1917.   V. 25 3.35

Concrete block cottages at Crayford, Kent    Illus    Rural housing organiza-
    tion society directing scheme    Illus
    *Concrete and Constructional Engineering*, March, 1915    V 10 3 137–45

Attractive, Evanston (Illinois) residence, Illus    Plans    Depends for its
    beauty not upon any special molding or cut, but upon plain surfaces
    with attractive color and texture effects
    *Concrete-Cement Age*, June, 1913    V 2 6 297–9S

Some attractive dwellings near Pittsburgh, Pa    Homes at Rosslyn, Pa
    Farms built under the direction of W H Parrish.    Cost data given
    Illus    Diags
    *Concrete-Cement Age*, Dec , 1912

Suggestion for poured concrete house to cost $3000    Illus    Plans    Design
    by W C Larkey of Buffalo, N Y , and was awarded second prize in
    contest conducted by the Blaw Steel Construction Co
    *Concrete-Cement Age*, Feb , 1913    V 2 2 80

A concrete house may have walls of beautiful texture    Illus    House of
    "Telecrete" concrete with stucco finish given dry dash of chips of white
    marble, blue stone and yellow pebbles
    *Concrete-Cement Age*, Feb , 1913    V 2 3 107–08

Three distinct types of concrete homes    Illus    Cast concrete stone poured
    concrete    Aiken system
    *Concrete-Cement Age*, March, 1913    V 2 3 110

Fireproof houses on western plains    Oklahoma for $2000    Illus    Finished
    with cement inside and outside    Some have flat roofs
    *Concrete-Cement Age*, March, 1913    V 2 3 115–16

Smith Morgan A
    Building a concrete residence on hillside, Pittsburgh, Pa    Illus    Plans
    A permanent chute was built from the mixer down the hillside and at
    the lower end a movable trough distributed the concrete
    *Concrete-Cement Age*, March, 1913    V 2 3 134–35

Concrete block cottages built complete for $1500 by U S. Portland Cement
    Co    Illus    Plans
    *Concrete-Cement Age*, March, 1913    V 2 3 137–38

House built of concrete to resist fire attack    Green Laurel, Miss    Walls of
    solid reinforced concrete furred with terra cotta blocks    Illus
    *Concrete-Cement Age*, March, 1913    V 2:3 143

Industrial cottages in England at low cost    Illus    Plans    Tab    Detailed
    cost data given for cottages at York
    *Concrete-Cement Age*, March, 1913    V 2 3 144–45

Concrete and plaster houses on Mojave Desert    Blocks of concrete and
    gypsum plaster prove very satisfactory in a hot dry country    Illus
    Diag
    *Concrete-Cement Age*, July, 1913    V 3 1 25

Robinson, Reed
    "An instance of economy and simplicity in concrete house building
    Irving Gill, architect "    A typical Gill house, artistic though some-
    what severe in line and low in cost
    *Concrete-Cement Age*, April, 1914    V 4 4 1–55

Manufacturing concrete houses at low cost at Midland, Pa '    Pittsburgh
    Crucible Steel Co , builders    House building machine equipment
    reduces hand labor or effort to about 10 per cent
    *Concrete-Cement Age*, April, 1914    V 4 4 156–60

Unger, C O, Calif, Los Cerritos
"Unusual features in residence construction made possible by use of concrete" Walls, partitions, beams in ceilings, roof, floors, bathing pool (instead of bath tub), garage and even the chicken coop all of reinforced concrete
Concrete-Cement Age, April, 1914 V 1 4 165–67

"House built of concrete block with interesting facing" Illus Specially faced block used for house at Scarborough-on-Hudson Illus
Concrete-Cement Age, April, 1914 V 4 4 167

Newman, Rolf R
"A review in the development in the construction of concrete houses, 1907–1914" Illus
Concrete-Cement Age, April, 1914 V 4 4 168–70

Comoli, P P
Architectural possibilities in concrete, particular reference to stucco Artisans called upon to do surface work should be an intelligent group skilled in the proper use of cement and concrete
Concrete-Cement Age, April, 1914 V, 4 4 111–13

"The use of sand coat concrete veneer slabs in Louisville residence" Mason Maury architect Illus After seven years, the walls have retained a light uniform tone
Concrete-Cement Age, April, 1914 V 4 4 176

"Concrete block houses in England" Chief claims to interest are low cost, double wall construction and absence of any imitation of the construction types which belong to other materials
Concrete-Cement Age, April, 1914 V 4 4 185

"Advancing the architectural appeal of concrete wall units Hydrostone an outgrowth of the Ferguson system
Concrete-Cement Age, April, 1914 V 4 4 195–98

Squires, Frederick
Sage Foundation Houses at Forest Hill Garden Long Island Precast hollow concrete floor, wall and roof units and exposed aggregate Illus System developed by Grosvenor Atterbury, a New York architect, and perfected for commercial work by Ernest Ransome
Concrete-Cement Age, Jan , 1915 V 6 1 3–8

Hering, Oswald C
Stucco in suburban architecture Notes on Angony Hill, Philadelphia Illus Architectural possibilities of stucco
Concrete-Cement Age, Jan , 1915 V 1 9 14

Havlik, R
Concrete block used in attractive and economical house construction Floor plans and comparative cost data House built of faced Hydrostone at saving of 19 7 per cent over faced clay brick Illus Diag
Concrete-Cement Age, Jan , 1915 V 6 1 15–16

Smith, A Morgan
Some worked-out details in concrete house construction Illus Plans
Concrete-Cement Age, Jan , 1915 V 6 1 17–18

Two-story house with walls and floors of concrete built for less than $3000, 24 by 25 feet in plan Lambie forms used Itemized cost data Surface brushed while concrete was still green Illus
Concrete-Cement Age, Jan , 1915 V 6 1 50–52

Kinney, Wm M , and others
Good practice in concrete block house construction Discussed by Wm M Kinney, R R Newman, O C Hering, A F Cline, J K Harridge, G R Knapp
Concrete-Cement Age, June, 1915 V 6 6 305–08.

Roobick, Eloise
    Outside life in California as expressed in the new architecture of
    Irving J Gill   Illus   Home built around a court in San Diego
    Not a single ornament mars the pure symmetry of its line
    *Craftsman*, July, 1913

Consulman, John E
    Ready-made houses built of concrete includes such houses as may be
    built by standardized sections even though these units are made on site
    *Eng and Cement World*, Jan , 1918   V 21 1 57

Perkins, Frank C
    Concrete cottages for employees   Whitlingham Sewage Farm, Nor-
    wich England   Illus   Blocks molded on the site on a Winget
    machine   Gravel taken from farm
    *Engineering and Contracting*, May 31, 1916   V 45 22 505-06

Large reinforced-concrete building at Walkerville, Ont   Illus   General
    methods of construction
    *Engineering Record*, Jan 26, 1907   V 55, p 91

The Mount Carmel Wing of the Chateau Frontenac, Quebec   Architectural
    and mechanical design and concrete specifications
    *Engineering Record*, July 24, 1909   V 60, p 97

One hundred concrete dwellings built as one contract job in Donora, Pa
    Standard designs, steel forms and contract methods similar to those
    used on large construction permit completion of one house every three
    days   Illus   Plans
    *Engineering News-Record* Sept 6, 1917   V 79 10 442-45

"Reinforced concrete house built without forms"   Donaldson system using
    metal lath both for forms and reinforcements very effective for small
    residences   Illus   Diag   Plans
    *Engineering News-Record*, Dec 5, 1918   V 81-23 1043

Unit built concrete cottages to house foreign labor   Dwellings in Youngstown
    (Ohio) Sheet and Tube Company's village built in precast slabs erected
    by traveler   Illus   Diag   Plans
    *Engineering News-Record* April 11, 1918   V 80 15 698

Concrete for house building   General discussion of relative merits of concrete
    block and monolithic concrete house construction
    *Municipal Engineering*, Jan , 1906   V 30 p 74

A stucco house in Menah, Wis   Two-story, nine room house, with shingle
    roof and white wood trimming   National Builder Design No 386
    Cost data   Illus
    *National Builder*, Sept , 1914   V 56 9 35-41

Milton Dana Morill
    Washington architect has reduced the cost of concrete houses to a mini-
    mum   House was built at Brentwood, near Washington, D C , by M
    Morill to demonstrate his ideas
    *Rock Products*, Sept 22, 1911   V 11 3 51

# REPORT OF COMMITTEE ON CONCRETE AGGREGATES

This committee, working in close co-operation with Committee C-9 on Concrete and Concrete Aggregates of the American Society for Testing Materials, has had the progress of its work seriously interfered with by the active participation of many of its members in Government work, and more recently by urgently pressing business demands and lack of assistants in laboratories. The committee has, through its sub-committees, continued some of its investigations along lines previously laid out and has considered a large mass of data made available by various investigators in the field covered by this committee. Some of this data relates to the concrete and mortar making qualities of aggregates, both fine and coarse, as indicated by their "Fineness Modulus" proposed by Prof. Abrams, their "Surface Area" proposed by Mr. Edwards, and their "Surface Modulus" proposed by Prof. Talbot, and also to the effect on the strength of concrete or mortar of the "Water-Cement Ratio" proposed by Prof. Abrams.

To get a better idea of the relative value and importance of these functions, a special sub-committee is now engaged in the conduct of a series of tests, which it is hoped will be carried out by a considerable number of co-operating laboratories designed to duplicate some of the work already done by one or two laboratories in their own investigations, and so to furnish a basis for some general comparisons of the functions mentioned in the last paragraph above. This sub-committee met in Chicago on November 17 and 18 last and spent the two days considering data placed before it, and at the end of the session drew up an outline of a series of tests designed to touch the high spots of the work previously done at enough points to indicate the relative value of the functions under investigation. These tests are now progressing.

## THE SUB-COMMITTEE ON WEIGHT, VOIDS, SPECIFIC GRAVITY, AND CONSISTENCY.

Cloyd M. Chapman chairman, made an extended report in 1917 of the work done and results obtained in investigating some eight methods of determining the unit weight of sand. At that time it was suggested that another method which had been in use at Lewis Institute might prove of value, and consequently the committee undertook an additional series of tests to compare this newly proposed method with those previously investigated.

This new method has been called for the want of a better name the Rod Method, and is operated as follows:

Fill the measure one-third full of the aggregate, then with a pointed iron rod of a prescribed size jab or puddle the aggregate twenty-five times, distributing the strokes over the surface of the aggregate and avoiding penetrating through the layer of aggregate so as to hit the bottom of the measure. Then add another one-third to the contents of the measure and again jab with the iron rod twenty-five times, penetrating only the last layer of aggregate placed in the measure. Next, fill the measure to overflowing and repeat the jabbing, then strike off the surplus with the iron rod and weigh.

This method appears equally applicable to fine or coarse aggregate or mixtures thereof, and its simplicity and convenience recommend it to consideration, since the results obtained are of a degree of concordance equal to that obtained with the best of the other methods considered in the 1917 report.

To investigate this method, it was desirable that the same aggregates be used that were used in the previous tests, so that results would be directly comparable without repetition of the earlier tests. Inquiry, however, developed the fact that only two of the laboratories co-operating in the 1917 series had retained their samples, so it was decided to have the new method investigated in only one laboratory, using the same old samples, but having five different operators make five tests each with the same measures used in the previous tests, with the two grades of fine aggregate each of them used in a dry and in a damp condition. These tests were, therefore, conducted in the laboratory of Westinghouse Church Kerr & Co., under the direction of the chairman of the sub-committee.

The six measures, described and illustrated in the 1917 Proceedings, were used. They were a 100 cc cylindrical measure, a 1,000 cc cylindrical, a ⅕ cu ft cylindrical, a ¼-cu ft cubical, a 1-cu ft cylindrical and a 1 cu ft cubical measure. The rods used were ¼ in diameter by 18 in long for the 100 cc and 1,000 cc measure, ½ in by 18 in (long for the quarter) for cubic foot measures and ¾ in x 18 in for the cubic measures. The aggregates were a coarse siliceous Long Island sand and a fine siliceous New Jersey sand. These aggregates were used room dry' and moistened to the extent of 3% for the coarse sand and 5% for the fine sand.

In order to make a comparison between the results obtained by this Rod Method and those reported on in 1917, a set of tables similar to those previously published are given below, for the Rod Method.

By comparing this table with Table I on Page 319 of the 1917 Proceedings it will be noted that the Rod Method gives average weights about equal to those given by Methods B and C or about midway between the light weights given by Methods A, F and G and the heavy weights given by Methods D and the Cone Method.

In Table II is shown the average difference between the highest and lowest weights obtained by all operators with all sizes of measures.

TABLE I — AVERAGE WEIGHTS OBTAINED BY ALL OPERATORS WITH ALL SIZES OF MEASURES

| Sand | Rod Method, lbs |
|---|---|
| 1   Coarse Dry | 107 5 |
| 2   Coarse Wet | 93 4 |
| 3   Difference | 14 1 |
| 4   Fine Dry | 99 5 |
| 5   Fine Wet | 82 9 |
| 6   Difference | 16 6 |
| 7   Dry | 103 5 |
| 8   Wet | 88 7 |
| 9   Difference | 15 3 |
| 10   Average of all | 95 8 |

TABLE II — AVERAGE OF DIFFERENCE BETWEEN HIGHEST AND LOWEST WEIGHTS OBTAINED BY ALL OPERATORS WITH ALL SIZES OF MEASURES

| Sand | Rod Method lbs |
|---|---|
| Coarse Dry | 3 8 |
| Coarse Wet | 7 5 |
| Fine Dry | 4 4 |
| Fine Wet | 6 1 |
| Dry (Coarse and Fine) | 4 1 |
| Wet (Coarse and Fine) | 6 8 |
| Difference | 2 7 |
| Average of all | 5 4 |

A comparison of this table with Table III on page 323 of the 1917 Proceedings shows that the Rod Method gives as little average difference between highest and lowest results as does Method D, and not appreciably more than the Cone Method. The Rod Method gives a small maximum difference as compared with other methods.

Taking up next the average variation from the mean, there is shown in Table III this average for all operators with all sizes of measures.

TABLE III — AVERAGE FOR ALL OPERATORS FOR ALL SIZES OF MEASURES OF THE VARIATION FROM THE MEAN WEIGHT OF ALL OPERATORS

| Sand | Rod Method lbs |
|---|---|
| Coarse Dry | 0 8 |
| Coarse Wet | 1 6 |
| Fine Dry | 0 8 |
| Fine Wet | 0 9 |
| Dry (Coarse and Fine) | 0 8 |
| Wet (Coarse and Fine) | 1 3 |
| Difference | 0 5 |
| Average of all | 1 0 |

This table indicates, as will be shown by comparison with Table V of the previous reports, that the Rod Method gives more concordant results than any method used except the Cone Method, which is slightly better in this particular

Coming now to a summary of the results obtained with all of the nine methods employed there is shown in Table IV data which gives a very concise idea of the relative values of these methods

From this data it is apparent that the Rod Method gives medium weights per unit volume that it gives a low maximum variation and a very low average variation. The only method offering lower maximum and

TABLE IV — EFFECT OF METHOD ON AVERAGE WEIGHT DIFFERENCE BETWEEN HIGHEST AND LOWEST WEIGHTS OBTAINED BY ALL OPERATORS FOR ALL RESULTS AND AVERAGE VARIATION FROM MEAN WEIGHT

| Method | A | B | C | D | E | F | G | Cone | Rod |
|---|---|---|---|---|---|---|---|---|---|
| Average Weight | 88.4 | 98.8 | 103.2 | 104.3 | 98.0 | 83.9 | 87.2 | 116.1 | 95.8 |
| Average Maximum Variation | 7.0 | 7.0 | 7.9 | 5.3 | 6.5 | 6.3 | 5.8 | 4.1 | 5.4 |
| Average Variation | 1.9 | 2.1 | 2.2 | 1.4 | 1.7 | 1.7 | 1.6 | 0.8 | 1.0 |

average variations is the Cone Method but as stated in the previous report the unit weights obtained by the Cone Method are so high as to be of little value in practice and therefore not considered a desirable standard method for use in determining unit weights

This Committee has, in view of all the data available, voted in favor of the adoption of the Rod Method as the standard method for the determination of the unit weight of concrete aggregate and proposes to prepare during the coming year, standard specifications for the manipulation of the method for presentation at the next convention

SANFORD E. THOMPSON

*Chairman*

CLOYD M. CHAPMAN,

*Secretary.*

Mr John W Lowell.—I would like to make a few suggestions regarding some work of a practical nature that this committee might do. Did you ever stop to think that the contractor buys his aggregates by the ton and sells by the cubic yard? Did you ever stop to think that there are very few real data as regards the volume per weight of aggregate that the contractor buys? Not long ago I thought of getting some information on this myself and called up a number of sand and gravel dealers and one of them told me the sand weighed 2300 lb per cu yd. I asked him if he would guarantee that the weight of a cu yd was 2300 lb, and he said no. Contractors in the paving business use a large amount of aggregate and I will venture to say that under the assumed weight per cu yd the contractor is liable to lose 10 per cent or 15 per cent in changing from weight to volume not only in sand, but in pebbles and crushed stone. I wonder if this committee could formulate something in that line that would be of value to the contractor?

Mr D A Abrams.—It might be of interest to point out, in reference to what Mr Lowell said, that we have been carrying out in our laboratory an extensive study of the unit weights of aggregate of different size and grading, and there is no doubt that there is great confusion as to the quantity of materials secured under the present form of contract. It is of course impractical to attempt to work to extremely fine limits in this direction, but we should attempt to get somewhat closer than we now are. We are preparing a report on this subject which will no doubt be of interest to this committee, and probably will result in the formulation of some definite recommendation in this direction.

Mr R B Young.—We have made a few studies in the Laboratories of the Hydro Electric Power Commission of Ontario, on the effect of moisture in changing the volume of sands. We found that the increases in volume because of small additions of moisture to a dry sand were for coarse materials seldom less than 20 per cent, and for the finer materials as high as 35 per cent. This bulking seems to be a function of the grading and its amount can be predicted very closely with ordinary concrete sands if the grading and moisture content of the aggregate are known.

Mr C M Chapman.—Mr Lowell brought up a point that the committee has considered that is that the method chosen should be one that would be useful in determining the amount of the aggregate that went into a yard of concrete. If, in purchasing concrete aggregate, a determination of its unit weight is made by the rod method, it will be found that it agrees very closely with the amount of that aggregate that went into a yard of concrete. In other words, the aggregate in the measure when treated by this method is about the same degree of compactness that it is in concrete placed in the form, so that by this method you may determine the concrete of an aggregate in the number of pounds that will be required to make a given volume of mortar

Mr W A Collings —As I understand Mr Lowell's inquiry, the commercial sellers usually sell sand by weight because they can weigh it easily I would like to ask Mr Lowell if he could suggest a better way than this?

Mr Lowell —No I could not suggest a better way unless they sold it by volume Of course I suppose that the sealers of weights and measures would put them under some law for selling by volume that would take care of it On the other hand if each dealer and each producer of aggregates would know exactly what his material weighed per cu yd for the various classifications, and let it be understood how much it weighed, the contractor then would have some information on which to make his figure As it is it does not seem to me that the general producer over the country has that information at his disposal. I know I have asked at least two dozen producers during the last six months and they have not been able to give me the weight of their material per cu yd, and say that they would guarantee it to weigh that much or anywhere near that or that it would weigh more than that

Another thing that comes up in the selling of sand and gravel is that one producer has more water in his material than the other For instance a company that dredges directly out of a river and loads onto scows or else loads directly onto cars from a nearby point, would perhaps weigh its material at their plant Some other producer may not have the scales and would weigh his material at the nearest weighing point on the railroad There is going to be a difference there as to the amount of water weighted into the material It is all right for the contractor to pay for water provided he knows he is getting a certain amount of sand too It is not a question how much the contractor pays for his material but a question of knowing how much material he is getting, because he charges for what he pays in the amount of his contract, but if he charges wrongly, he may lose the amount of money he expected to earn on the contract

The Chair —As many of you know, the Hydro-Electric Power Commission of Ontario is putting in a number of thousand yards of concrete according to a method of designing mixtures by quality of the aggregate I would like to ask Mr Young of the Commission to describe the method

Mr R B Young —Most of the concrete put in during last season —some 25,000 cu yd —was placed by the methods described by the speaker in an article in *Engineering News Record* Jan 1, 1920

In brief this method attempts to fulfil the requirements of the designer, that the finished concrete shall have a definite quality and of the construction man that the concrete mixtures shall be workable The first result is obtained by maintaining the water cement ratio of the mixture constant at a value found experimentally to give a concrete of the desired compressive strength The second result is obtained by maintaining the relation of cement and water to surface area at a ratio which has been found experimentally to give concrete mixtures of the desired plasticity. The former is based on Professor Abrams' conclusions that a definite relation exists between the compressive strength of a concrete and the quality of its cementing medium as expressed quantitatively by the ratio of the volume of water to the volume of cement present, and the latter is based on studies made independently by Mr. Edwards and the writer, which tend to show that the water required to bring a concrete mixture to a given plasticity depends upon the surface area of its aggregates.

An example will illustrate the measure of control we have been able to attain under average conditions. We have a small job on which as yet only a thousand yards have been placed. The design called for concrete having a minimum compressive strength of 1500 lb. per sq. in. when 28 days old. To cover contingencies the concrete mixture was designed to give 1800 lb. per sq. in. at this age. The concrete was to be placed by the pneumatic method and the conditions demanded that the consistency of the concrete be kept uniform. By using our method the desired consistency was maintained continuously although the sand used varied considerably both in grading and moisture content. In the same way concrete of the required strength was obtained as was shown by the results of the tests on concrete cylinders made from concrete taken directly from the forms on the job. The average compressive strength of the first 14 of these cylinders which have been tested to date is 1775 lb. per sq. in., only 25 lb. per sq. in. less than the strength for which the concrete was designed. Two of the cylinders tested slightly below 1500 lb. per sq. in., the minimum requirement of the specification and one slightly above 2000 lb. per sq. in., the minimum requirement of the next higher class of concrete. When you consider that the 14 cylinders were taken in most cases on different days and each represented a different pouring of concrete the result shows excellent control.

We have had experience with the other method even as late as this year on work being done by us to another firm's specifications. Our experience with the ordinary method is that both consistency and strength vary widely. In one case where the design was based on concrete having a compressive strength of 2500 lb. per sq. in. when 28 days old the strength as given by the field cylinders varied from 1440 to 3670 lb. per sq. in. with the majority testing at nearer the former value.

Another distinctive feature of our method is the way we overcome the question of consistency. Usually on a concreting job it is a continual fight as to whether or not the consistency used is "right." With us we place the decision as to what is the best consistency on the construction superintendent. Our engineer sets proportions based on a normal consistency, an arbitrary consistency chosen for convenience which happens to be approximately the limit of dryness we have found possible to place successfully in the field. The superintendent new to our method invariably pronounces it too dry, which in many cases is true although probably not as much too dry as he believes   Our engineer says to him, "Use any consistency you want to, but one thing you must do, and that is to maintain the ratio of water to cement which has been set "  To do this means that for every three gallons of water the superintendent adds to his mixture, he is forced also to add approximately one-half bag of cement   It does not take him long to see the economy of the dryer mixture and to strike a balance between the additional cost of their placing and the advantages of the wetter but more expensive concrete mixtures   The result is usually the best consistency for the particular conditions on the job in question

Mr W A Slater—I would like to ask for information on two points  I assume that one of the main features of the adoption of this method of grading is economy   If so, what was the probable saving per cu yd over using an arbitrary mix which would have given a strength high enough to insure 1500 lb per sq in   If you have had to estimate on the 2500-lb concrete in order to be sure of 1500 lb, what would you save by using this method?  Would this method be applicable with economy to ordinary small jobs where much smaller quantities of concrete were to be used?

Mr Young—I can only answer the first question by citing a specific experience   We are doing some work to the specifications of an outside firm which call for the usual arbitrary proportions   This work is being done with the same concrete gangs as we are using elsewhere and the inspection is similar   Here we have found that to get the quality of concrete required it is necessary to use one bag of cement per yard batch in excess of what is used elsewhere on our work where our own methods are in force

The second question is more difficult to answer but my opinion is that the method can be developed so as to be applicable to the smaller jobs  As yet we have not attempted it, but we have studies under way which we expect will give us a cheap method of getting the necessary data

You will appreciate we are doing our own construction work and have never had to apply our method to a contract job   Whether it can be done or not we do not know   Personally I think it can   One of the difficulties lies in the type of specifications we use   We classify all concrete into four classes  A, B, C and D, having compressive strengths at the age of 28 days of 2500, 2000, 1500 and 1000 lb per sq in, respectively   If we specify class A concrete our construction department is required to produce concrete of that quality, and we place very little limit upon the material which they use other than that it shall not be structurally deficient in some important respect

The question arises in this form of specification whether we can specify the quality of the finished concrete and at the same time specify the method of producing it without being in some measure responsible for the quality produced   Then, too, how can we penalize the contractor for bad work?  These things remain to be worked out

Mr Slater—How much inspection cost was necessary to save that one bag of cement per cu yd?

Mr Young—We have the same number of inspectors on the job in both cases

Mr S H Wightman—I would like to ask Mr Young in connection with his statement that they have established a definite relation between cement and water paste and the areas of your aggregate, if that theory does not suggest the obtaining of better strength results or a less amount of cement for equal strength by the use of large aggregate, particularly in mass work using 1¼ in and 1½ in gravel or crushed stone. Would it not be possible to employ 3 in and in heavy work 4 in stone to advantage or economy?

Mr Young—Under the surface area theory it would of course be true that less cement would be required by using the coarser than by using the finer aggregates. However, the cost of cement is but one factor in the cost of concrete, and in my opinion the use of large sized materials would not be as economical, all things considered, as the use of materials graded within the usual limits

I will give a recent experience to illustrate what I mean. On a certain job we had trouble with our crushing plant which for a time was producing 3½ in stone which we had to use or shut down the job. When this material was first used the resident engineer began to have difficulty with his concrete. Proportions which up to that time were giving satisfaction, ceased to be workable when the grading of the crushed stone changed from the "2½-in and down" to "3½-in and down" and the proportions and consistency had to be altered to overcome the trouble. This started him experimenting and he found by reducing the size of the crushed rock to "1 in and down," he could add one wheelbarrow more of stone to each one-half yard batch and still maintain the desired degree of workability. I have never made any experiments to check this, but I have wondered if this might not mean that possibly the use of the coarse aggregates of the smaller sizes would not really be more economical, all things considered, than using aggregates graded to the larger sizes

Mr Slater—I want to call attention to one other feature brought out by a remark Mr Young has made. Suppose that concrete in being worked to a specified strength rather than an arbitrary mix, and he says, 2000 lb of concrete is required, how long does he have to wait after it is placed to be able to form an opinion to see whether he is going to have 2000 lb of concrete?

Mr Young—We have been able to predict the probable compressive strength of concrete at 28 days from tests of the same material made at 7 days. We are putting a small hydraulic press on one of our jobs to make these and other tests. It is almost impossible to make tests at the early ages unless a laboratory of some kind is readily accessible. If this procedure proves successful we will adopt it as general practice. Our experience with field tests is that they check up satisfactorily with laboratory tests for the same conditions, that is cylinders made up in the field will have compressive strengths similar to laboratory-made specimens of the same cement and water content and of similar materials

# REPORT OF COMMITTEE ON STANDARDIZING THE SPECIFICATIONS FOR STEEL BARS FOR CONCRETE REINFORCEMENT.

The committee presented a report which, after discussion, was modified on the floor to read as follows:

A reduction in the number of areas with equivalent sizes of concrete reinforcing bars was recommended by the War Service Committee on Reinforcement to the United States War Industries Board during the summer and fall of 1918, as a conservation measure, which would have been adopted by the Government had the war continued. The necessity for this conservation continues, and the committee submits for adoption by the Institute the following areas with equivalent sizes for concrete reinforcing bars:

| Area. | Equivalent Size. |
| --- | --- |
| 1.560 | 1¼ in. Square |
| 1.265 | 1⅛ in. Square |
| 1.000 | 1 in. Square |
| 0.785 | 1 in. Round |
| 0.601 | ⅞ in. Round |
| 0.440 | ¾ in. Round |
| 0.307 | ⅝ in. Round |
| 0.250 | ½ in. Square |
| 0.196 | ½ in. Round |
| 0.110 | ⅜ in. Round |

The appended diagram drawn to scale shows the above areas with equivalent sizes.

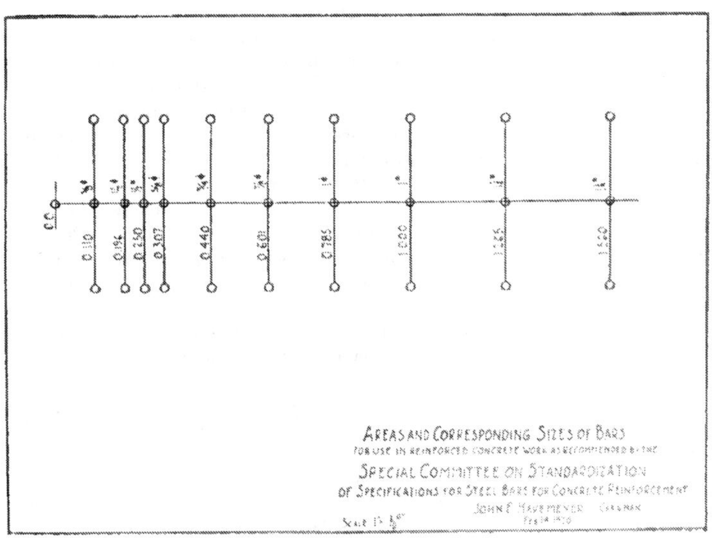

In view of the present difficulty in obtaining finished steel and the conditions in the steel market in general, engineers and contractors should allow a wide latitude in the grade of steel to be used in their work, and the members of the Institute are advised that the steel manufacturers and the bar companies have, in the present emergency, agreed to limit the number of specifications for steel bars and will manufacture generally an intermediate and hard grade material conforming to the "Manufacturers Standard Specifications of Concrete Reinforcement Bars Rolled from Billets" as adopted by the "Association of Steel Manufacturers, March 22, 1910, and Revised April 21, 1914," and also to the "Standard Specifications for Rail Steel Concrete Reinforcing Bars Adopted by the American Society for Testing Materials," Aug 25, 1913

## REPORT OF SPECIAL COMMITTEE ON UNIT VALUES FOR
## VERTICAL SHEAR IN REINFORCED CONCRETE DESIGN

[The Special Committee on Unit Values for Vertical Shear in Reinforced Concrete Design prepared a report which was printed and mailed to the membership of the Institute thirty days in advance of the Convention It submitted at the Convention this report with a number of amendments and asked that the amended report be submitted to letter ballot by the Institute as Recommended Practice It was later round, however, that the Committee on Reinforced Concrete and Building Laws had adopted the report of this Committee on Shear *in toto* and had incorporated it in the proposed Building Regulations which became a standard of the Institute under letter ballot vote of April 17 1920 The committee therefore, asked that the report be received by the Convention and printed in the Proceed ings as information The report of the Special Committee on . . Shear will be found as Section 44 of the Standard Building Regulations on p 283 of this volume

The following discussion is based on the shear provisions as preprinted
—EDITOR ]

DISCUSSION

Mr. Edward Godfrey.—I would like to ask one thing. The report reads, "Properly anchored bent-up longitudinal bars may be considered as web reinforcement. The maximum unit shearing stress shall not exceed $0.12 f_c'$ in any case." Is not that out of agreement with the paragraph (44h) where only 0.06 is allowed for bent-up longitudinal bars?

Mr. A. R. Lord.—Paragraph 44h takes care of the case where you have bent up truss rods in a single plane, and for that we propose a limit of 120 lb. per sq. in. shear. If you desire to use a greater shearing stress than 120 lb. per sq. in. you must provide a series of bent up rods or vertical stirrups in addition to truss rods in a single plane.

Mr. Godfrey.—I understand then that if there are stirrups or short shear members, or bent-up rods that are bent up sharply at different distances from the support they have twice the advantage of a single bar in the shape you describe in the figure.

Mr. Lord.—The limit in stress permitted is twice as great in the case of a series of web bars as in the case of a single bar.

Prof. A. N. Talbot.—It is quite probable that the paragraphs (44l) concerning critical section for shear in beams do not bring out clearly enough for recommended practice that that is not the only section to be provided for. I would like to suggest that the committee add "to bring that to any other design," if it is not in the provisions elsewhere. I should like to ask a question concerning the test on which this coefficient of 0.12 compressive stress value of shear is based. I wish to ask if it applies to rectangular beams, or whether it is based upon T beams and upon beams with I sections.

Mr. Lord.—The data upon which this is founded are not alone of I sections and T sections but also rectangular sections. The series included several rectangular sections in which shears greater than 600 lb. per sq. in. were carried. There is no indication whatever but that we could have gotten as high shearing resistances from rectangular beams as I sections if we had employed the same percentage of web reinforcement.

Mr. S. C. Hollister.—I should like to ask Mr. Lord at what unit shear the rectangular beams which he cites develop their initial crack in diagonal tension?

Mr. Lord.—The shearing stress at initial crack was approximately 400 lb. to the sq. in., sometimes greater, sometimes less.

Mr. Godfrey.—Then I understand you would allow 300 lb. on the concrete that showed an initial crack at 400 in shear?

Mr. Lord.—Yes, sir, with properly designed web reinforcement. Section 44l would apply to the case that you mention. With reference to the allowance of $0.12 f_c'$, may I state that several members of the committee are

( 242 )

of the opinion that that limit is simply placed there because it is as high as it is necessary and desirable to go at the present time in designing web reinforcement of beams  If it were necessary or desirable to go higher, I for my part would not hesitate to go to very much higher stresses in shear than the stresses which are here stated as a maximum  The design of concrete ships did, of course, embody even higher shearing stresses than these  and I have no feeling that that allowance was not in every way safe

MR HOLLISTER —I should like to say  in connection with concrete ships that the shearing unit stress was 10 per cent of the ultimate compressive strength as intended before the concrete was mixed  In other words, for a 4000 lb per sq in ultimate strength of concrete, the shearing unit stress of 400 lb per sq in on the rectangular members was adopted

MR LORD —I may also state that the results of the test showed that with different grades of concrete the result in shearing strength was very slightly affected  that is, with concretes of differing strengths and the same amount of web reinforcement, you secured practically the same shearing resistance regardless of the quality of the concrete  That is not an absolute statement because the quality has to be sufficiently good to take the diagonal compression stresses, but as far as diagonal tension is concerned, the quality of the concrete is not of first importance

MR W  A  SLATER —There are two points on which I wish to speak  I fear there will be a misunderstanding on a certain point involved in this discussion  Prof  Talbot asked a question regarding rectangular beams and Mr  Lord stated that rectangular beams were included  Mr  Hollister then asked the question as to the shear at which the cracks occurred  The answer which Mr  Lord gave referred to the rectangular beams  as I understand Mr  Lord in personal conversation  but it is likely to be misleading because I believe Mr  Hollister's question refers to all the beams which are covered by the recommendation, whether rectangular or I section  Beams of I-section showed cracks at shearing stresses between 200 and 300 lb per sq in , generally, and in order to avoid later confusion I wanted to make that clear now

This leads to the other question which I wish to discuss  A number of the recommendations in this report apparently are based upon the concrete-ship investigational work, data of which have not yet been published  It is expected that they will be published in the near future and it does not seem wise to me that the report go finally to vote before the data on which some of the recommendations are based have been made public and an opportunity given to everybody to examine them

Another feature which would lead to the same conclusion regarding passing this report over is the fact that there are now working on this same subject two other committees, the Committee on Reinforced Concrete and Building Laws of this Institute and the new Joint Committee which has just been organized and is getting to work  On both committees there are members of the Institute  It has been known in the past that when the members of a committee have committed themselves to a certain report, it embarrasses them in making any change when they come to considering a later report. Now since these committees have somewhat the same personnel it seems to me that it is in the interest of finally getting a report on which we can all agree that this report should not come up for approval, at least until the data are made public and if possible until the other committees have gotten together and can show whether they will agree on these things or not  If it is not possible to agree on these things, then it is proper to report independently, but if we can get together on them I believe that the better time to do it is before anyone has committed himself on any report

Mr C A P Turner (by letter) —Shear failure in reinforced concrete beams as pointed out by the committee, is not a vertical cross breaking or sliding of the material in a vertical plane, but it is a diagonal rupture of the material termed a diagonal tension failure  That such failures, in the opinion of the committee are not proportional to the unit vertical shearing stress is made evident by their recommendation that the vertical unit shearing stress in punching shear be limited to $0.1f_c'$ in contrast to a limiting vertical unit shear in simple beams with steel in the bottom throughout of $0.2f_c'$ where $f_c'$ is the unit compressive strength of the concrete  That the same intensity of vertical shearing stress may be five times as dangerous in one case as in another as is here assumed by the committee, would seem to the uninitiated to be a thing so inexplicable as to require a thorough investigation of the character of the diverse deformations that may result from the same identical vertical unit shearing stress under different conditions  but we look in vain for any such elucidation of this mystery in the report of the committee  It is a matter however which is susceptible of explanation on the basis of the accepted principles of beam theory

Under load a beam is said to be subjected to a transverse stress—i e, subjected to combined bending and shearing stresses  This involves longitudinal strains consisting of horizontal compressions and elongations of the outer fibers with no change of length at the neutral surface and to the extent that the material is elastic these strains are proportional to the distances of the fibers from the neutral surface  Transverse vertical strains also occur but these are of an order so much lower than the longitudinal strains that they are commonly disregarded  These strains together produce angular rotational distortion of the material of the web of the beam  Where this angular shearing distortion exceeds a certain limiting value elastic failure begins and cracking occurs

An initially plane right section of a beam will not, after flexure, be in general either vertical or normal to the curve of flexure, but will lie between the vertical and the normal  The angle between the vertical and the normal will be equal to the slope $a$ of the deflection curve of the beam, while the angle between the normal and the plane section is the horizontal shearing detrusion $h$ at that section, and in case of material regarded as perfectly elastic is proportional to $a$ at that point—i e, $h = Aa$, in which $A$

is a constant for a given beam and is dependent upon its cross-section and other physical properties.  Let $B$ represent the amount of bending produced by a given bending moment $M$, then $B = M/EI$, in which $E$ is the modulus of elasticity and $I$ the moment of inertia of the beam.

Then from the differential equations of beam theory we have[*]

$$\frac{1}{A}\frac{dh^2}{dx^2} = \frac{d^2a}{dx^2} = \frac{dB}{dx} = \frac{1}{EI}\frac{dM}{dx} = \frac{S}{EI} \quad \ldots\ldots\ldots\ldots\ldots \quad (1)$$

in which $S$ is the shear to which the rate of increase $dm/dx$ of the bending moment at any point is due.

$$\text{Now, } a = \Sigma B = \Sigma M/EI \ldots\ldots\ldots\ldots\ldots\ldots\ldots\ldots\ldots \quad (2)$$
$$\text{and } h = Aa = A \Sigma M/EI \ldots\ldots\ldots\ldots\ldots\ldots\ldots\ldots \quad (3)$$

hence, in any given beam we have $h$ proportional to $\Sigma M$.

It therefore appears from this equation that the detrusion, or the liability to failure by angular distortion at any point, depends directly upon the total area of the moment curve between that point and some point where the detrusion is zero, while equation (1) shows that it is not the detrusion $h$ that is directly proportional to the vertical shear $S$, but that it is merely the second differential coefficient of $h$ that is proportional to $S$, a quantity that has no proportional physical relation to failure by shearing distortion.

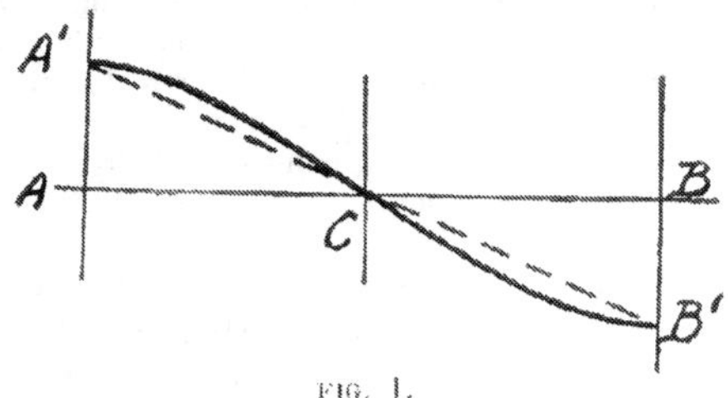


FIG. 1.

It is commonly assumed that diagonal failure is so related to vertical shearing stress that the intensity of the shear is the controlling factor, but such is not the case, since diagonal shear failure is due to detrusion, which by equation (3) is proportional to $\Sigma M$ and not to $S$.

These relations may be represented graphically[†] by treating the moment areas whose ordinates are $M$ as a kind of loading whose summations give the ordinates $h$ of the detrusion curve in the same manner as the summation under an ordinary curve gives a shear curve.

Such a detrusion curve $A'ACB'$ is shown in Fig. 1, whose ordinates measured from $AB$ represent the magnitude of the detrusions $h$ for a simple beam.  Here the maximum detrusion $h$ occurs at the end of the simple

*See Concrete Steel Construction, Eddy & Turner, 2nd ed, 1919, pp. 180-185.

†See Concrete Steel Construction, Eddy & Turner, 2nd ed, 1919, p. 182.

beam and is represented in relative magnitude by $AA'$ at the left and $BB'$ at the right

But for a beam fully restrained at the ends and having a constant moment of inertia, the detrusion is measured from the line $A'B'$, in which case $h$ is zero at the supports and at mid span, while the maximum values of $h$ which occur at the points of inflection are only about one-fifth the values at the ends of the simple beam of the same length loading and cross section

It is to be specially noticed that the detrusion curve $A'CB'$ is unchanged by any restraints at the supports just as is the curve of shears, but the line of zero detrusion from which the detrusion ordinate $h$ is measured is changed in position by the restraints at the supports  In the case of perfect restraint the line of zero detrusion is revolved about $C$ from $AB$ to $A'B'$, while complete restraint at the end $A$ alone would change it to a new position, one point of which would be $A'$  The same principles apply to the zero line of detrusions and the moment area as a kind of loading that apply to the line of zero shears when we have given the profile of the load area for homogeneous loading

Since by (3) it appears that $h$ is inversely proportional to $EI$, it is evident that the higher the steel ratio the higher becomes the unit vertical shear that can be resisted before failure by cracking  Now $I = Ajd^2$, and $A = pbd$, in which $p$ is the steel ratio  $b$ the breadth of the cross section, and $d$ its depth  But since $M$ is proportional to the span length, it follows that the limiting shear deformation is inversely as the ratio of the depth to the span length, $L$  Consequently, the variation in safe values between shallow and deep beams is wide  For $N = L/d = 30$, the committee's values are at least twice too large, but too small where $N = 10$ with the steel at the bottom throughout

The failure of the committee to differentiate between the deep and shallow beam is accounted for by the limited range of the tests upon which their report is based and their complete failure to apply mathematical reasoning to the problem in hand

Having briefly presented the analysis of shear deformation in terms of homogeneous material, it is now in order to investigate the differences involved in the non homogeneous make-up of reinforced concrete members

First, where the steel is straight and in the bottom of the beam the angular shear deformation would not before slipping occurred vary greatly from that in the homogeneous beam  The increment of bond shear along the reinforcing element would cause some irregularity of distribution across the beam  Bending up a part of the steel in the simply supported beam places the steel in position to resist directly a portion of the vertical shear, thereby reducing the increment of shear deformation resisted by the concrete  In the continuous beam such bending of part of the steel downward from the top across the inflection point is especially effective in reducing bond stress between the steel and concrete and increasing the shear resistance of the member

In the continuous beam the magnitude of the angular shear distortion varies not only with the steel ratio and ratio depth to span length but in accord with the mechanical law of the distribution and apportionment of moments where the moment of inertia is variable instead of constant This fact is obvious from equation (3), by which $h$ varies as $\sum M$, the apportionment when restraint is complete being such that the positive and negative moment areas divided by the respective moments of inertia where the positive and negative bending occur are equal

The committee states that the shearing resistance of flat slabs is not known to them   Such slabs present a state of plane hydraulic stress about the column which accounts for their remarkably high resistance which is so much in excess of that of continuous beams

Nevertheless the steel ratio and the ratio of thickness to span are as important in determining their shear resistance as is the case with the ordinary beam   One hundred fifty pounds per inch in stress on a thin slab may be relatively higher than 300 pounds per square inch on a thick slab properly reinforced

The flat slab differs from the beam in that the moment of inertia of the steel mat is affected by the difference in curvature between the beam and the slab   In the beam the curvature is cylindrical and the moment of inertia is determined by the cross section of the steel normal to the element of the cylinder   In synclastic curvature, however the mode of operation is different, in that, like a thin shell, curvature in one direction changes the curvature in the opposite direction in the reverse order  and the moment of inertia of the steel by this operation is increased for any given direction as compared with cylindrical curvature two and one-half times   Therefore the angular detrusion of the plate is reduced inversely as the increase of the effective moment of inertia   Such reduction, however, does not apply to antielastic curvature, whether produced by non uniform distribution of metal or by restraints affecting the curvature

Scientific advance is supposed to be accomplished by the painstaking application of scientific theory corroborated and checked by experiment Heterogeneous experiments may substantiate such theory while failing by themselves to substantiate broad conclusions   The committee's complete failure to apply analytical methods of investigation deprives their conclusions of any weight other than that which may be assigned to a mere mechanical average of the limited and heterogeneous tests compared by them

That the report apparently recommends that the resistance of the entire area of the cross section of a continuous plain concrete beam be figured on the same unit value under punching shear as is recommended for that part only of the cross section below the reinforcement in case of a continuous reinforced beam of the same external dimensions strikes the writer as such a grotesque absurdity that it can seemingly be accounted for only as a misprint in a preliminary report.

The resultant principal strain at rupture is in general a composite

of the angular detrusion and direct fiber elongation because the latter may
occur independently of angular shear distortion   The apparent state of
stress arrived at by finding the resultant of the vertical unit shear stress
and the static horizontal stress due to bending is wholly unrelated to the
true principal strain, since the vertical shear is not proportional to the
angular shear distortion   As the laws governing the latter become more
generally understood weak and unsatisfactory designs for light loading
on the one hand   and unreasonably expensive and excessively heavy con
struction for heavy loading on the other hand   will be less frequent and
our building codes in course of time may become somewhat rational and
scientific

The report states that the recommended shear values are derived from
experiment, not by theoretical reasoning checked by experiment

In the sketches of beams shown in the preprinted report the loading is
shown to have been applied at the third points of the beam   The question
therefore, arises whether shear values obtained from such experiments are
directly comparable to the ordinary case of building construction in which
the loads are uniform   The general equations before quoted permit this
matter to be readily investigated by computation

Consider the case of a given beam   uniformly loaded with a given
weight $W$ as Case I   that of the same beam having the same weight $W$
applied equally at the third points as Case II

The relative detrusion curve for uniform load Case I is given in
Fig 1

With the load concentrated at the third points the bending moment
at the center is $WL/6$ for Case II as against $WL/8$ in Case I, so that the
tangent of intersection of the detrusion curve of Case II with the axis of
reference $AB$ at $C$ will be one third greater than for Case I Fig 1

For the load applied as in Case II equally at the third points there is
no shear in the middle third of the beam   Hence $\dfrac{d^2h}{dx} = 0$   The change
in direction of the detrusion curve is therefore zero between the points
of loading, and it is a straight line between the points of application of
the load   Since the shear $S$ is constant between the load and the support
$\dfrac{d^2h}{dx} = \dfrac{EI}{S}$ equals a constant for this portion of the beam

Hence the detrusion curve for the end portion of the beam is a para
bolic arc tangent to the straight line portion of the curve at the load point,
$i = L/3$   The apex of this arc lies on $AA'$ on the left or $BB'$ at the right
of the curve   The new ordinate $AA'$ for a load at the third point is one
third greater for Case II than for Case I, as appears from the summation
of the moments in the respective cases   The parabolic arc being short
differs little from a circular segment whose center lies on $AA'$ to the right
and on $BB'$ to the left

Because of these differences in the detrusion curves in the two respec
tive cases the critical section Case I would not occur at the same point

along the beam as with Case II, the latter being nearer the end of the
beam  Hence, the selection of the same locus as the critical section by the
committee for any loading  uniform or concentrated  which presents the
same unit vertical shear, is arbitrary and irrational  Moreover, because
the same unit vertical shear at the end of the beam produced by the same
total load $W$ distributed uniformly on the one hand and concentrated at
the third points on the other, produce an angular shear distortion 33 per
cent greater in one case than in the other and a different ratio of increase
safe unit values for vertical shear figured on the cross section of the beam
in the horizontal elongations  with the change in the moment curve the
should be nearly 50 per cent higher for uniform load than for the same
total load concentrated at the third points of the beam

The committee's recommendation of the same value for these different
conditions based upon test of but one of them is thus approximately 50
per cent in error, as an application of the principles of the elastic theory
of flexure shows for the ordinary case of uniform loading

As this theory is the basis of all acceptable analyses of concrete in
flexure, the empirical deductions of the committee will fall short of general
acceptance as a standard until they are corrected to harmonize therewith

Mr  Edward Godfrey (*by letter*)  It is gratifying to observe that
others are beginning to see the things I have been pointing out for nearly
fifteen years  The loose stirrup and short unanchored shear member are
beginning to find their proper place in oblivion  Real anchorage of main
reinforcing rods that are depended upon to reinforce a beam for diagonal
tension is also given a place in your report  Many years ago I was ridiculed
for proposing such things

But your report still has many pieces of the old shell hanging to it
The stirrup dressed up with an end anchorage and restricted in its girth,
is a stirrup still and never has been and never could be shown by analysis
to be a proper element in design  The short diagonal shear member,
restricted to an inclination of 60 degrees with the vertical is only a little
better than the stirrup  The analysis is self evident  but analysis is
asked for

In the first place it is inconceivable that a vertical stirrup in a whole
beam could take any stress  There is no force in a beam that elongates
its vertical dimension  hence there can be no stress in the stirrup  for
the concrete in which the stirrup is embedded remains exactly the same
dimension in the direction of the axis of the stirrup

If the stirrup is for a broken beam  what about the portion of the
shear that the concrete is to take?  What will take that shear if the
concrete web has failed?

Stirrups and short shear members do not relieve the concrete between
these members of shear or diagonal tension  The beams of Figs  1 and 2
are not relieved of failure on the lines indicated  by the presence of the
short shear members, anchorage or no anchorage

The careful restriction in paragraph 11 of the report to an inclination of 60 degrees for web members, and the general disregard in the report of the only web reinforcement capable of analysis (rods bent up at the quarter point with a long, flat angle) are bad. In Figs. 3 and 4 on any of the diagonal lines there is no provision for web reinforcement. Only horizontal steel crosses these lines, and the shear in all of these sections may be greater than the unaided concrete can safely carry.

There is one, and only one, system of reinforcement for diagonal

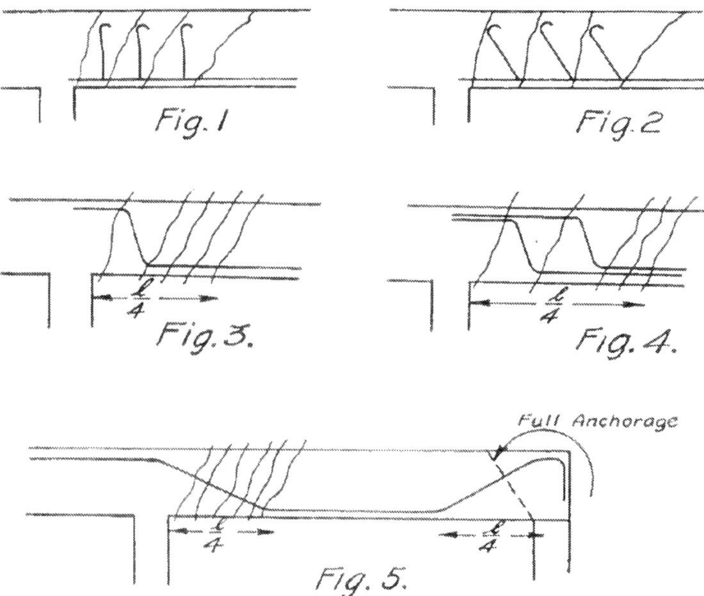



tension that admits of logical analysis, and this seems to be the one system not sanctioned by this report.

The system of reinforcement referred to is illustrated in Fig. 5.

No matter what sections may be cut in the end quarter of span, where the shear is in excess of that allowed on the concrete, diagonal steel is cut; and this steel is capable of taking the stress, for it is fully anchored. It happens, too, that this is the only system of reinforcement that has ever been shown by measurement, so far as the writer knows, to have any considerable stress under test.

Figs. 6, 7 and 8 illustrate how and why the diagonal tension reinforcement shown in Fig. 5 is effective and takes stress. These figures show also how and why vertical stirrups and diagonal shear members with a steep inclination are not effective and take little or no stress; this is in addition to their failure to be located where they can do much good in a beam.

Paragraph 1a of "Recommended Practice" in the report allows $0.12f'$ for unit shear where "properly anchored bent-up longitudinal bars" are used, and Fig. 14 of the report shows examples, presumably, of these

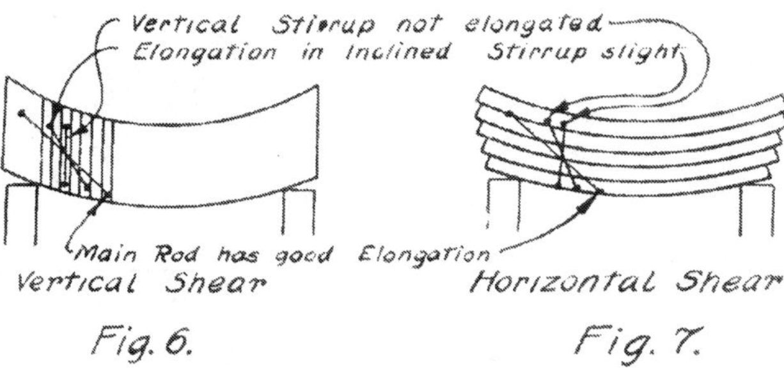


Fig. 6.          Fig. 7.



Fig. 8.

properly anchored bars.  This figure also shows critical shear sections. But there is not a scintilla of diagonal steel crossing any of these critical sections.  What takes the shear?  All of the bent-up bars rise at a sharp angle with the vertical.  Furthermore, they are bent at a considerable distance from the support, and yet the report says, on page 4, paragraph 8: "The construction in which the bent-up bars reach the top of the slab at a considerable distance from the edge of the support were decidedly erratic."

It is astounding that this report, whose author states that erratic results were found in tests of a certain kind of web reinforcement, should allow in that very kind of reinforcement double the shearing unit on any other style of reinforcement and double what has heretofore been used as a maximum

Prof W. K. Hatt in 'Proceedings," American Concrete Institute, Vol XIII, p 285, says "The principles of action of such reinforcing are on a very insecure experimental basis and have little rationality ' I can appreciate the predicament of a professor of engineering who is up against the proposition of trying to square up with any kind of logic the standard practice of reinforcing the web of a concrete beam and the standard treatment of the same in textbooks and committee reports. It can't be done  A student of ordinary intelligence can ask the professor questions about how the standard stirrup or shear member acts that no wise professor can answer Here are a few sample questions  Does the vertical dimension of a whole concrete beam increase or diminish under a load? The only answer possible is no  How then can the stirrup take either tension or compression, since the concrete in which it is embedded remains exactly the same dimension in the direction of the axis of the stirrup? If, then, the stirrup takes neither tension nor compression, does it take the vertical shear of a beam? No it is not in a position to take vertical shear  Can a stirrup take horizontal shear in a beam? Yes, a trifling amount, but this would not aid the concrete in carrying the vertical shear to the support  What, then, is the nature of the "stress" which reports apportion to stirrups, since it is equally absurd to attribute either tension compression, or shear to these members? I have been waiting for an answer to this question for many, many years

It is possible by making up freak test beams with a large number of stirrups welded to the horizontal steel to show large ultimate shearing strength  A few stirrups will add some strength to a beam  A peck of nails would do the same thing, if the nails were loosely distributed in the beam  Any kind of crisscross steel reinforcement strengthens the concrete of a beam for tension, shear and compression  But it is a far cry from making this acknowledgment to the proposition that a stirrup has any definite value in a beam or the proposition that stirrups as placed in the standard way are safe design

In 1907 I publicly pointed out in commenting on some tests that seemed to show high shearing values for concrete, that the high results were exhibited only in the case of concrete where the tensile stress in the same was inhibited  Earlier than this I pointed out that it is absolutely essential that concrete beams be tied into the supports by steel extended over and anchored to these supports  I have been ridiculed and harshly condemned for advocating that the web steel be anchored over the supports, the very thing that the report before us insists upon and I call attention to the fact that this is something brand new in reports

Plain common sense and reason tell me that if the concrete can safely

take only a portion of the shear in any vertical section and the actual
shear in that section is in excess of the amount the concrete can safely
take, there must be steel in that section capable of carrying the excess
shear by tension in that steel    If that steel is inclined to the horizontal,
the stress in the steel will have a vertical component which, in proper
designs will equal the excess shear    Common sense and reason also tell
me that that steel whose office is to reinforce the web must be integral with
the bottom reinforcement of the beam at mid-span and must be fully
anchored over the support    Now web reinforcement to meet this requirement
of common sense and reason is precluded by this committee's report    They
do not allow a flatter angle than 30 deg with the horizontal, and the shape
of most beams would demand the very inclinations that this committee
prohibits

I know of one building that was reinforced in accordance with this
committee's allowance or requirements    The girder is illustrated in Fig  9
These girders failed along the heavy lines    Why?    Because there was no
diagonal steel crossing these lines    Great open cracks appeared on these
lines, though the bottom of the girder showed no cracks visible in a photo
graph    Plainly the girder was not properly reinforced for shear

Another example of improper shear reinforcement is in the Edison
Building    Details of the girder reinforcement can be seen in the Journal
of the American Concrete Institute  Aug , 1915  pages 662 and 664

Fig  10 shows how these girders were reinforced and how one of them
broke

A photograph of the broken girder may be seen in *Engineering News*
Dec  17, 1914, p  1234    The reinforcement of this girder is almost good    It
had bent-up and anchored rods  but the bend did not extend clear across the
high shear zone of the girder  and the break occurred in the part of the
girder where the diagonal steel was lacking    Note that the stirrups were
distributed over this high shear zone, and the break occurred in spite of
the stirrups

Another fault in the reinforcement of Fig  10 is that the steel that
was bent up did not reach the top of the girder at the support

In contrast with this girder I refer to a beam the detail of whose
reinforcement is shown on page 662 in the Journal of the American Con
crete Institute    This beam is reinforced for shear with rods bent up with
a long sweep, as I have recommended    On page 649 there are photographs
of some of these beams that stood up remarkably well    With the rods
burnt apart the beams did not drop and the load is carried by cantilever
action from the supports

As illustrating the method of shear reinforcement here recommended
assume a beam as per sketch in Fig  11 with a total uniform load of
48 000 lb    The bending moment is 48 000 × 1618 = 96,000 ft  lb    The depth
from centroid of compression to steel is 18 in  and the steel stress is then
96,000 × 12 — 18 = 64 000 lb    The steel area required is 4 sq  in , which
may be made of four 1 in  square rods    If two of these rods be bent up at
the quarter point, as indicated in the figure, some of the shear will go

through these rods. If we allow the concrete beam to take a share of the end shear at 50 lb. per sq. in. (and the writer believes in taking the full area of the rectangle regardless of where the steel is located), we can deduct from the end shear of the beam, which is 24,000 lb., the amount taken by the concrete, or $12 \times 22 \times 50 = 13,200$ lb. This leaves 10,800 lb.

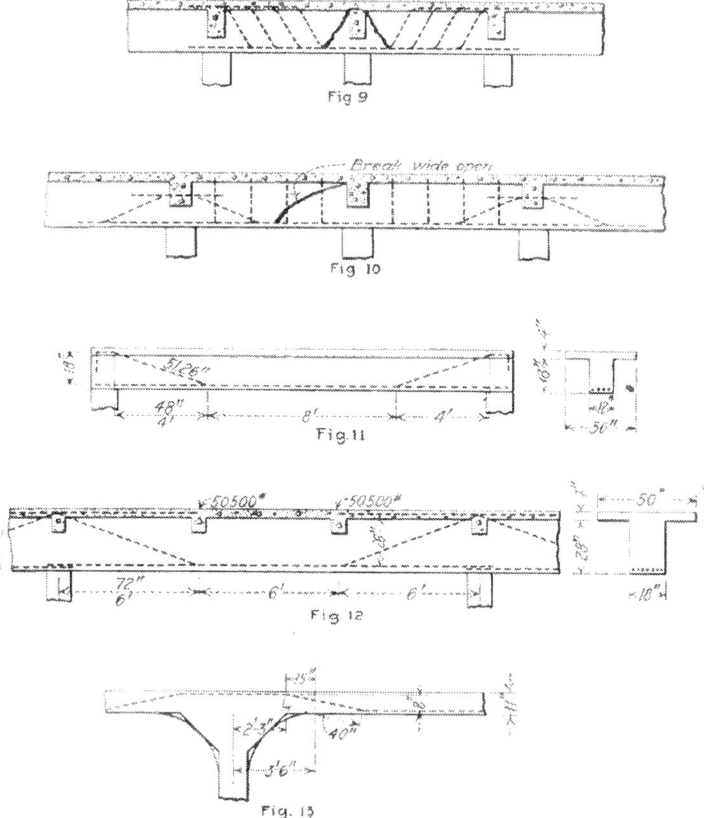

Fig 9



Fig 10

Fig. 11

Fig 12

Fig. 13

to be taken by the bent-up steel rods. If we multiply this shear by the secant of the angle of inclination of the rod with the vertical (in exactly the same way as in the resolution of forces in any other engineering work), we shall have the stress in the rods. The shear is thus resolved into two components, one in a horizontal direction, to be taken in compression by the concrete of the beam and the other in the direction of the inclined rods.

to be taken by the tension in those rods  The latter stress is
10,800 × .5126 — 18 = 30 760  If two 1 in sq rods are bent up this will
give an area of 2 sq in and a stress of 15 380 lb per sq in

Given a girder as in Fig 12  The moment on this girder using 8/10 of
the simple beam moment on account of continuity, is 259 000 ft lb  The depth
from centroid of compression to steel is 26 4 in  Steel stress is then 118,100
lb  Area reqd 7 4 sq in  Use four 1¼ in round rods = 4 91 and two
1⅜ in round rods = 2 97, total 7 88 sq in  The shear next to the support
is 50 500 + 5000 = 55,500 lb  Allowing 32 × 18 × 50 or 28 800 lb on the
concrete, this leaves 26,700 lb to be taken by the bent up rods
26,700 × 76 55 — 26 = 78,600 lb  the stress in the rods  If the four 1¼ in
round rods be bent up the area is 4 91 sq in and the stress is 16,000 lb
per sq in

In the case of a flat slab the maximum punching shear is in a cylinder
around the column head  Hence the reinforcing rods across the column
head should begin to dip at the circumference of the column head, if the
unit shear here exceeds 50 lb per sq in, so that there will be diagonal steel
in any section where the punching shear is in excess of this limit  The
intensity of punching shear diminishes rapidly around the column head
because of the increase in the section in shear and the decrease in the
load carried  It is not proper, in a slab where shear reinforcement is needed
to make the bend in rods at the point of inflection in the slab, for this is
not the section of maximum shear  Given a slab of 20 ft square bays
designed for a total load of 400 lb per sq ft, slab thickness 11 in, column
head 4 5 ft in diameter, reinforcement for negative moment over column
heads nine 1-in sq rods in each of four directions  The punching shear
around the column head is 82 lb per sq in  In a circle 7 ft in diameter
around the column the punching shear is 50 lb. per sq in  But there are
two reasons why the rods should not be brought down to the bottom of the
slab in the 15 in between these two circles  The first is because the rods
are needed for tension in the upper part of the slab beyond this seven foot
circle, and the second is that they are not needed in the bottom of the
slab within the circle of points of inflection of the slab  The reason why
they need not be given even as steep an inclination as would result in
dropping them to the bottom of the slab in 15 in is because it will be
found that there is ample steel to take the tension even at the flat slope
indicated in Fig 13  The fact seems to be lost sight of that steel rods
can support loads by a suspension system as well as through the medium
of bending moments

The foregoing illustrations are given to show just how I would take
care of shear or diagonal tension  This is an answer to those who have
been so severely criticising me because I do not go into these details  My
dissenting note in the Joint Committee Report is just as definite as any
example in bridge stresses  The analysis is just as simple and exact as any
problem in the resolution of stresses  This is infinitely more than can be
said of any analysis of the stresses in stirrups ever attempted

A striking difference between the efficiency of bent-up rods, such as I recommended, and the inefficiency of stirrups is seen in a beam in the Edison Building   The beam referred to was reinforced somewhat similar to that of my Fig 11, but the rod was bent up half way between the support and the first concentrated load, instead of being bent up at the concentrated load

Also there were stirrups all the way from support to concentrated load   The beam cracked apart with a great open crack just at the foot of the bent rod   The portion containing the inclined part of the rod held together  but the portion containing the horizontal rod and the stirrups— that is the part that this proposed standard attributes double value to— failed   (See *Engineering News* Dec. 17, 1914, p 1235, and "Journal," American Concrete Institute  Aug  1915  pp  662 664 )   This is most significant  and I have failed to find an engineer anywhere who is willing to discuss the relative merits of stirrups and bent up main rods

MR  I  OI STERBLOOM (*by letter*) —The writer has read with very great interest the report of the Special Committee on Unit Values for Vertical Shear in Reinforced Concrete Design   The question is by no means a simple one, the best proof of which is the great amount of experimental work which has been done for years and which still leaves a doubt as regards the interpretation of the results

Permit me to inquire in connection herewith if the fear that sufficient anchorage may not be provided has not been overstated   It would appear to the writer that for each increment of tensile stress in the bar between two closely adjacent intersecting planes there should be provided an adequate bond strength between the same planes

Near the center of any beam naturally this would offer no difficulty, but the problem may be a serious one near the supports, and this particularly so if the bar for the design has been selected too heavy in proportion to the span   Assuming now that an error in the selection of size is thought to be safeguarded by means of a special anchorage provided at or beyond the supports  the question may well be raised whether this would prevent the construction from failure

Is it not to be expected that the bar may fail in bond at the support and subsequently to an initial failure further from the support, progressively, while the anchorage were quite sufficient to provide for the full tensile stress of the bar?   But if such failures appear and develop under progressive loading the results would not be a reinforced-concrete structure, but two independent elements, one in compression acting as an arch and the other in tension, co operating by means of the two anchorages so as to carry a certain amount of loading

This, however, is hardly a result to be desired, and while anchorages might provide for some sort of insurance against ultimate and rapid destruction which might be disastrous  it would seem that the question of proper selection of size should rather be stressed and the design be made so that there should be absolutely no question as regards provision of adequate bonding strength for any particular part of the bar, which alone would justify the assumption and execution of steel and concrete design in combination to serve for load carrying purposes

Even if we assumed that the arch with a tension rod would carry the same load as the reinforced concrete originally designed, have we the right to assume likewise that the steel in this manner separated from the concrete will be thoroughly protected against corrosion?

The statement has been made, and it appears very reasonable, that the bond is not merely a close physical contact, but an alloy between certain elements in the cement and the steel. This intimate relation is destroyed by an overstressed bond and no anchorage which may be provided will serve as a sufficient substitute for the intimate bond relation thus destroyed. Or has the committee experimental data to prove the contrary? If so, the writer would like to know.

If any of the above comments can find support in experimental work it might eventually lead to a somewhat different formulation as regards the safeguards which should be employed. Possibly the question about anchorage would be put forward as a question of insurance, and greater stress be laid upon the necessity to compel rational determination of the size of the bars required and means whereby in commercial work same can be done without undue waste of time and labor.

Mr. A. R. Lord (*by letter*).—Mr Godfrey has appealed to me to refrain from all personal references in discussing this matter, and I shall certainly endeavor to do so but I submit it is difficult if not impossible to answer his discussion without bringing out facts that will cause him some personal discomfort. The report is based on *facts* almost entirely— largely on data of tests conducted for the express purpose of establishing the proper limits for design. When Mr Godfrey states that vertical stirrups do not and cannot take tension in the web of a concrete beam, and that they leave areas of concrete between the stirrups which are not reinforced, and which, presumably would cause failure of the beam, the sufficient answer is found in the facts. The identical construction has been built and tested and the vertical stirrups do carry tension, increasing regularly with the load until the yield-point strength is reached, at which time the beam fails in diagonal tension, due to the overstress in the vertical stirrups. This is not the exception. It is rather the universal experience, and the data have long been a matter of public record.

Further, the areas of 'unreinforced concrete" between the vertical stirrups did not fail, even though the computed shearing unit stress exceeded 2000 lb per sq in in some cases, and very commonly exceeded by two to three times the value of 600 lb per sq in mentioned several times in the discussion at the convention as being 2½ times the maximum shearing unit stress permitted for 2000 lb concrete by the report. The facts are such that I do not feel justified in entering upon any lengthy discussion of Mr Godfrey's contentions.

In the tests by several authorities and made over a period of 12 years, on which data the report is founded, only a few beams have stirrups "welded to the horizontal steel,' and these few show about the same results as the vast majority in which no welding was done

The report does allow the type of reinforcement advocated by Mr Godfrey, and such reinforcement was sanctioned in the earliest draft of this report   There are peculiar difficulties in drawing up regulations for this type, and it may easily be that more liberal allowances may be safe I have personally felt that a slope as flat as 20° with the horizontal might be used  and there are data to support this view   The majority felt, however, that the limit should be placed at 30° for the present   There is a real question as to the sufficiency of this type of reinforcement for the portions of the beam immediately adjoining the support where the shear is greatest and where the inclined truss rods are very considerably above the neutral axis   The report sanctions this type of web reinforcement, and has gone as far in the matter of allowances and detailed specifications as the data and theory would seem to establish as thoroughly safe

Some of his discussion would indicate that Mr Godfrey had not read the report with sufficient care   The report does not permit the type of web reinforcing which was found in tests to be "decidedly erratic"—far from allowing double the shearing unit on that type

## REPORT OF COMMITTEE ON CONCRETE ROADS
## AND PAVEMENTS

[This committee presented to the Convention certain changes in the Standard Specifications for Concrete Roads, Streets and Alleys, but as they had never been submitted to the membership they could not be acted upon The committee also moved that the Amendments to Recommended Practice for Concrete Roads and Street Construction, printed in the *Proceedings*, Vol XV, 1919, p 405 be sent to letter ballot for adoption as standard

By vote of April 17, 1920, these Amendments were accepted as Standards of the Institute —EDITOR ]

## DISCUSSION ON CONCRETE ROADS

———

Tin: Chair—We have a number of gentlemen here today who are interested in the whole question of concrete road construction and it is the intention of the Program Committee to make this an opportunity for bringing up several matters of interest  We will be glad to hear from anyone

Mr J T Voshell.—The first matter I would discuss is how best to utilize classes of aggregate not hitherto considered available for concrete roadwork  I do not know of any change in the construction of concrete roads that would justify us now in using aggregates that we have hitherto considered unsuitable  Frankly, I dislike to see sources of material developed that are unsuitable  If we once get them on the market they are hard to get off and the engineers are simply in trouble  There are efforts being made to have them change the specifications, or rather write the specifications, so that these poor materials may be used  I do not believe we are building our concrete roads any better than we ought to, and I do not believe we ought to do anything that would cause us to build them any poorer than we are now doing

Another subject of interest is the use of reinforcement versus thicker slabs to meet heavy traffic demands.  I have been getting all the information for the last two years that I can find on reinforcing concrete roads, and I find that it is about "fifty-fifty", that is, about 50% of the people who have used it say that they do not see that it does any good  and about 50% think that it is a success  I might say, however, that the reinforcing that has been used heretofore has been such small amounts that it could hardly be said to be a reinforcement for strength  About all that is done is simply to keep the cracks from opening up wider than they might otherwise have done had the reinforcing not been placed

There is lack of information as to where we should put the reinforcement if we should attempt to reinforce for strength  There seems to be about as much argument in placing it 2 in from the bottom as there is in placing it, say, 2 in from the top  Probably the only sure way we could do would be to put in double the amount of reinforcing and put it in both the bottom and the top of the slab

There is another thing to consider—that is that impact may be one of the greatest causes of the breaking down of concrete roads  If this is so  reinforcement may not be of as great value in preventing that as would be increasing the thickness of the slab

A third matter is the practical application of the dryer mixture requirements to actual construction and practice  It certainly has been true that a great many jobs of concrete roads were laid with the mixture too wet, that is, it was absolutely soupy, it would run like water almost,

There never was any reason for that, and there is not any reason now There is a limit, of course as to the dryness of the mix I do not know how to describe that limit but I will say that the concrete which in putting in structures we consider is dry concrete is too dry in general for concrete roadwork It must be plastic and readily moved about in order that we may secure satisfactory finish

Mr A T Goldbeck.—It may be of some interest to introduce at this time some information on the design of concrete roads We know that in the past roads have not been designed—that is they have simply been built of a thickness which has been agreed upon, and we do not know exactly why we made the roads of that thickness In the design of any structure we must first know the forces that are exerted on the structure, and at the Bureau of Public Roads we are now making an effort to determine something of the amount of force being exerted on concrete roads, and also something regarding the supporting value of the sub grades

We have made static load tests on a concrete road in which we have measured the distribution of pressure between the sub grade and the road by means of a pressure-gage instrument, and in that way we have determined what that distribution is We have gone further and calculated the tensile stress existing under the load We find that tensile stress to be quite small when the slab is adequately supported on the subgrade, and the indications are that the concrete slab could certainly not fail under static loads—that is, under the static load such as we get today, even taking into consideration the very heaviest trucks That leads us to the idea that impact is the all governing factor, not in the cracking of concrete roads, because we all realize that other forces than the mere force of traffic cracks concrete roads, but impact is the thing that certainly shatters the concrete roads when they are shattered

We have conducted a number of tests, using trucks of different size, in order to determine something of the amount of impact exerted on concrete roads, and it is rather surprising to find out just how much this impact can be For instance, say you have a heavy truck, a three ton army truck, which is very often a five-ton truck, and that truck has a total weight on one rear wheel of 7,500 lb when the truck is loaded with five tons When one rear wheel of that trucks falls through a height of ¼ in the impact on the road may be as high as 20,000 lb that is the impact pressure produced may be as high as 20,000 lb, almost three times as much as the static load pressure If the truck falls through a height of 3 in, which would of course, mean an exceedingly bad road you may get an impact pressure as high as 43,000 lb

We have gone further than that, and constructed a number of concrete slabs of different thicknesses varying from 2 up to 10 in, laid directly on the subgrade, and we have constructed a machine which is designed to resemble the impact condition existing on the rear wheel of a heavy truck The machine consists of an unsprung weight, on top of which is supported a spring weight   The idea would be to exert impact on these slabs, repeated impact, until the slabs fail   In that way we will be able to determine something of the impact resistance of slabs of different thicknesses, and we hope to be able to determine something of the load carrying capacity of slabs of different thicknesses when laid on different kinds of subgrade

We have varied the subgrade   In one case the subgrade is purposely kept very moist and the bearing power low, in another case the subgrade is purposely kept dry, to keep the bearing power high   We hope when we get through with the investigations that we will be able to say, with some degree of definiteness, just what thickness of slab will be suitable for carrying heavy truck loads on subgrades of different kinds   We must not forget that we have, throughout the country, subgrades of different bearing power which will call for different thicknesses of slabs best suited to support the same loads

Mr K. H Talbot—I would like to bring out another possibility, and that is to obtain, during the next year or so, some actual field specimens cut out of roads built under the usual conditions in the slabs   I have felt for a long time that concrete pavement is subjected to moisture on three sides, and as a result the strengths are quite a good deal higher than they are on laboratory specimens   I understand that such work is being done by the State of Pennsylvania at the present time   It seems to me that that, in conjunction with the work on design is going to help a great deal in knowing what quality of concrete we are getting

I have also felt that there is a point where it is desirable to increase the cement rather than cut down the water   The question of labor versus material cost is just as acute in road construction as it is in building construction, and if by slight increase in cement, we can use a more fluid material which we can place at a cheaper cost we are in better shape   I am reminded of two States, one used a 1   1½ · 3 mix, the other a 1   1 · 3½ mix, and one got its work done at practically the same cost as the other   The first State guaranteed the quality of road by cement, the other by work   In other words, the contractor in the second State found it necessary to increase his bid by some thousand or fifteen hundred dollars because he did not know just what his labor costs were going to be under the conditions that were in existence

Mr W A Collings—I should like to ask Mr Talbot if he cannot tell us, in view of the fact that a number of States are specifying in their roadwork more reinforcing and no concrete roads without reinforcing, what was the purpose in discontinuing those recommendations?

Mr K H Talbot—The purpose in discontinuing reinforcement recommendations was the fact that it is impossible to write any specifications showing a cross section area of steel of a certain minimum weight to fit local conditions   The recommendation was not struck out, but the statement was made that where reinforcement was called for it should be placed in accordance with the plans and in the amount specified   The com mittee did not feel in position to recommend either the retaining of the present amount or adopting a greater amount, because none of the members of the committee had been able, in their own minds, definitely to determine the relative efficiency of the amount which we specified as against a little more or a little less  We felt it desirable to leave that to the individual engineer who knew his local conditions and for what he was reinforcing  The reinforcement in the past has been in a blind way and not a structural reinforcement.

Mr S P Arnsby —Mr Talbot has brought up the question of the desirability of having concrete for roadwork more fluid  and suggests a way to accomplish that  I would like to call the attention of the Institute to the growing use of a material which has not been much discussed in these committee reports  You are all aware of the fact that the use of hydrated lime in concrete mixtures has increased during the past few years at a great rate  The advantages or disadvantages of it have not been fully determined  either by laboratory tests or field tests  There is considerable field evidence, however available, and practically all the field reports indicate that greater ease of placing concrete can be accomplished by the use of this material without detriment to the finished job

The indications are that there are certain advantages to be obtained from the use of hydrated lime  We do not know just what the advantages may be  but I should like to see the American Concrete Institute consider the matter to the extent of investigating it both in laboratory tests and in field tests  I believe that much of interest may be ascertained regarding the advisability of using a material which is already growing in use and is of concern to all of us

Mr W. W. Horner —I would like to ask Mr Talbot if there was a decided sentiment in the committee in favor of reducing the proportion of cement in road concrete?

Mr K H Talbot —There was not, there was a decided sentiment among those members of the committee who were from New York in trying to develop a scheme by which the proportion of cement could be varied depending on the aggregate used  For instance, there are many aggregates the material of which ranges from ¼ to 3 in. and other materials with part of that range removed  which are now in piles and not allowed to be used  It was thought that possibly some of those materials might be used by a change in the proportions  My understanding is that Prof Abrams has prepared something on that  If that thing can be done so that with a variation of aggregate, with a change in the size of aggregate not a change in the quality of aggregate, but simply a change in the size of aggregates, the proportion will be changed  The State of Wisconsin is doing something of the same kind  There is a basis however, for the adoption of all this 1 2 3 mix  As far as reduction of the richness of concrete goes, the only tendency in that respect is toward a 1 2 4 mix instead of a 1 2 3 mix, where aggregates will permit that additional stone  However, it seems to be the general consensus of opinion that anything leaner than a 1 2 2 mix is too lean to hold up under the very heavy traffic conditions to which our roads are subjected today

Mr A Foster, Jr—May I ask if the committee has investigated means to prevent change in elevation between adjacent slabs due to various subgrades?

Mr A H Talbot—That matter did not come up in the committee report The adoption of the steel contraction joints, at least an inch below the surface was one of the outcomes of a study made some years ago to adopt something where the slabs would be locked so that they would not climb The other results have been the discontinuance of all joints in the State of Illinois and several other States, so that where the concrete is cracked due to contraction, it will be locked and will not raise one slab over another Where a bulkhead is put in some people have used bar connections but the result of that is practically inch bars because even though you break those bars you do get some cohesion between the cement and the bars

Mr C R Egr—I think perhaps I might add a word to what Mr Talbot has said in regard to the selection of materials and the possibilities in that line The intention which I think the committee had in mind was not to permit materials of a lower grade structurally to be admitted to the specifications, but it was to adjust the specifications particularly as to sizes and grading to permit of materials which are available in a number of localities throughout the country to be used for concrete pavements There are many parts of the country where there is not a wide range of selection in the choice of materials particularly as to the coarser aggregates There is a situation of that kind I believe, in Nebraska, where the principal materials they have available come from the Platte River and contain practically none of the coarser sizes Through the study of the State Engineer's office of Nebraska a proportion has been devised which will enable them to make use of those materials successfully for concrete pavements, and several jobs have been done with the proportion that they worked out using that material, none of which I believe is over $\frac{3}{4}$ in in maximum size

There are many localities throughout the country that are somewhat similarly situated There are places where they do not have the coarser sands which are available in the Mississippi Valley and throughout most of the eastern sections, and some proportion must be worked out whereby those materials may be utilized and concrete of the desired strength secured The work Prof Abrams is doing along that line has been mentioned and we hope very much to have something ready for announcement on that subject within the next few months

## REPORT OF COMMITTEE ON CONCRETE SEWERS

Your Committee on Concrete Sewers submits herewith specifications entitled ' Proposed Standard Specifications for Monolithic Concrete Sewers and Reinforced Concrete Pipe Sewers, with Recommended Rules for Concrete Sewer Design, Revised 1920 '

These specifications are in revision of those submitted by the committee at the 1919 meeting  The committee has carefully considered the action of the 1919 meeting in regard to the specifications then submitted

As instructed by the last meeting, the committee has, as far as possible, eliminated the word "Contractor ' from these specifications  If this matter had not come as an instruction from the meeting, it appears that the committee should have preferred to have retained the so called contract clauses, as in many cases they seem to be almost integral parts of necessary specifications  The committee does not however consider their inclusion as of vital importance  and does not feel that it is advisable to present this point for further discussion

The committee has accepted the amendments as to speed of mixers which were made on the floor of the 1919 meeting, but wishes to voice a feeling that standard mixer speeds can be somewhat slowed down with resultant advantage to the product

The committee does not concur in the amendment from the floor of the 1919 meeting introducing blast furnace slag as a good coarse aggregate  This material is however included in the accompanying specifications, and is to be considered as having been included by the 1919 meeting without the approval of the committee  In taking this action, the committee wishes to make clear that it has no data on which to approve or disapprove of this material in sewer construction

In the matter of quality of crushed stone aggregate  the committee has decided to substitute a French coefficient of wear of 8 for the coefficient of hardness of 16 formerly recommended  It does not feel that this will materially change the character of stone permitted, but the change is made in order to eliminate the recollection of the discussion on the floor of the 1919 meeting, in which many of the members apparently mistook the coefficient of hardness for the French coefficient of wear  The committee wishes to call attention that all of the discussion on this point at the last meeting was apparently based on this error, and cannot therefore be considered

The French coefficient of wear is fully described in bulletins 347 and 370 of the United States Department of Agriculture and the test on which it is based has been standardized by the American Society for Testing Materials  The probable results of the limiting of the coefficient of wear, to not less than 8, can be fairly judged as regards the stone from any particular locality by an inspection of the tests given in bulletin 370 above referred to

Other minor changes have been made in the line of suggestions offered at the last meeting

The committee recommends the presentation of these specification as a new standard of the Institute*

Respectfully submitted

W. W. Horner (Chairman),
Arthur S. Bent,
Alfred H. Hartman,
W. S. Lea
Frank A. Marston,
Langdon Pearse,
Coleman Merriwether,
W. R. Harris,
A. J. R. Curtis,
W. K. Hatt

---

* The specification was submitted to letter ballot and adopted as standard, April 17 1920 It is printed beginning on the next succeeding page —EDITOR

# AMERICAN CONCRETE INSTITUTE
## STANDARD SPECIFICATIONS NO. 24

### STANDARD SPECIFICATIONS FOR MONOLITHIC CONCRETE SEWERS AND REINFORCED CONCRETE PIPE SEWERS
### AND
### RECOMMENDED RULES FOR CONCRETE SEWER DESIGN[*]

#### PART I.—MATERIALS.

#### *Cement*

*Section 1.* All cement shall conform to the current specifications for portland cement of the American Society for Testing Materials and shall be tested in accordance with the methods of testing described in the specifications of that Society.

#### *Fine Aggregate*

*Section 2.* Fine aggregate shall consist of sand graded from fine to coarse and passing when dry a screen having holes one-quarter inch in diameter. It shall be clean, coarse, free from dirt, vegetable loam or other deleterious matter. Not more than 6 per cent shall pass a sieve having one hundred meshes per lineal inch[†]

*Section 3.* Fine aggregate shall be of such quality that mortar composed of the proportions of cement and fine aggregate hereinafter specified for the various classes of concrete shall show a compressive strength after fourteen (14) days at least equal to the strength of mortar made of portland cement and standard Ottawa sand in corresponding proportions and of the same consistency[‡]

#### *Coarse Aggregate*

*Section 4.* The coarse aggregate shall consist of crushed stone, gravel or blast furnace slag which is retained on a screen having ¼ in. diameter holes and graded from the smallest to the largest particles. It shall be clean, hard, durable, free from all deleterious matter and soft, flat or elongated particles. Crusher dust in sufficient quantity to weaken the

---

[*] Adopted by letter ballot of the Institute, April 17, 1920.

[†] Crushed stone screenings may be permitted for use as fine aggregate provided that they shall comply with all the specifications of Sections 2 and 3 and further that they shall be produced from stone having a French coefficient of wear of not less than 8, as described in Bulletins No. 347 and No. 370 of United States Department of Agriculture.

[‡] It is recommended that, if possible, available fine aggregates be tested before awarding contracts. If it appears necessary to use an aggregate of poorer quality than those specified the proportion of cement in the various classes of concrete should be increased in order that the strength of the mortar actually used shall not be less than that with the Ottawa sand. If, however, the strength of the resulting mortars is less than 70 per cent of those with the Ottawa sand, fine aggregate should be rejected entirely.

concrete will not be permitted   For reinforced-concrete arches or for plain concrete arches less than 6 in  in thickness  the maximum size of particles shall be such as will pass a screen having 1 in  diameter holes.  For inverts and plain concrete arches over 6 in  in thickness, the maximum size of particles shall be such as will pass a screen having 1½ in. diameter holes

*Section 5.*  Where crushed stone is used it shall have a French coefficient of wear of not less than 8, as described in bulletins No  347 and 370 of United States Department of Agriculture

(The above paragraph is for use in locations where limestone or sandstone of a questionable value are common   If all available stone is suitable, the paragraph may be omitted )

**Aggregate**

*Section 6*  Samples of not less than ½ cu. ft  of fine aggregate and not less than one cubic foot of coarse aggregate shall be delivered in suitable boxes or containers.  All samples shall be plainly labeled with the places where taken, where to be used, the date, and the name of the collector

*Section 7*  For the purpose of determining proportions of materials for concrete, each bag of cement containing 94 lb  shall be considered as containing one cubic foot   Sand and coarse aggregate shall be measured loose in approved boxes or hoppers

## Water.

*Section 8*  Water used for concrete shall be free from oil, acid, alkalies, or organic matter

## Concrete Reinforcement Bars.

*Section 9*   All steel reinforcement shall consist of cold drawn steel wire fabric having an elastic limit of not less than 55,000 lb  per sq in , or of expanded metal having an elastic limit of not less than 55,000 lb  per sq in., and expanded cold from steel sheets, or of reinforcing bars

*9 1.*  Steel bars for reinforced-concrete sewers shall conform to the current specifications of the American Society for Testing Materials for (A) Billet Steel or (B) Rail Steel except that rail steel bars may be used in sizes of 1 in  and under only, and hot twisted bars will not be permitted

*Section 10*   Dimensions of bars given on the plans are based on square sections   The net area and weights of bars shall not be less than 95 per cent of the values for square bars as indicated   In computing the weights of steel, one cubic inch of steel shall be regarded as 0 283 lb

**Measurement and Payment.**

*Section 11.*  The quantity of metal to be paid for shall be the number of pounds actually placed, as shown on the drawings or as ordered   It shall not include any waste metal due either to the nature of the construction or to the fact that the lengths supplied are too long or too short for their purpose

The quantity paid for shall, however, include extra metal in laps, where authorized, due to the fact that a single bar would be unreasonably long

All bars shall be of the length ordered and shall be in one piece where required up to 30 ft in length

The compensations shall cover the cost of furnishing and delivering metal, including any royalty, the cutting, bending, placing, fastening in position, coating with cement and all other work and materials connected therewith.

### Castings

*Section 12.*   Circular cast iron frames and covers for manholes and catch basins and any other iron castings shown on the drawings, or specified herein, necessary to complete the work shall be furnished and placed — Description

*Section 13*   All castings shall be of tough, close-grained gray iron, free from blow-holes, shrinkage, and cold-shuts  They shall be sound, smooth, clean, and free from blisters and all defects — Cast Iron

*Section 14*   All castings shall be made accurately to dimensions to be furnished and shall be planed where marked or where otherwise necessary to secure perfectly flat and true surfaces  Allowances shall be made in the patterns so that the thickness shall not be reduced.  Manhole covers shall be true and shall seat at all points — Workmanship

*Section 15*   All castings shall be thoroughly cleaned and painted before rusting begins, and before leaving the shop, with two coats of high-grade asphaltum or other suitable varnish that the engineer may direct.  After the castings have been placed in a satisfactory manner, all foreign adhering substances shall be removed and the castings given two additional coats of asphaltum or other varnish as directed by the engineer — Cleaning and Painting

*Section 16*   No casting shall be accepted the weight of which shall be less than that computed to its dimensions by more than five per cent.

### Material for Lining Inverts

*Section 17*   All vitrified brick shall be uniform in size, and be not less than 8 in by 4 in by 2 in, nor more than 10 in by 4½ in by 2½ in in length, width or thickness, respectively  The brick shall be free from lime or other impurities, uniformly vitrified and annealed, and shall have one edge face such that if the brick is laid on a horizontal plane on that face no portion thereof shall be more than ⅛ in from the plane

*Section 18*   Concrete block for sewer lining shall be uniform in size, not more than 18 in by 12 in in surface area and not less than 3 in in thickness  They shall be made of Class "A" or better concrete, as hereinafter specified in satisfactory molds, and thoroughly cured  They shall have an ultimate compressive strength at 28 days of not less than 2000 lb per sq in

*Section 19*   Tile liners for inverts shall not be more than 8 in by 12 in in surface area, and not less than 2 in in thickness  The back of the tile shall be roughened and equipped with lugs or projections for bedding in mortar  They shall be manufactured under the general requirements covering vitrified sewer pipe and shall comply with the standard tests of the American Society for Testing Materials for clay sewer pipe in so far as applicable

PART II— CONCRETE FOR MONOLITHIC CONCRETE SEWERS

*Section 20.* Concrete shall consist of a mixture of cement, fine and coarse aggregate and water of the qualities hereinbefore specified

Concrete shall be of three classes proportioned as follows

| Class | Cement | Fine Aggregate, cu ft | Coarse Aggregate, cu ft |
|---|---|---|---|
| A | 1 sack | 2 | 4 |
| B | 1 " | $2\frac{1}{2}$ | 5 |
| C | 1 " | 3 | 6 |

**Mixing.**

The relative proportions of fine and coarse aggregates may be modified at the direction of the engineer, provided that the proportions of cement to the total of the aggregates measured separately shall not be changed

*Section 21* Concrete shall be machine mixed   The concrete mixer shall be designed to take one completed batch of materials (using whole bags of cement) and to mix that batch thoroughly before any portion of it is withdrawn or any portion of the succeeding batch is introduced.   The mixer shall be equipped with a tank so designed that when once set it will automatically supply to the mixer the amount of water so determined   The mixer shall be equipped with an instrument for measuring the time of mix

*Section 22*   Concrete shall be mixed at least one minute after all the ingredients, including water, have been discharged into the mixer   Where the character of the work will permit, concrete shall be mixed in batches of one-half to one cubic yard and the mixer speed shall not be less than 12 nor more than 19 revolutions per minute.   Where small mixers are used, the speed shall not exceed 22 revolutions per minute

*Section 23*   No concrete shall be hand-mixed except relatively small quantities, and then only by special permission of the engineer

*Section 24*   Where concrete is mixed by hand, the cement and fine aggregate shall be mixed dry on a properly constructed wooden or steel platform built for the purpose until it shall have obtained an even and uniform color throughout   This mixture shall then be spread to make a bed of uniform thickness, on which shall be spread the coarse aggregate and the whole wet with the required amount of water and turned with square-pointed shovels at least three times or until a uniform mixture is secured, water being added from time to time if necessary

**Rubble or Stone in Concrete**

*Section 25*   In all plain concrete where the thickness is 15 in or more, there may be embedded broken pieces of sound stone, the greatest dimension of which does not exceed 6 in, and the least dimension of which is not less than three-quarters of the greatest dimension   These stones shall be set in the concrete as layers are being rammed, in a satisfactory manner, and so placed that each stone is completely and perfectly embedded   In general, there shall be a space of 4 in between the stones and no stone shall come within 4 in of any exposed face   The stone shall be thoroughly cleaned and wet before placing.

*Section 26*   In mixing concrete, it is advisable to use the least possible **Consistency** amount of water required to obtain a workable mix and when the aggregate is dry, 6 gal of water to a sack of portland cement is the maximum which should be used   (For slag aggregate this may be somewhat increased ) Where comparatively dry mix is to be used as in inverts, and near the crown of the arches the concrete must be thoroughly tamped until the water flushes to the surface

*Section 27*   Concrete shall not be mixed nor deposited in the work in **Work in** freezing weather except as directed   If the work on concrete structures is **Freezing** **Weather** prosecuted in cold weather proper precautions shall be taken for removing ice and frost from the materials, including heating the water and aggregates, for protecting the newly-laid masonry from freezing and for securing work satisfactory in all respects   Satisfactory covering for the newly-laid concrete and such additional appliances and materials as may be required therefor, including steam pipes for keeping them warm beneath the said covering shall be provided

## *Transportating and Placing Concrete*

*Section 28*   Provision shall be made for quickly transporting the **Transporting** concrete from the mixer to the work and with as little shaking as possible, so that the tendency of water to rise to the top may be reduced to a minimum   Any concrete which may have been compacted during transportation shall be satisfactorily remixed before being placed in the work   Any concrete delayed one half an hour in transit shall not be used in the work and must be removed from the premises

*Section 29*   Concrete shall be deposited so as to maintain a nearly **Placing Concrete** level surface and avoid flowing along the forms   It shall be continuously and sufficiently worked to expel air and to force the aggregate away from the forms   In special cases, as where concrete is deposited on slopes, a comparatively dry mixture may be used, but great care shall be exercised to spread such concrete evenly in layers not more than 6 in in thickness and to ram it thoroughly   In general, the methods used shall be such as to give a compact, dense and impervious concrete with a smooth surface

*Section 30*   For the proper bonding of new and old concrete, such **Joining New** provisions shall be made of steps dovetails, or other devices as may be **Work to Old** required   Whenever new concrete is joined to old, the contact surface of the old concrete shall be thoroughly cleaned, using a stiff brush and a stream of water, if required, and shall be clean and wet at the moment the fresh concrete is placed   Where ordered, a thick wash of rich mortar shall be run over the contact surface of the old concrete   Where it is of importance that the joint between the new and old work shall be as strong and tight as possible, especial precautions shall be taken such as picking off the top one or two inches of the old work so as to remove the laitance or washing the old cement off the surface with acid or alkali and later with water to remove all traces of them, or both, as may be required

*Section 31*   Special care shall be taken that all concrete surfaces shall **Finish of Concrete** be smooth and free from indentations or projections   All surfaces shall be **Surfaces**

free from voids, exposed stones and other imperfections. If such imperfections are found upon removing the forms, the faults shall be corrected at the contractor's expense by filling with mortar or otherwise, as directed, even to the extent of taking down and replacing unsatisfactory concrete

**Plastering of Concrete Surfaces.**  *Section 32* No plastering of any concrete surface shall be done unless expressly permitted and if so permitted shall be done in strict accordance with directions No payment will be made for plastering done to correct defective work.

**Masonry not to be Laid in Water.**  *Section 33* No concrete or other masonry shall be deposited under water without permission and then only in accordance with directions Water shall not be permitted to rise on any masonry until the mortar shall have set at least 12 hours.

## Forms

**Forms**  *Section 34* There shall be provided suitable collapsible centers or forms with smooth surfaces of ample strength and rigidly braced  The bracing shall be adequate to prevent deviations from the correct lines

*Section 35* All steel forms shall be neatly and accurately made with all similar parts in each longitudinal section of form interchangeable with other sections  Bent plates required to fit shall be rolled and fabricated to the correct curves before assembling  Suitable forms shall be provided for bends in the sewer  Steel filler plates shall be furnished

*Section 36* All wooden forms shall be built of clean, sound lumber, reasonably free from knots, dressed on all sides and neatly fitted  Tongued and grooved material shall be used where required  The form surface shall be watertight, securely fastened to the ribs or supports

*Section 37* No forms built up in the trench or ribs with separate pieces of wooden lagging, piece by piece will be allowed except for specials or curves.

*Section 38* No center or form shall be used which is not clean and of proper shape and strength and in every way suitable  Before placing concrete or reinforcement the forms shall be coated with vaseline, form grease or other suitable approved substance, to prevent adherence of concrete

## Placing Reinforcement

**Placing Concrete.**  *Section 39* All steel reinforcement shall be placed in the exact positions and with the spacing shown on the drawings or as ordered and it shall be so fastened in position as to prevent displacement while the concrete is being deposited

**Shaping and Splicing**  *Section 40.* The reinforcing steel shall be bent to the shapes shown on the drawings or as required  The ends of the bars shall be bent or hooked over if required  The length of the laps for bonding the adjacent bars shall not be less than thirty times the diameter of the bar when the steel is designed for working stress of 12,000 lb and not less than forty times the diameter of the bar when the steel is designed for working stress of 16,000 lb per sq in.  Where the bars are of different sizes, the diameter of the larger bar shall be used

*Section 41.*  Steel must be stored in such manner that its condition will Storing at all times correspond to that under which the samples were taken

### Part II-A—General Construction, Monolithic Sewers

*Section 42.*  The width of trench for circular sewers shall be equal to Width of Trench the greatest outside width of the sewer  Below the springing line for such sewer the trench shall be accurately shaped to the form of the outside of the masonry and the concrete shall have a firm bearing on the natural soil or rock at all points below the springing line *

*Section 43*  In general the width of the trench for sewers of the horse-shoe and similar types shall be one foot greater than the outside width of masonry to allow for satisfactory bracing

*Section 44*  Underdrains of agricultural tile laid in gravel or crushed Underdrain stone, shall be constructed of the size and where directed for the purpose of keeping the work free from water during construction, such drains to be abandoned when the work is completed  underdrains so laid shall lead to sumps or manholes, and water flowing to them shall be removed by pumping  Such pumping shall be carried on continuously, day and night, and the level of the ground water shall be maintained below any cement or concrete which may be placed in the work for a period of at least twelve hours after such cement or concrete is placed  When the temporary underdrains above described are abandoned, they shall be cut and plugged where directed and the sump holes above described shall be solidly filled with approved material

*Section 45*  On all sections having a comparatively flat invert, the Construction of<br>Inverts. complete invert shall first be built, while on all circular sections a center strip of not less than one-fourth circumference shall be built  The invert or center strip shall be placed in sections of not over 16 ft  where the surface is to be finished with end guides and a longitudinal straight edge, and not more than twenty feet if a separate lining of vitrified brick tile or concrete block is to be provided

*Section 46*  A granolithic finish shall be applied to the fresh concrete Finish. as soon as the condition of its surface will permit  This finish shall consist of a mixture of one part of cement to two parts of granite or other hard rock chips, graded from $\frac{1}{8}$ in  to $\frac{1}{2}$ in  in size, and shall be laid $1\frac{1}{2}$ in  thick  The upper surface shall be formed by means of screeds and shall be floated and troweled to a smooth surface  As soon as this surface is dry enough to receive it, a dry mixture of two parts of cement and one part of sand, free from crushed dust and particles larger than $\frac{1}{4}$ in  shall be sprinkled over it and then the surface shall be floated and troweled  This treatment shall be repeated at least once, and where the proportion of very fine material in the aggregate necessitates it, a total of three dry coats shall be applied  Where the placing of the dry coat must be deferred until the day following the pouring of the concrete invert, the concrete shall be first moistened and covered with neat cement, which shall be thoroughly broomed into the concrete in the form of a thick paste

---

* Where there is a probability that wet ground will make the shaping of circular inverts impossible, an alternate section of a suitable type shall be used

**Lining.**
**(Alternate to Sec 46)**
**Brick or Concrete Block Lining**

*Section 47.* * Where required, the inverts shall be lined with concrete is laid. A mixture made of one part of portland cement and three parts of sand, without the addition of water, shall be spread on the finished surface block, title or vitrified brick, as shown on the plans

*47.1.* The concrete bottom shall be accurately shaped up to a line one-half inch below the bottom of the lining and allowed to set before the lining to the depth required to bring the block or brick to the required grade The lining units shall be laid in straight lines and in a workmanlike manner and so that all joints shall be broken. After being laid, it shall be rolled with a hand-roller weighing from 300 to 500 lb or tamped until every unit shall have a solid bearing and the top of the finished work shall present a smooth and even surface and conform accurately with the shape of the invert as shown on the plans. The joints between the units shall be grouted with mortar made of one part portland cement and two parts sand and the surface shall be brushed until every joint is completely filled

**Tile Lining.**

*47.2* Where vitrified tile is used, the units shall be carefully bedded in wet mortar, the mortar bed to be approximately ½ in in thickness

**Protection.**

*47.3* The bottom must be kept free from water until the work is completed and no water will be allowed to run over the completed work until it shall have set

*Section 48* The unfinished surface of the invert on which the concrete of sidewalls or arches is to be placed, shall be made as rough as possible In unreinforced work dovetails shall be formed as provided in Section 31 In reinforced work, where projecting bars may interfere with the formation of dovetail joints the invert concrete shall be thoroughly cleaned by a pressure stream of water or scrubbed and every precaution shall be used to prevent earth or material from the forms falling on the surface after cleaning.

**Keeping Concrete Moist.**

*Section 49* Precaution shall be taken to prevent concrete from drying until there is no danger of cracking from lack of moisture Concrete shall be kept moist for at least one week, unless sooner covered with earth This may be done by covering of wet sand, burlap, continuous sprinkling or by some other method approved by the engineer

*Section 50* Forms for slabs or very flat arches as in box sections or roofs of special chambers, shall remain in place for at least seven days No load shall be placed on the concrete for fourteen days, and then only with permission

**Removal of Arch Forms.**

Arch forms shall not be slackened until the backfilling has been carried to a height of at least one foot above the top of the arch and tamped Arch forms shall remain in place for forty-eight hours when conditions are most favorable for the hardening of the concrete and for a longer time, as may be directed during inclement weather, or where unusual conditions exist Permission for dropping center must be secured for each arch unit †

---

* This construction is particularly applicable to sewers having comparatively flat inverts, and is more difficult to carry out with circular sewers.

† For small arches, 6 ft or less, and under the most favorable conditions, forms may be dropped in 24 hours

*Section 51.* Backfill, over and around arch sewers, shall be placed as soon as possible after the cement has set   The filling up to a plane 2 ft above the top of the arch shall be made from the best earth and shall not contain a sufficient amount of large stones as to allow the pieces of stone to become wedged   It should be filled in layers of not over 6 in  and care fully tamped   If the remaining of the backfill is dumped from buckets, the contents of the buckets should not be allowed to fall more than 5 ft unless the impact is broken by timber grillage   Bracing should generally be removed only when the trench below it has become completely filled and every precaution shall be taken to prevent any large slips of earth from the side of the trench onto or against the green arch.  All voids left by withdrawal of sheeting shall be immediately filled with sand, by ramming with tools especially adapted to that purpose, by watering or otherwise as may be directed.

*Section 52*   During the construction of the sewer, care should be taken that no loose mortar or concrete shall be allowed to remain on the interior surface of the invert.  At the completion of the work all débris shall be removed and the invert shall be left clean and smooth.

### Part III-A.—Manufacture of Reinforced-Concrete Pipe.

*Section 53.*   Reinforced-concrete sewer pipe shall be made circular or egg shape in cross-section and circular pipe made in sizes from 24 in  to 96 in  inside diameter.  Opposite diameters shall be true with a permissible variation of not more than three-quarters of one per cent.

*Section 54.*   Reinforced-concrete sewer pipe shall be in sections of not less than 3 ft in length and ends so formed that when laid together and cemented they shall make a continuous and uniform line of pipe.

*Section 55*   The provisions of Sections 1 to 11  inclusive, specifying materials for monolithic sewers, shall apply to materials for concrete pipe, and the provisions of Section 20, 21, 22 and 26 shall apply to its manufacture   All concrete shall be of Class "A "

*Section 56.*   All pipe shall be made in forms composed of sheet steel cores and casings, and cast-iron bottom and top rings which form the joint  The forms shall be rigidly held together and the core and casing so placed as to insure uniform wall thicknesses

The top rings, cores and casings shall not be removed from the pipe until the concrete has obtained its final set

Under average climatic conditions pipe shall not be lifted from the bottom rings until concrete is from 60 hours to 72 hours old   In very warm, dry climates the engineer may permit the removal of the pipe after 24 hours.

After the cores and casings have been removed from the pipe they shall be kept constantly and thoroughly wetted by sprinkling with water three times a day or oftener so that they shall be kept wet until they are removed from the bases and yarded.  After being placed on the yard the pipes shall be sprinkled thoroughly at least three times a day until they are six days old.

All pipes shall be marked with the date of their manufacture and no pipe that is not 14 days old will be permitted to be laid unless it has been steam cured

**Steam Curing.** Pipe may be cured by the use of wet steam in the following manner After the pipes have been cast they shall be covered with canvas or other material known as steaming jackets and wet steam be turned into these jackets for one day after casting   Then the casings and cores may be removed and the steam again applied in the same manner for one day After this has been done the pipes may be removed from the bases and varded  no other curing being necessary   Steam cured pipes may be laid when they are six days old

### TABLE I
#### (Knife edge bearing )

| Diameter in | Load lb per lin ft |
|---|---|
| 24 | 2149 |
| 27 | 2369 |
| 30 | 2583 |
| 33 | 2830 |
| 36 | 3080 |
| 39 | 3300 |
| 42 | 3521 |

### TABLE II
#### (Sand bearing )

| Diameter, in | Load, lb per lin ft |
|---|---|
| 24 | 3070 |
| 27 | 3370 |
| 30 | 3690 |
| 33 | 4040 |
| 36 | 4400 |
| 39 | 4710 |
| 42 | 5030 |

**Samples for Testing.** *Section 57.* Any or all of the following tests may be applied to samples selected by the engineer from the pipe delivered on the work   For the purposes of making such tests  the contractor shall furnish and deliver, when directed, and at the place required five lengths of each size pipe used in the work

**Crushing Tests.** *Section 58*   (*a*) When supported at the bottom upon a knife edge one inch in width  in such a manner that an even bearing is provided throughout the whole length, exclusive of the bell, and load is applied at the crown uniformly through a similar knife edge, the various sizes of pipe shall withstand, without signs of distress  the loads shown in Table I.

(*b*) Sand bearing loads shown in Table II are equivalent in value to the knife-edge loads in Table I

(*c*) When supported upon a sand saddle which extends the full length of the pipe, exclusive of the bell and whose upper surface fits accurately the outer curved surface of the pipe, and whose width is equal to an arc of fifteen degrees in such a manner that an even bearing is provided throughout the whole length, and the load is applied at the crown uniformly through a knife edge one inch in width, the various sizes of pipes with diameters greater than 42 in shall withstand the following loads·

TABLE III

| Diameter, in | Load lb per lin ft |
| --- | --- |
| 48 | 3800 |
| 54 | 4400 |
| 60 | 5000 |
| 66 | 5500 |
| 72 | 6000 |
| 78 | 6500 |
| 84 | 7000 |
| 90 | 7500 |
| 96 | 8000 |

*Section 59*   The specimens for absorption tests shall be sound pieces **Absorption Test** with all edges broken and may be from pipes broken in the crushing test One specimen shall be selected from each pipe broken in the crushing test, or may be taken from other pipes   They shall be from 12 to 20 sq in in area, and shall be as nearly square as they can be readily prepared   They shall be free from observable cracks, fissures, laminations or shattered edges

Preparatory to the absorption test, the specimen shall be first **Drying** weighed and then dried in a drier or oven at a temperature of not less than 110 degrees C (230 degrees F) for not less than three hours   After removal from the drier the specimen shall be allowed to cool in dry air to room temperature and then weighed

If the specimen is comparatively dry when taken, and the second weight closely agrees with the first, it shall be considered dry   If the specimen is wet when taken it shall be placed in the drier for a drying treatment of two hours and reweighed   If the third weight checks the second, the specimen shall be redried for two hour periods, until check weights are obtained

The balance used shall be sensitive to five-tenths (0 5) grams when **Weighing** loaded with 1 kg, and weighings shall be read to the nearest gram   When other than metric weights are used, the same degree of accuracy shall be obtained

The specimen, after final drying cooling and weighing, shall be placed **Immersion** with other similar specimens in a suitable wire receptacle, packed tightly enough to prevent jostling, covered with distilled water or rain water, raised to the boiling point and boiled for five hours, and then cooled in water to room temperature

Reweighing
The specimen shall be allowed to drain for one minute and, the superficial moisture having been removed by towel, or blotting paper, the specimen is then placed upon the balance

Calculation of Absorption
The test result shall be calculated as percentage of the initial dry weight.

Reporting Results.
The results shall be reported separately for each individual specimen, together with the mean for all the specimens from the same shipment of pipe

Identification
Each specimen shall be marked so that it may be identified with the pipe used in the crushing test from which the specimen was taken The marking shall be applied so that the pigment shall not cover more than one per cent of the total superficial area of the specimen

Allowable Absorption
The maximum allowable absorption shall be 12 per cent

## Part III-B — Laying the Pipe

*Section 60*   After the trench has been properly prepared the pipes shall be laid true to line and grade with the spigot end extending toward the outfall   Where pipe are laid in rock or hard ground they should be thoroughly bedded in sand gravel or concrete   The joints shall then be filled with a mortar consisting of one part of portland cement and two parts of sand of the quality previously specified   After the joints have been made the trench shall be carefully backfilled in thin layers and the material shall be thoroughly compacted under the haunches, around the sides and over the top of the pipes to 1 ft above the top before the other backfilling material is thrown or dumped into the trench.   This additional material must be thoroughly tamped or compacted to the top of the trench

If wet ground or wet sand is encountered a timber platform of sufficient width and strength shall be constructed   Then the pipe shall be placed on this platform and wedged accurately to line and grade, using 2 x 6-in wedges 18 in long, four to each pipe   After this has been done the trench shall then be backfilled in the manner before specified

### General Note

No attempt has been made to include herein detailed specifications, for much of the work entered into sewer construction, such as earth and rock excavation, sheeting and bracing, etc

Statements relating to the responsibility of furnishing materials, performing work and giving directions have also been generally omitted

No specification has been included in regard to the measurement of materials or the amount of work covered in any particular compensation, other than for reinforcing steel, as it has been considered best to leave these clauses to be worked under the conditions prevailing on the particular piece of work.

## RECOMMENDED RULES FOR CONCRETE SEWER DESIGN

### (To accompany the Specifications for Concrete Sewers)

1   Concrete sewers without reinforcement are approved for sizes **Plain Concrete Monolithic Sewers** between 30 and 60 in mean diameter   Plain concrete sewers between these sizes are to be used only in rock or hard soils   It is recommended that the minimum thickness for a diameter of 36 in or under should be 5 in and for a 5 ft diameter 7 in with intermediate sizes in proportion   These thicknesses are to be taken as a minimum for circular sewers and used only under favorable conditions.

2   (a) *Steel Reinforcement*—The reinforcement for circular pipe **Concrete Pipe Sewers** shall consist of one or two rings of steel wire fabric or rods of the areas shown in Table IV   Special methods of reinforcement will be permitted if the requirements of Article 7 as to crushing strength are fulfilled

(b) *Thickness*—The thickness of pipe walls shall be as set forth in the following table, but thinner walls may be used provided the amount of steel reinforcement is increased to give sufficient strength to withstand the crushing loads specified in Article 7 of these specifications

| Size, in | Minimum Thickness of Shell, in | Cross Sectional Area of Steel per lin ft of Shell |
|---|---|---|
| 24 | 3 | 1 concentric ring of 0 058 |
| 27 | 3 | " 0 068 |
| 30 | 3½ | " " 0 080 |
| 33 | 4 | " " 0 107 |
| 36 | 4 | " " 0 146 |
| 39 | 4 | " " 0 146 |
| 42 | 4½ | " " 0 153 |
| 48 | 5 | 2 " rings 0 107 |
| 54 | 5½ | " " " 0 126 |
| 60 | 6 | " " " 0 116 |
| 66 | 6½ | " " " 0 168 |
| 72 | 7 | " " " 0 180 |
| 84 | 8 | " " " 0 208 |
| 96 | 9 | " " " 0 215 |

3   All sewers near the surface and subject to moving loads or vibration, should be reinforced   For sewers of 6 ft or less in diameter it is **Reinforced Concrete Monolithic Sewers** recommended that the reinforcement be ½ of 1 per cent placed near the inside at the crown, and near the outside at the springing lines

If it appears at all possible that the horizontal pressures on the sewer might be large reinforce for reverse stresses

4   It is recommended that for all sewers greater than 6 ft in diameter, several possible types of loading be assumed and stresses be calculated on the elastic arch theory   (The methods are indicated in Turneaure & Maurer's "Principles of Reinforced Concrete" or in Metcalf & Eddy's "American Sewerage Practice" Volume I)

5   It is also suggested that in sewers of greater than 6 ft in diameter, it may be found economical to adopt a section having a comparatively flat bottom, and an arch with or without intermediate side walls

6   The minimum thickness of concrete in sections of this type should be 8 in   This is recommended as a factor of safety against poor placing and also to secure waterproof structures

7   The specifications submitted provide for three classes of concrete It is recommended that all arches be built of Class "A" concrete and that the inverts be of Class "A" concrete except in rock or very hard soils, where Class "B" concrete may be used

8   For reinforced work in bad ground, the designer should provide for a raft of Class "C" concrete of from 4 to 6 in in depth, which is to be allowed to set before the reinforced structure is started   This is advisable to facilitate good workmanship and particularly to prevent contamination of the concrete around the reinforcement by mud or sand

9   The distance from the face of reinforcing steel to the face of the concrete in monolithic sewers should be not less than 2 in

10   In determining dimensions of concrete and reinforcement, the following working stresses should be the maximum used·

(a) The maximum working stress in the steel where structural grade is used should be not more than 12,000 lb. and for intermediate or hard grades, or for cold twisted bars, 16,000 lb per sq in

The maximum working stress in rail steel should not exceed 16 000 lb per sq in

(b) The maximum working stresses in concrete are based on the Report of the Joint Committee on Concrete and Reinforced Concrete are about 25 per cent less than the stresses there recommended.

Working Stresses in Pounds per Square Inch

| Aggregate | Class A | Class B | Class C |
|---|---|---|---|
| Granite or trap rock | 550 | 450 | 350 |
| Gravel or hard limestone | 500 | 400 | 325 |
| Soft limestone or sandstone (if permitted) | 375 | 300 | 250 |

Class 'B' concrete is not recommended for use in the sewer proper Soft limestone and sandstone are prohibited if the accompanying specification is rigidly carried out.

These stresses should be further reduced where construction conditions are likely to be very unfavorable to good workmanship, as in very wet or deep trenches

11   In all important work, specify that the reinforcement shall be held in place with steel chairs or holders and wire ties

12   Attention is called to the fact that with sewers having comparatively flat inverts, careful consideration must be given to the distribution of load across the invert,   Where soils are likely to be compressible, the

weight should be taken as uniformly distributed  The stresses in such inverts should be carefully analyzed, as they are generally more severe than the other parts of the sewer

It will generally be advisable to provide alternate details of the invert for use in rock cuts  when resting on rock  or nearly incompressible soils and for soft or wet ground

13  Accompanying specifications for monolithic work provide for either a granolithic finish on the invert or for a lining of concrete block, brick or tile  The use of the separate lining should be considered as an additional factor of safety where unsatisfactory construction conditions are likely to affect adversely the quality of workmanship and the strength or density of the finished invert concrete

## REPORT OF THE COMMITTEE ON REINFORCED-CONCRETE AND BUILDING LAWS

[The report of this committee for the current year consisted in the presentation to the convention of the proposed "Standard Building Regulations For the Use of Reinforced Concrete" as printed in the *Proceedings* of the American Concrete Institute, Vol XV, 1919, p 386, and as revised on the floor of the convention  The revised "Standard Building Regulations for the Use of Reinforced Concrete" were adopted by the vote of the convention and sent to letter ballot, and by letter ballot vote of the Institute canvassed April 17, 1920, were adopted as a Standard of the American Concrete Institute  The revisions of the current year consisted mainly in the insertion of the report of the Special Committee on Unit Values for Vertical Shear in Reinforced-Concrete Design as Section 44 of the Regulations.

These "Standard Building Regulations" are printed on the next succeeding page —EDITOR ]

# AMERICAN CONCRETE INSTITUTE.
## STANDARD SPECIFICATIONS No. 23

### STANDARD BUILDING REGULATIONS FOR THE USE OF REINFORCED CONCRETE *

#### I. GENERAL

1. The term "Reinforced Concrete," as used in these regulations, shall mean an approved mixture of portland cement with water and aggregates in which metal (generally steel) has been embedded in proportionately small sections, in such a manner that the metal and the concrete assist each other in taking stress  — *Definition of Reinforced Concrete*

2. Reinforced concrete may be used for all classes of buildings if the design is in accordance with good engineering practice, and stresses are calculated as indicated in these regulations  — *Use*

3 There shall be no limit upon the height of buildings of reinforced concrete, except as limited by general height restrictions, for all types of buildings or by the strength requirements in these regulations  — *Height of Buildings*

4 Before permission is granted by the Building Department to erect any reinforced-concrete building, complete general plans accompanied by specifications signed by the engineer or architect must be filed with the Building Department  This shall include a statement giving the dead- and live-loads, wind and impact, if any, and working stresses  Sufficient details shall be included in the plans submitted to make clear the exact dimensions and construction of the reinforced-concrete portions of the building and the arrangement of the reinforcement so as to permit computation of all stresses. specifications shall state the qualities and proportions of the materials to be used  — *Permits*

Copies of approved plans and specifications must be left on file with the Building Department for public inspection until the building is completed

5 Materials used for the concrete as well as for the reinforcement shall be carefully inspected and tested  The construction of the building shall be inspected in detail by a representative of the architect or engineer who will keep a complete record of the progress of the work, including dates of placing concrete and dates of removing forms  He shall also check the quantity of the materials used, and the placing of same in the different parts of the building  He shall insure that the work completed from day to day is kept moist for a period of not less than 5 days  These records shall be available for inspection by the Building Department  — *Inspection*

---

* Passed by letter-ballot of the Institute, April 17, 1920

**Load Tests**

6   The Building Department may require the owner to make load tests on portions of the finished structure   Under such tests when made, covering at least one full panel, with a load of twice the specified live load, the permanent deflection 7 days after the load is removed should be not more than 20 per cent of the total deflection under the test load, which total deflection should not be more than $\frac{1}{800}$ of the spans for beams, girders and slabs supported by beams   Load tests shall not be made before the concrete has been in place 60 days   In the event that the deflection is in excess of the specified amount the building may be tested again at a later time to determine when the concrete has developed adequate strength to permit specified loading, otherwise the allowable floor loads shall be reduced

**Posting of Floor.**

7   The Building Department shall issue signed certificates to be posted on each floor of the building stating the allowable carrying capacity per square foot

## II   MATERIALS

**Specifications Cement**

8   Only portland cement shall be used in reinforced-concrete structures   Cement shall meet the requirements of the Standard Specifications for Cement of the American Society for Testing Materials as in effect at the time of the adoption of this regulation   (Standard 1, Am  Conc  Inst )

**Tests of Cement**

9   All cement used shall be tested and record of such tests shall be kept at the building site for inspection by the Building Department   No cement which has not met the requirements of the above specifications shall be used without the written approval of the Building Department.

**Aggregates— General.**

10   All aggregates shall be of clean material, free from dust, soft particles, lumps of clay, vegetable loam, and all organic matter

**Fine Aggregates**

11   Fine aggregate shall consist of sand, or the screenings of gravel or crushed stone, graded from fine to coarse, and passing, when dry, a screen having $\frac{1}{4}$-in  diameter holes, it preferably shall be of siliceous material, and not more than 30 per cent by weight shall pass a sieve having 50 meshes per linear inch   It shall have a satisfactory freedom from organic material as indicated in the colorimetric test described in the reports of Committee C-9, American Society for Testing Materials   (Proc  A S T M , Vol  XIX, 1919, Part 1, p  321 )

**Test of Fine Aggregates**

12   The suitable character of the cement, water, fine aggregate and coarse aggregate, mixed in the proportions to be used in the work and for the same length of mixing time, shall be established to the satisfaction of the Building Department by tests of 6 x 12 in  or 8 x 16 in  cylinders   Seven-day tests shall show at least 50 per cent and 28 day tests at least 100 per cent of the ultimate strength upon which the working stresses are based in accordance with Sections 40 and 41   Work may proceed upon the satisfactory completion of the 7-day tests   If the 28-day tests prove unsatisfactory, the water-cement ratio shall be sufficiently decreased or other materials substituted to provide the required ultimate strength   Additional cylinder tests may be required from time to time as the work progresses to further demonstrate the satisfactory strength of the concrete   Subsequent to the comple-

tion or preparation of such tests the materials used on the work shall not be changed without the consent of the Building Department

13  Coarse aggregates shall consist of crushed stone, gravel, or slag, which is retained on a screen having ¼ in  diameter holes and graded in size from small to large particles   The maximum size of the coarse aggregate shall be such that the concrete will flow freely around the reinforcement Bank gravel shall be separated from the sand before mixing   Slag shall be clean, dense, air-cooled, blast-furnace slag, weighing not less than 70 lb per cu ft when loosely placed in the measure and containing not more than 1 3 per cent of sulphur as sulphides   *Coarse Aggregates*

14  Cinders shall not be used as coarse aggregate in concrete for rein- forced-concrete structures without tests acceptable to the Building Department showing the strength of such concrete   Cinder concrete may be used for fireproofing, for floor and roof slabs, not exceeding 8-ft span and for partitions   Where cinders are used as the coarse aggregate they shall be composed of hard, clean, vitreous clinker, free from sulphides, unburned coal or ashes   *Cinders*

15  The water used in mixing concrete shall be free from oil, acid, alkalies or organic matter

16  Steel for reinforcement of concrete shall conform to the requirements of the specifications of the American Society for Testing Materials for Con- crete Reinforcement Bars, as in effect at the time of the adoption of this regulation

Cold-drawn steel wire made from billets may be used in floor and roof slabs, column hooping, and for temperature and shrinkage stresses   This steel shall have an elastic limit between fifty thousand (50,000) and sixty-five thousand (65,000) lb per sq in  and an ultimate strength of not less than eighty-five thousand (85 000) lb per sq in

All reinforcing steel shall be free from flaking, rust, scale, or coatings of any character which will tend to reduce or destroy the bond

## III. Details of Construction

17  Forms must be substantial and unyielding and sufficiently tight to prevent the leakage of mortar   Before placing concrete all forms shall be first thoroughly cleaned of all débris and preferably oiled to prevent adhesion of the concrete   *Forms*

18  All bars must be carefully bent as required by plans   *Preparation of Reinforcement*

19  Reinforcement shall be accurately located in the forms and secured against displacement   *Placing of Reinforcement*

20  Where it is necessary to splice reinforcing steel, this shall be done by providing a lap sufficient to transfer the stress between bars by bond and shear, or by a mechanical connection such as screw coupling   Splices at point of maximum stress should be avoided   *Steel Splices*

21. Vertical fill lines between two fills of concrete must be selected so that the resulting joint will have the least possible effect upon the strength of the structure   Before making the second fill, the concrete previously   *Construction Joints*

placed shall be thoroughly cleansed of foreign material and laitance, drenched and slushed with a mortar consisting of one (1) part portland cement and not more than two (2) parts fine aggregate

Construction joints for columns should be made at underside of floor construction, haunches and column capitals being considered as part of the floor construction, and should be poured monolithically. Where reinforced-concrete columns have flaring heads or where structural steel columns are used, concrete for slab and column heads may be poured immediately after the concrete for the column shaft

In general, fill lines in floors should be selected near the center of spans of slabs, beams and girders  Unless a beam intersects a girder at this point, in which case the joint shall offset a distance equal to twice the width of the beam  Where shear is present at the joint, adequate provision shall be made for resisting same by inclining joint or providing sufficient reinforcement

**Measuring Ingredients**

22  Methods of measuring of the various ingredients of concrete, including the water, shall be used which will secure separate and uniform measurements, of the proportions required  Measurements shall be made by volume; 94 lb of cement to be considered as a cubic foot.

**Mixing—General**

23  The ingredients of concrete shall be thoroughly mixed to the desired consistency and the mixing shall continue until the cement is uniformly distributed and the mass is uniform in color and homogeneous

**Machine Mixing**

24  In mixing by machine a mixer of a type which insures the uniform distribution of the materials throughout the mass, and in which the required portions of the water-cement and aggregates can be accurately measured, shall be used

**Hand Mixing.**

25. When it is necessary to mix by hand, the mixing shall be done on a watertight platform, and all ingredients shall be turned together at least six times and until the resulting mass is homogeneous in appearance and color

**Consistency.**

26  The materials must be mixed wet enough to produce a concrete of such a consistency that it will flow sluggishly into the forms and about the metal reinforcement, and at the same time can be conveyed from the mixer to the forms without separation of the coarse aggregate from the mortar

**Re-tempering**

27. Mortar or concrete shall not be re-mixed with water and used after it has partly set

**Placing of Concrete**

28  Concrete after the completion of the mixing shall be transported as rapidly as practicable from the place of mixing to the place of final deposit  The concrete shall be deposited in such a manner that it will flow sluggishly around the steel reinforcement and shall be rammed or agitated by suitable tools in such a manner as to produce thoroughly compact concrete

Where concrete is conveyed by spouting, the plant shall be of such a size and design as to ensure a practically continuous stream in the spout. The angle of the spout with the horizontal shall be such as to allow the concrete to flow without a separation of the ingredients, in general an angle of about 27 degrees, or one vertical to two horizontal will be required

**Placing in Water**

29  Concrete shall not be placed in water unless unavoidable, if necessary to do this a tremie or other method demonstrated to be especially effective shall be used to prevent the cement from being separated from the aggregate

30  The concrete at the end of each fill shall be cleaned of laitance or other deleterious material which would detract from the quality of the concrete.  After forms are removed, any porous sections of concrete shall be cleaned out and filled in a manner to meet the approval of the Building Department. *Finishing*

31.  Newly placed concrete shall be protected from rapid drying and kept damp for a period of at least 5 days. *Protection in Warm Weather*

32  Concrete shall not be mixed or deposited during freezing temperatures unless it is maintained at a temperature not less than 50 degrees F during mixing, placing, and for at least 72 hours thereafter, and until the concrete is thoroughly hardened *Protection in Cold Weather*

33  Under no consideration shall forms be removed until the concrete has hardened sufficiently to permit their removal with safety *Removal of Forms*

Where there is danger of frozen concrete being mistaken for properly hardened concrete, heat shall be applied before tests for hardness are made

34  Before a section of form is removed, shoring shall be provided as necessary to carry the weight of the new concrete and other loads brought upon the construction in acting as a support for upper floors  Careful consideration must be given to the loads carried and the strength of the new concrete before any shoring is removed *Temporary Supports*

## IV.  Design

35  All reinforced-concrete construction shall be designed to meet the conditions of loading (including bending in columns) without stressing the materials used beyond the safe working stresses specified *Conditions*

36  The dead-loads shall be the weight of the permanent structure.  The weight of reinforced stone, gravel or slag concrete shall be taken as 144 lb. per cu ft , the weight of cinder concrete as 100 lb per cu ft *Dead-Loads*

37  The live-load shall be the working or variable load for which the structure is designed *Live-Loads*

38  All parts of a structure shall be designed to carry safely the entire combined dead- and live-loads with the exception that the loads on columns and foundations may be reduced by considering that columns in top story carry the total live- and dead-load above them, columns in next to top story carry the total dead-load and eighty-five (85) per cent of the total live-load above, columns in the next lower story, the total dead-load and eighty (80 per cent of the total live-load above,  and thus on downward, reducing it each story the percentage of total live-loads carried, by 5, until a reduction of fifty (50) per cent is reached   The columns in this and in every story below this point, shall be proportioned to carry the total dead-load and at least fifty (50) per cent of the total live-load of all the floors and roofs above them *Reduction of Loads*

For warehouses the increment of reduction per story shall be $2\frac{1}{2}$ per cent instead of 5 per cent.

**General Assumptions**

39  As a basis for calculations for the strength of reinforced-concrete construction the following assumptions shall be made

(a) Calculations shall be made with reference to working stresses and safe loads rather than with reference to ultimate strength and ultimate loads

(b) A plane section before bending remains plane after bending

(c) The modulus elasticity of concrete in compression within the usual limits of working stresses is constant.

(d) In calculating the moment of resistance of beams, the tensile stresses in the concrete are neglected

(e) Perfect adhesion is assumed between concrete and reinforcement  Under compressive stresses the two materials will, therefore, be stressed in proportion to their moduli of elasticity

(f) The ratio of the modulus of elasticity of concrete shall be taken as follows

1  One-fortieth that of steel when the strength of the concrete is taken as not more than eight hundred (800) lb per sq in

2  One-fifteenth that of steel when the strength of the concrete is taken as greater than twelve hundred (1200) lb per sq in or less than twenty-two hundred (2200) lb per sq in

3  One-twelfth that of steel when strength of the concrete is take as greater than twenty-two hundred (2200) lb per sq in or less than thirty-three hundred (3300) lb per sq in

4  One-tenth that of steel when the strength of the concrete is taken as greater than thirty-three hundred (3300) lb per sq in

**Strength of Materials**

40  The ultimate strength of concrete shall be that developed at an age of 28 days in cylinders 8 in in diameter and 16 in in length or 6 in in diameter and 12 in in length of the consistency and proportions to be used in the work, made and stored laboratory conditions, but in no case shall the values exceed those allowed in the table below  In the absence of definite knowledge in advance of construction as to just what strength may be developed, the following values may be used

TABLE OF STRENGTHS OF DIFFERENT MIXTURES

| | Proportion of Cement to Aggregate. | | | | |
|---|---|---|---|---|---|
| Aggregate | 1·3* | 1·4½* | 1·6* | 1·7½* | 1·9* |
| For stone, gravel or slag with water-cement ratio† of | 0 8 | 0 9 | 1 0 | 1 11 | 1 22 |
| Strength of concrete | 3000 | 2500 | 2000 | 1600 | 1300 |
| Cinders | 800 | 700 | 600 | 500 | 400 |

**Safe Working Stresses**

41  Reinforced-concrete structures shall be so designed that the stresses, figured in accordance with these regulations, in pounds per square inch, shall not exceed the following

*Total volume of fine and coarse aggregate, measured separately
† Water-Cement Ratio = Ratio of water to cement by volume

(*a*) Extreme fiber stress in concrete in compression 37½ per cent of the compressive strength specified in Section 40  Adjacent to the support of continuous members, 41 per cent provided the member frames into a mass of concrete projecting at least 50 per cent of the least dimension of the member on all sides of the compression area of the member

(*b*) Concrete in direct compression 25 per cent of the compressive strength specified in Section 40

(*c*) Shearing stress in concrete when main steel is not bent and when steel is not provided to resist diagonal tension, as specified in Section 44

(*d*) Where punching shear occurs, provided the diagonal tension requirements are met, a shearing stress as specified in Section 44 will be allowed

(*e*) Vertical shearing stresses, as specified in Section 44

(*f*) Bond stress between concrete and plain reinforcing bars—4 per cent of the compressive strength

(*g*) Bond stress between concrete and approved deformed bars—5 per cent of the compressive strength

(*h*) Compression applied to a surface of concrete of at least twice the loaded area, a stress of 50 per cent of the compressive strength shall be allowed over the area actually under load

(*i*) Tensile stress in steel—16,000 lb per sq in , except that for steel having an elastic limit of at least 50,000 lb , a working stress of 18,000 lb per sq in. will be allowed

42  In determining the bending moment in slabs, beams and girders, the load carried by the member shall include both the dead- and the live-loads **Girder, Beam, and Slab Construction**

The span of the member shall be the distance center to center of supports, but not to exceed the clear span plus the depth of the member, except that for continuous or fixed members framing into other reinforced-concrete members the clear span may be used

For continuous members supported upon brackets making an angle of not more than 45 degrees with the vertical, and having a width not less than the width of the member supported, the span shall be the clear distance between brackets plus one-half the total depth of the member

If the brackets make a greater angle than 45 degrees with the vertical, only that portion of the bracket within the 45 degrees slope shall be considered  Maximum negative moments are to be considered as existing at the end of the span as here defined

For members uniformly loaded the bending moment shall be assumed as $\dfrac{WL}{F}$ , where $W$ = total load, $L$ = span, and $F$ = 8 for members simply supported, 10 for both negative and positive bending moment for members restrained at one end and simply supported or partially restrained at the other, and 12 for both negative and positive bending moment for members fixed or continuous at both supports  The above bending moments for continuous members apply only when adjacent spans are approximately equal.

A special condition of loading to be reduced to equivalent uniformly distributed loading in accordance with approved engineering practice   For members having one end simply supported or partially restrained, at least fifty (50) per cent of the tension reinforcement required at center of span shall be bent up and adequately anchored to take bending moment at exterior support

At the ends of continuous beams, the amount of negative moment which will be developed in the beam will depend on the condition of restraint or fixedness, and this will depend on the form of construction used   In the ordinary cases a moment of $\frac{w^2}{16}$ may be taken, for small beams running into heavy columns this should be increased but not to exceed $\frac{w^2}{12}$

43   The main tensile reinforcement shall not be farther apart than two times the thickness of the slab   For slabs designed to span one way, steel having an area of at least two-tenths of one per cent (0 2%) of section of slab shall be provided transverse to main reinforcement, and this transverse reinforcement shall be further increased in the top of the slab over girders to prevent cracking, and the main steel in slabs parallel and adjacent to girders may be reduced accordingly   Where openings are left through slabs, extra reinforcement shall be provided to prevent local cracks developing   This reinforcement shall in no case be less than ¼ sq in  in section and must be securely anchored at ends   Floor finish when placed monolithic may be considered part of the structural section

Where adequate bond and shearing resistance between slab and web of beam is provided, the slab may be considered as an integral part of the beam, but its effective width shall not exceed on either side of the beam one-sixth of the span length of the beam nor be greater than six times the thickness of the slab on either side of the beam, nor greater than one-half of the distance between beams on either side, the measurements being taken from edge of web



44   (a) The notation used in this section is as follows:

$V$  = Total vertical shear at any section  
$V'$ = Vertical shear carried by the web reinforcement  
$v$  = $V/bjd$ = Unit vertical shearing stress  
$d$  = Depth from compressive face to e g  of tensile steel in inches  
$b$  = Breadth of beam  
$b^1$ = Breadth of stem of T-beam or web of I-beam  
$A_s$ = Area of longitudinal steel  
$A_v$ = Area of shear steel in section of beam considered  
$j$  = Ratio of lever arm of resistance couple to depth d  
$p$  = $A_s/bd$ = Longitudinal steel ratio.  
$r$  = $A_v/ba$ = Shear steel ratio  
$a$  = Spacing of shear steel measured perpendicular to its direction.  
$f'_c$ = Ultimate strength of concrete cylinders at 28 days (or at time of test in considering test data)  
$f_v$ = Tensile stress in web reinforcement

Except where $v$ is noted as the unit punching shearing stress, it is used as a shearing stress index governing the value of the diagonal tension in the web as is the present common practice

(b) All allowances for design unit shearing stresses in the following sections are predicated on proper design of the longitudinal reinforcement to effectively resist all positive and negative moments, as prescribed in other sections of these standards  Wherever web reinforcement is used it must be adequately anchored at both ends

(c) *Members with Web Reinforcement* —When adequate mechanical anchorage of both web and longitudinal rods is provided, the concrete may be figured to carry a unit vertical shearing stress equal to $0.025f'_c$ and the remainder of the shear shall be carried by web bars designed according to the formula

$$A_v = \frac{V'a}{f_v jd}$$

Properly anchored bent-up longitudinal bars may be considered as web reinforcement

The maximum unit shearing stress shall not exceed $0.12f'_c$ in any case.

(d) When adequate mechanical anchorage of the longitudinal rods as defined in the next paragraph is not provided, the maximum unit shearing stress shall not exceed $0.06f'_c$, of which $0.02f'_c$ may be considered to be taken by the concrete and the remainder of the shear taken by the web bars designed as above  Web rods must be adequately anchored in all cases

(e) Adequate mechanical anchorage of the bottom longitudinal steel for positive moments shall consist of carrying the reinforcement a sufficient distance beyond the point of inflection to develop the assumed tension in the reinforcement at the point of inflection by bond between the end of the bar and the point of inflection of the member (never to a less distance than one inch from the center of the support or in case of wide supports to not less than 12 in of embedment in the support), or of bending the end of the bars over the support to a half circle of diameter not less than 8 times the diameter of the bar, or by any device that will transmit the tension on the bar to the concrete over the support at a compressive stress of not over $0.50f'_c$  The tension in the bar, at the point of inflection to be resisted by the anchorage, shall be taken for this computation as not less than one-third of the maximum safe tension in the bar  Reinforcement for negative moment shall be thoroughly anchored at the support and extend into the span a sufficient distance to adequately provide for negative tension by bond  Simply supported beams shall have the longitudinal steel anchored by hooks of diameter specified above or by an equivalent anchorage, the tensile stress at the edge of the support being taken as one-third of the maximum safe tension in the bar  (Figs 1, 2 and 3)

(f) Anchorage of the web steel shall consist of continuity of the web member with the longitudinal member, or of carrying the web member

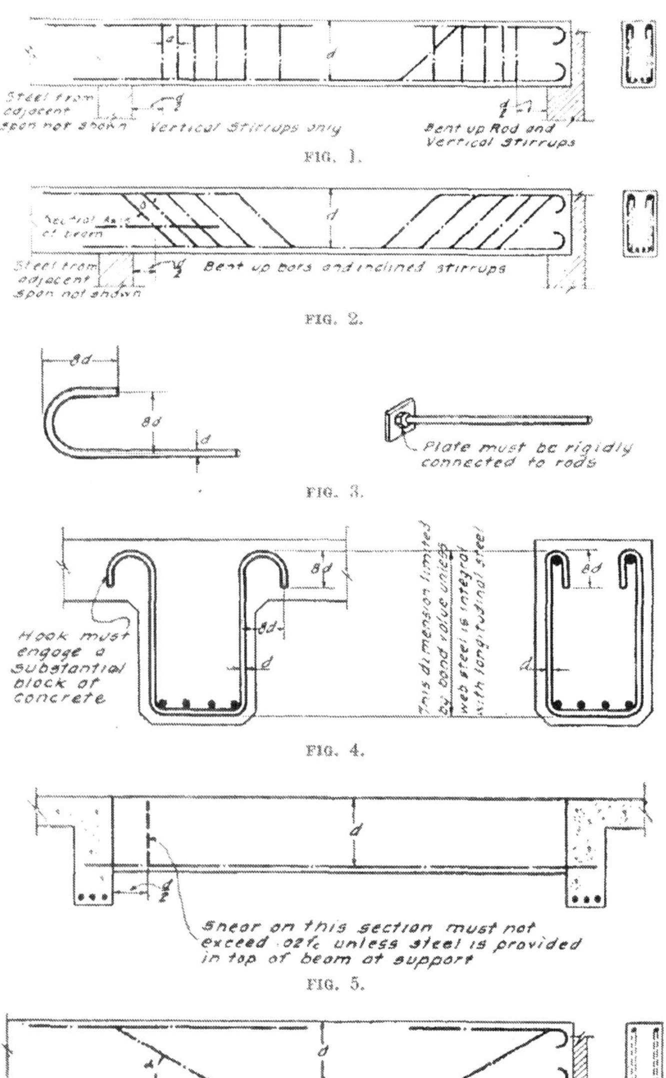
Steel from
adjacent
span not shown
Vertical Stirrups only
Bent up Rod and
Vertical Stirrups
FIG. 1.
Neutral Axis
of beam
Steel from
adjacent
span not shown
Bent up bars and inclined stirrups
FIG. 2.
8d
8d
d
Plate must be rigidly
connected to rods
FIG. 3.
8d
Hook must
engage a
substantial
block of
concrete
8d
d
This dimension limited
by bond value unless
web steel is integral
with longitudinal steel
8d
d
FIG. 4.
d
Shear on this section must not
exceed .02 f_c unless steel is provided
in top of beam at support
FIG. 5.
d
d
FIG. 6.

about at least two sides of a longitudinal bar at both ends, or of carrying the web member about at least two sides of a longitudinal member at one end and making a half circular hook at the other end of a diameter not less than eight times the diameter of the web rod. In all cases, the bent ends of web bars shall extend at least eight diameters below or above the point of extreme height or depth of the bar. In case the end anchorage is not in bearing on other reinforcing steel, the anchorage shall be such as to engage an adequate amount of concrete to prevent the bar from pulling off a portion of the concrete. In all cases the stirrups shall be carried as close to the upper and lower surfaces as fireproofing requirements will permit. The size of web reinforcing bars which are not either a part of the longitudinal steel or welded thereto shall be such that not less than two-fifths of the maximum design tensile stress in the bar may be developed at design bond stresses in a length of rod equal to $0.4d$. This condition is satisfied for plain round stirrups when the diameter of the bar does not exceed $d/50$. The balance of the tensile stress in the bar may be considered as taken by adequate end anchorage as specified above. (Fig 4.)

(g) Beams in which no longitudinal reinforcement is provided in the upper portion of the beam adjacent to the support and in which the ends of the beam are built monolithic with other parts of the concrete structure, shall not carry a unit shearing stress in excess of $0.02f'_c$, regardless of amount of web reinforcement provided. (Fig 5.)

(h) When the shear reinforcement consists of bars bent up at an angle so as to reinforce all sections of the beam in which the unit shearing stress exceeds $0.02f'_c$ the design may be made as follows

$$A_0 f_v = V' \sec a$$

Where $A_0$ = Area of bent up shear bars

$f_v$ = Stress in bent up shear bars

$V'$ = Total shear at end of span as prescribed for moment less the shearing resistance of the concrete at a unit stress of $0.02f'_c$ over the area $b'jd$

$a$ = Angle between bent up rod and the vertical (Fig 6.)

The maximum unit shearing stress shall not exceed $0.06f'_c$ with this arrangement of web steel and the longitudinal steel shall be adequately anchored as defined above in all cases.

(i) In case the web reinforcement consists solely of inclined shear bars the first bent bar shall bend downward from the plane of the upper reinforcement directly over or within the edge of the support.

(j) Where additional web reinforcement is provided the same may be figured in accordance with Section 14 (e). The total shearing resistance of the beam shall be taken as the sum of the resistances under Section 44 (e) and 14 (h).

(k) *Beams without Web Reinforcement.*—When the longitudinal steel is not fully anchored, as prescribed above, the unit shearing stress shall not exceed $0.02f'_c$. When the longitudinal steel is fully anchored, as prescribed above, the unit shearing stress shall not exceed $0.03f'_c$.

(*l*) *Critical Section for Shear in Beams.*——The critical section for shear as governing diagonal tension shall be taken at a distance not greater than one-half the effective depth of the beam ($\frac{1}{2}d$), from the end of the span as prescribed for moment.

The effective depth of the critical section for shear as governing diagonal tension shall be taken as the depth $jd$ of the beam in the plane of the critical section.

The breadth of the critical section shall be the full breadth of rectangular beams or the breadth of the stem of T-beams or the thickness of the web in beams of I section.

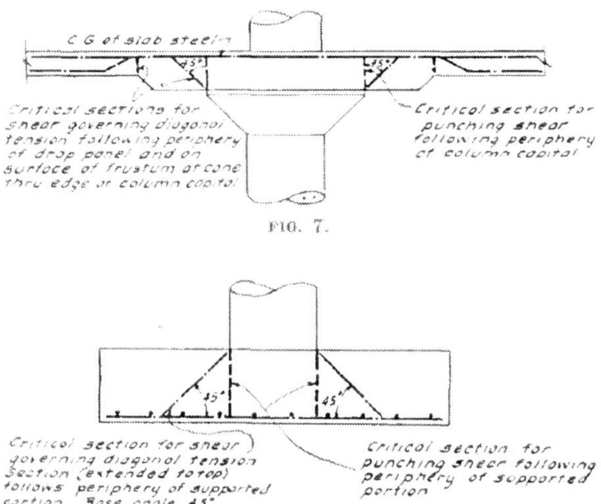


FIG. 7.



FIG. 8.

(*m*) *Tile and Concrete Joist Construction.*——The shearing stresses in tile and concrete joist construction shall not exceed those in beams or slabs of similar reinforcement.   The breadth of the effective section for shear, as governing diagonal tension, may be taken as the thickness of the concrete joist plus one-half the thickness of the vertical webs of the tile, provided that the joints in one row come opposite the centers of tile in adjoining rows on either side.

Where the tile joints are not staggered, only the concrete joists may be considered effective in resisting shear.

(*n*) *Flat-Slab Construction.*——In flat-slab construction where a drop panel is used adjoining the column, the shearing stress, as governing diagonal tension, figures on the $jd$ depth on a vertical section along the periphery of the drop, shall not exceed $0.03f'_c$.   (See Fig. 7.)

(*o*) In flat-slab construction, with or without drop panels, the shearing stress, as governing diagonal tension, figured between the compression face of the slab or drop and the level of the center of gravity of the reinforcing steel, on the surface of the frustum of a cone or pyramid passing through the periphery of the column capital and having a base angle of 45 degrees, shall not exceed $0.035f'_c$

(*p*) *Footings* —In footings carrying a single column or load, the shearing stress, as governing diagonal tension, figured between the level of the centroid of the compressive stresses and the level of the center of gravity of the reinforcing steel on the surface of the frustum of a cone or pyramid passing through the base of the supported column or loaded member and having a base angle of 45 degrees the unit stresses shall not exceed those in beams without web reinforcement. Especial attention shall be given to bond in footings. The total vertical shear on this section shall be taken as the upward pressure on the area of the footing outside the base of this section.

(*q*) If adequate anchorage is provided for the tensile steel and adequately anchored web reinforcement is also provided such web reinforcement may be figured in accordance with the formula given in Section 11 (*c*) above. Such calculations may be made for vertical sections concentric with the supported column.

(*r*) For footings supporting two or more columns, the shearing stresses shall be figured as for beams or slabs.

(*s*) *Arrangement of Web Reinforcement* —The spacing of web reinforcement as measured perpendicular to their direction shall not exceed $3d/4$ in any case where web reinforcement is necessary. Where vertical stirrups or web members inclined less than 30 degrees to the vertical are used, the spacing shall not exceed $d/2$. When the unit shearing stress exceeds $0.06f'_c$ the spacing of the web reinforcement shall not exceed $d/2$ in any case, nor $d/3$ for vertical stirrups or web steel inclined less than 30 degrees with the vertical.

The first vertical stirrup shall be placed not farther than $d/2$ from the face of the support in any case. The first inclined stirrup or bent-up rod shall reach the level of the upper longitudinal steel at a distance not greater than $d/2$ from the edge of the support if the bottom longitudinal steel is adequately anchored and at the edge of the web support if the longitudinal steel is not anchored. Web members may be placed at any angle between 0 and 60 degrees with the vertical, provided that, if inclined they shall be inclined in the proper direction to take tension, rather than compression, in the web.

(*t*) *Punching Shear* —Punching shear shall be figured on a vertical section through the periphery of the smaller member. The unit shearing stress in punching shear, figured on the full depth $d$ to the center of gravity of the reinforcement, shall not exceed $0.1f'_c$

(*u*) When the depth of the supported or supporting member is less than one-fifteenth of the span in the case of beams or slabs, or less than one-third of the overhang in the case of cantilevers (including footings) the unit shearing stress in punching shear shall not exceed $0.06f'_c$

Tile and
Joist Floors.

45. Wherever floors are built with a combination of tile or other fillers between reinforced-concrete joists, the following rules regarding the dimensions and methods of calculations of construction shall be observed:

(a) Wherever a portion of the slab above the fillers is considered as acting as a T-beam section, the slab portion must be cast monolithic with the joist and have a minimum thickness of two (2) in.

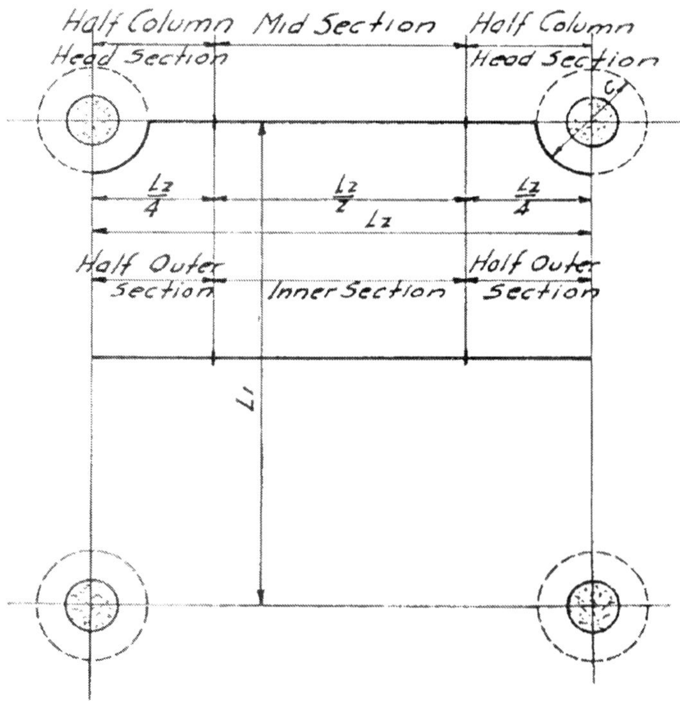



FIG. 9.

(b) Wherever porous fillers are used which will absorb water from the concrete, care must be taken thoroughly to saturate same before concrete is placed.

(c) All regulations given above for beam and girder floors shall apply to tile and joist floors.

(d) The sections of fillers shall be together and all joints reasonably tight before concrete is placed.

46. Continuous flat-slab floors, reinforced with steel rods or mesh and supported on spaced columns in orderly arrangement, shall conform to the following requirements: **Flat-Gird**

(a) *Notation and Nomenclature.*—In the formula let

$w$ = total dead-and-live-load in pounds per square foot of floors

$l_1$ = span in feet center to center of columns parallel to sections on which moments are considered.

$l_2$ = span in feet center to center of columns perpendicular to sections on which moments are considered.

$c$ = average diameter of column capital in feet at plane where its thickness is $1\frac{1}{2}$ in.

$q$ = distance from center line of the capital to the center of gravity of the periphery of the half capital divided by $\frac{1}{2}c$. For round capitals $q$ may be considered as two-thirds and for square capitals as three-quarters.

$t$ = total slab thickness in inches.

$L$ = average span in feet center to center of columns, but not less than 0.9 of the greater span.

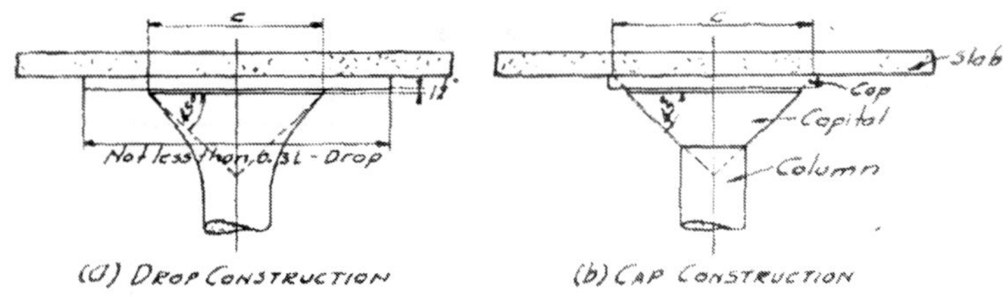


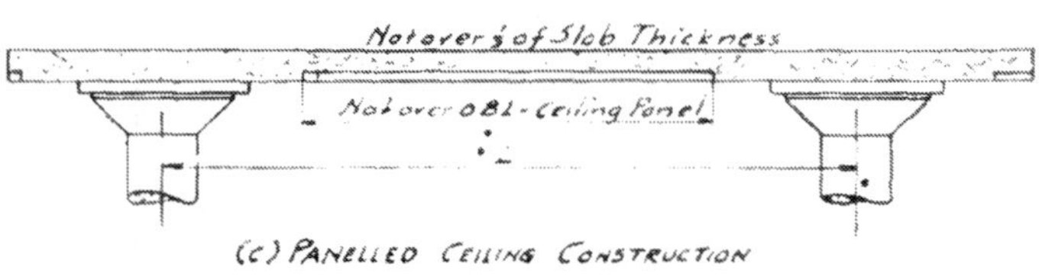


FIG. 10.

The column head section, mid section, outer section, and inner section are located and dimensioned as shown in Fig. 9. Corresponding moments shall be figured on similar sections at right angles to those shown in Fig. 9.

(b) *Structural Variations.*—Flat-slab floors may be built with or without caps, drops or paneled ceilings. These terms are illustrated in Fig. 10.

Where caps are employed they shall be considered a part of the columns and the column capital dimension $c$ shall be found by extending the lines of the capital to an intersection with the plane of the under surface of the slab as indicated in Fig 10*b*. The cap shall be large enough to enclose this extension of the capital lines.

The column capital profile shall not fall at any point inside an inverted cone drawn as shown in Fig 10*a*, from the periphery of the designed capital of diameter $c$ and with a base angle of 45 degrees. The diameter of the designed capital $c$ shall be taken where the vertical thickness of the column capital is at least $1\frac{1}{2}$ in.

The drop, where used, shall not be less than $0.3\,L$ in width.

Where paneled ceilings are used the paneling shall not exceed one-half of the slab thickness in depth and the dimension of the paneling shall not exceed 0.8 of the panel dimension. (See Fig 10*c*.)

(c) *Slab Thickness.*—The slab thickness shall not be less than

$$t = 0.02L\sqrt{w} + 1 \text{ in}$$

In no case shall the slab thickness be less than $\frac{1}{32}L$ for floor slabs nor less than $\frac{1}{40}L$ for roof slabs.

(d) *Design Moments.*—The numerical sum of the positive and negative moments in foot pounds shall not be less than $0.09\,wl_1\,(l_2 - qc)^2$. Of this total amount not less than 40 per cent shall be resisted in the column head sections. Where a drop is used, not less than 50 per cent shall be resisted in the column head sections.

Of the total amount not less than 40 per cent shall be resisted in the mid section.

Of the total amount not less than 18 per cent shall be resisted in the outer section.

Of the total amount not less than 12 per cent shall be resisted on the inner sections.

The balance of the moment shall be distributed between the various sections as required by the physical details and dimensions of the particular design employed.

(e) *Exterior Panels.*—The negative moments at the first interior row of columns and the positive moments at the center of the exterior panel on sections parallel to the wall, shall be increased 20 per cent over those specified above for interior panels. If girders are not provided along the column line, the reinforcement parallel to the wall for negative moment in the column head section and for positive moment in the outer section adjacent to the wall, shall be altered in accordance with the change in the value of $c$. The negative moment on sections at the wall and parallel thereto should be determined by the conditions of restraint, but must never be taken less than 80 per cent of those for the interior panels.

(f) *Reinforcement.*—In the calculation of moments all the reinforcing bars which cross the section under consideration and which fulfil the requirements given under "Arrangement of Reinforcement" may be used. For a column head section reinforcing bars parallel to the straight portion of the section do not contribute to the negative resisting moment for the column head section in question. The sectional area of bars, crossing the section at an angle, multiplied by the sine of the angle between these bars and the straight portion of the section under consideration may be taken to act as reinforcement in a rectangular direction. Calculations for shearing stress shall be made in accordance with Section 44.

(g) *Point of Inflection.*—For the purpose of making calculations of moment at sections away from the sections of negative moment and positive moment already specified, the point of inflection shall be taken at a distance from center line of columns equal to $\frac{1}{5}$ $(l_2 - qc) + \frac{1}{2}qc$. This becomes $\frac{1}{5}$ $(l_2 + c)$ where capital is circular. For slabs having drop panels the coefficient of $\frac{1}{4}$ should be used instead of $\frac{1}{5}$.

(h) *Arrangement of Reinforcement.*—The design should include adequate provision for securing the reinforcement in place so as to take not only the maximum moments but the moments of intermediate sections. If bars are extended beyond the column capital and are used to take the bending moment on the opposite side of the column, they must extend to the point of inflection. Bars in diagonal bands used as reinforcement for negative moment should extend on each side of the line drawn through the column center at right angles to the direction of the band a distance equal to 0.35 of the panel length, and bars in the diagonal bands used as reinforcement for positive moment, should extend on each side of the diagonal through the center of the panel a distance equal to 0.35 of the panel length. Bars spliced by lapping and counted as only one bar in tension shall be lapped not less than 80 diameters if splice is made at point of maximum stress and not more than 50 per cent of the rods shall be so spliced at any point in any single band or in any single region of tensile stress. Continuous bars shall not all be bent up at the same point of their length but the zone in which this bending occurs should extend on each side of the assumed point of inflection.

(i) *Tensile and Compressive Stresses.*—The usual method of calculating the tensile and compressive stresses in the concrete and in the reinforcement, based on the assumptions for internal stresses, should be followed. In the case of the drop panel, the section of the slab and drop panel may be considered to act integrally for a width equal to a width of the column head section. Within the column head section the allowable compression may be increased as prescribed in Section 44 for continuous members.

(j) *Provision for Diagonal Tension and Shear.*—In calculations for the shearing stress which is to be used as the means for measuring the resistance to diagonal tension stress, it shall be assumed that the total vertical shear on a column head section constituting a width equal to one-half the lateral dimension of the panel, for use in determining critical shearing stresses, shall be considered to be one-fourth of the total dead-and-live-load on a panel for a slab of uniform thickness, and to be 0.3 of the sum of the dead- and live-loads on a panel for a slab with drop panels. The formula for shearing unit stress shall be $v = \dfrac{0.25W}{bjd}$ for slabs of uniform thickness and $v = \dfrac{0\ 30W'}{bjd}$ for slabs with drop panels, where $W$ is the sum of the dead-and-live-load on a panel, $b$ is half the lateral dimension of the panel measured from center to center of columns, and $jd$ is the lever arm of the resisting couple at the section

The calculation for punching shear shall be made on the assumption of a uniform distribution over the section of the slab around the periphery of the column capital and also of a uniform distribution over the section of the slab around the periphery of the drop panel, using in each case an amount of vertical shear greater by 25 per cent than the total vertical shear on the section under consideration

The values of working stresses should be those recommended for diagonal tension and shear in Section 44

(*k*) *Walls and Openings* —Additional slab thickness, girders, or beams shall be provided to carry walls and other concentrated loads which are in excess of the working capacity of the slab    Beams should also be provided in case openings in the floor reduce the working strength of the slab below the required carrying capacity    Where lintels are used with flat-slab construction the depth of the lintels being greater than the combined depth of the slab and depressed panel, they shall be designed to carry a uniformly distributed load equal to $\frac{1}{8}$ of the total panel load in addition to any other loads superimposed upon the lintel and the dead weight of the lintel

(*l*) *Unusual Panels* —The coefficients, steel distribution, and thicknesses recommended are for slabs which have three or more rows of panels in each direction and in which the sizes of the panels are approximately the same    For structures having a width of one or two panels, and also for slabs having panels of markedly different sizes, an analysis should be made of the moments developed in both slab and columns and the values given herein modified accordingly

(*m*) *Oblong Panels* —The requirements of design herein given for flat slab floors do not apply for oblong panels where the long side is more than four-thirds of the short side

(*n*) *Bending Moments in Columns* —Provision shall be made in both wall columns and interior columns for the bending moment which will be developed by unequally loaded panels, eccentric loading, or uneven spacing of columns    The amount of moment to be taken by a column will depend on the relative stiffness of columns and slab, and computations may be made by rational methods such as the principle of least work or of slope and deflection    Generally the largest part of the unequalized negative moment will be transmitted to the columns and the columns shall be designed to resist this bending moment.    Especial attention shall be given to wall columns and corner columns    Column capitals shall be designed, and reinforced where necessary, with these conditions in mind

The resistance of any wall column to bending in a direction perpendicular to the wall shall be not less than $0\ 04\ wl_1\ (l_2 - qc)^2$ in which $l_2$ is the panel dimension perpendicular to the wall    The moment in such wall column may be reduced by the balancing moment of the weight of the structure which projects beyond the center line of the supporting wall column Flat Slabs (cont'd)

Where the column extends through the story above, the resisting moment shall be divided between the upper and the lower columns in proportion to their stiffness  Calculated combined stresses due to bending and direct load shall not exceed by more than 50 per cent the stresses allowed for direct load.

47. Reinforced-concrete columns, for the working stresses hereinafter specified, shall have a gross width or diameter not less than one-fifteenth of the unsupported height nor less than twelve (12) in   All vertical reinforcement shall be secured against lateral displacement by steel ties not less than ¼ in  in diameter, placed not farther apart than 15 diameters of the vertical rods or more than 12 in Columns— General

For columns supporting flat-slab floors or roofs, the diameter shall be not less than one-thirteenth of the distance between columns

The length of columns shall be taken as the maximum unstayed length

48  For columns having not less than 0 5 per cent nor more than 4 per cent of vertical reinforcement, the allowable working unit stress for the net section of the concrete shall be 25 per cent of the compressive strength specified in Section 40, and the working unit stress for the steel shall be based upon the ratio of the moduli of elasticity of the concrete and steel   Concrete to a depth of 1½ in  shall be considered as protective covering and not a part of the net section Columns with Longitudinal Reinforcement

49  Columns, having not less than 1 per cent nor more than 4 per cent of vertical reinforcement and not less than 0 5 per cent nor more than 2 per cent of lateral reinforcement in the form of hoops or spirals spaced not farther apart than one-sixth of the outside diameter of the hoops or spirals nor more than 3 in  shall have an allowable working unit stress for the concrete within the outside diameter of the hoops or spirals equal to 25 per cent of the compressive strength of the concrete, as given in Section 40, and a working unit stress on the vertical reinforcement equal to the working value of the concrete multiplied by the ratio of the specified moduli of elasticity of the steel and concrete, and a working load for the hoops or spirals determined by considering the steel in hoops or spirals as four times as effective as longitudinal reinforcing steel of equal volume   The percentage of lateral reinforcement shall be taken as the volume of the hoops or spirals divided by the volume of the enclosed concrete in a unit length of column   The hoops or spirals shall be rigidly secured at each intersection to at least four (4) verticals to insure uniform spacing   The percentage of longitudinal reinforcement used shall be not less than the percentage of the lateral reinforcement   Spirals shall be manufactured of steel having a yield point of not less than 50,000 lb  per sq. in Columns with Longitudinal and Lateral Reinforcement

50  For steel columns filled with concrete and encased in a shell of concrete at least 3 in  thick, where the steel is calculated to carry the entire load, the allowable stress per square inch shall be determined by the following formula·  $18,000 - 70\dfrac{L}{R}$, but shall not exceed 16,000 lb  —where $L =$ un-

supported length in inches and $R =$ least radius of gyration of steel section in inches. The concrete shell shall be reinforced with wire mesh or hoop weighing at least 0.2 lb. per sq. ft. of surface of shell.

When the details of the structural steel are such as to fully enclose or encase the concrete, or where a spiral of not less than one-half of 1 per cent of the core area, and with a pitch of not more than three inches is provided for this purpose, the concrete inside the column core or spiral may be loaded to not more than 25 per cent of the ultimate strength specified in Section 40, in addition to the load on the steel column figured as above.

Composite columns having a cast iron core or center surrounded by concrete which is enclosed in a spiral of not less than one-half of 1 per cent of the core area, and with a pitch of not more than three inches, may be figured for a stress of $12,000 - 60\ L/R$, but not over 10,000 lb. per sq. in. on the cast iron section and of not more than 25 per cent of the compressive strength specified in Section 40 on the concrete within the spiral or core. The diameter of the cast iron core shall not exceed one-half of the diameter of the spiral.

**Footings—General**

51. Symmetrical, concentric column footings shall be designed for punching shear, diagonal tension, and bending moment.

**Punching Shear in Footings**

52. Punching shear shall be figured in accordance with Section 44.

**Diagonal Tension in Footings**

53. Shearing stresses shall be figured in accordance with Section 44.

**Bending Moment in Footings**

54. The bending moment in isolated column footings at a section taken at edge of pier or column shall be determined by multiplying the load on the quarter footing (after deducting the quarter pier or column area) by six-tenths of the distance from the edge of pier or column to the edge of footing. The effective area of concrete and steel to resist bending moment shall be considered as that within a width extending both sides of pier or column, a distance equal to depth of footing plus one-half the remaining distance to edge of footing, except that reinforcing steel crossing the section other than at right angles, shall be considered to have an effective area determined by multiplying the section area by the line of the angle between the bar and the plane of section.

**Bond Stresses in Footings**

55. In designing footings, careful consideration must be given to the bond stresses which will occur between the reinforcing steel and the concrete.

**Walls—General**

56. Walls shall be reinforced by steel rods running horizontally and vertically. Walls having an unsupported height not exceeding fifteen times the thickness may be figured the same as columns. Walls having an unsupported height not more than twenty-five times the thickness may be figured to carry safely a working stress of $12\frac{1}{2}$ per cent of the compressive strength specified in Section 40.

**Exterior Walls**

57. Exterior walls shall be designed to withstand wind loads or loads from backfill. The thickness of wall shall in no case be less than 4 in.

**Protection**

58. The reinforcement in columns and girders shall be protected by minimum thickness of 2 in. of concrete, in beams and walls by a minimum of $1\frac{1}{2}$ in.; in floor slabs by a minimum of $\frac{3}{4}$ in., in footings by a minimum of 3 in.

# Standard Recommended Practice for Portland Cement Stucco.

AMERICAN CONCRETE INSTITUTE.
STANDARD NO 25.

# AMERICAN CONCRETE INSTITUTE.
## STANDARD NO. 25.

### STANDARD RECOMMENDED PRACTICE FOR PORTLAND CEMENT STUCCO *

#### General Requirements

1) *Design*—Whenever the design of the structure permits, an overhanging roof or similar projection is recommended to afford protection to the stucco. Stuccoed copings, cornices and other exposed horizontal surfaces should be avoided whenever possible. All exposed stuccoed surfaces should shed water quickly, and whenever departure from the vertical is necessary, as at water tables, belt courses, and the like, the greatest possible slope should be detailed. Stucco should not be run to the ground whenever other treatment is possible. Should the design of the structure require this treatment, the backing should be of tile, brick, stone, or concrete, providing good mechanical bond for the stucco, and should be thoroughly cleaned before plastering. Unless special care is taken to thoroughly clean the base and each plaster coat from dirt and splash before the succeeding coat is applied, failure of the stucco may be expected.

2. *Flashing*—Suitable flashing should be provided over all door and window openings wherever projecting wood trim occurs. Wall copings, cornices rails chimney caps etc. should be built of concrete, stone, terra cotta, or metal with ample overhanging drip groove or lip, and water-tight joints. If copings are set in blocks with mortar joints, continuous flashing should extend across the wall below the coping and project beyond and form an inconspicuous lip over the upper edge of the stucco. Continuous flashing with similar projecting lip should be provided under brick sills. This flashing should be so installed as to insure absolute protection against interior leakage. Cornices set with mortar joint should be provided with flashing over the top. Sills should project well from the face of the stucco and be provided with drip grooves or flashing as described above for brick sills. Sills should also be provided with stools or jamb seats to insure wash of water over the face and not over the ends. Special attention should be given to the design of gutters and down spouts at returns of porch roofs where overflow will result in discoloration and cracking. A 2-inch strip should be provided at the intersection of walls and sloping roofs and flashing extended up and over it, the stucco being brought down to the top of the strip.

3. *Preparation of Original Surface*—All roof gutters should be fixed, and downspout hangers and all other fixed supports should be put in place before the plastering is done, in order to avoid breaks in the stucco.

Metal lath and wood lath should be stopped not less than 6 inches above grade to be free from ground moisture.

All trim should be placed in such manner that it will show its proper projection in relation to the finished stucco surface, particularly in overcoating.

---

*Adopted by letter ballot of the Institute, April 17, 1920

*The notes appearing on successive right-hand pages apply to the respective left hand page of the "Recommended Practice" Both the "Recommended Practice" and the notes were prepared by the Committee on Treatment of Concrete Surfaces*

Successful stucco work depends in large measure upon suitable design of the structure *for stucco* Exterior plaster of any kind merits whatever protection can legitimately be given it and while concession must sometimes be made to architectural requirements there is rarely any necessity for subjecting stucco to an exposure which it cannot reasonably be expected to withstand Even where stucco will remain structurally sound, it is sometimes wiser to use other treatment for the sake of appearance For example, it is better not to run stucco to grade not only because of the danger from frost action, but also to avoid staining of the stucco from dirt and moisture For the same reason special attention should be given to details of flashing and drips, wherein a little foresight will prevent much unsightly discoloration and possibly more serious defects

A fundamental rule in the design of a stucco structure is Keep water from getting behind the stucco" The architect should go even further than this and endeavor to keep any concentration of water flow from getting at the stucco at all Real study of methods of avoiding damaging leaks and drips and of providing properly for roof drainage will be well repaid

Paragraphs 1 to 3 contain definite suggestions for stucco protection These are supplemented on page 326 by simple drawings which show typical details for such protection

## MASONRY WALLS

4   *Tile* —Tile for exterior walls should preferably be not less than 8 inches thick, and should be hard burned, with dovetail or heavy ragged scoring   Tile should be set in cement mortar composed of one part cement, not more than one-fifth part hydrated lime and three parts sand, by volume   The blocks should not vary more than ½ inch in total thickness and should be set with exterior faces in line   Joints should not be raked, but mortar should be cut back to surface Neither wire mesh nor waterproofing of any type should be applied to tile walls before plastering   The surface of the tile should be brushed free from all dirt, dust and loose particles, and should be wetted to such a degree that water will not be rapidly absorbed from the plaster, but not to such a degree that water will remain standing on the surface when the plaster is applied

5   *Brick* —Surface brick should be rough, hard burned, commonly known as arch brick   Brick should be set in cement mortar with joints not less than ⅜ inch thick, and the mortar should be raked out for at least ½ inch from the face   The surface of the brick should be brushed free from all dust dirt and loose particles, and should be wetted to such a degree that water will not be rapidly absorbed from the plaster, but not to such a degree that water will remain standing on the surface when the plaster is applied

Old brick walls which are to be overcoated should have all loose, friable, or soft mortar removed from joints, and all dirt and foreign matter should be removed by hacking, wire brushing or other effective means   Surfaces that have been painted or waterproofed should be lathed with metal lath before overcoating.

6   *Concrete.*—Monolithic concrete walls should preferably be rough and of coarse texture, rather than smooth and dense, for the application of stucco   Walls of this type should be cleaned and roughened, if necessary, by hacking, wire brushing, or other effective means   The surface of the concrete should be brushed free from all dust, dirt, and loose particles, and should be wetted to such a degree that water will not be rapidly absorbed from the plaster, but not to such a degree that water will remain standing on the surface when the plaster is applied

7   *Concrete Block* —Concrete block for stucco walls should be rough and of coarse texture but not weak or friable   Block should be set with cement mortar joints, which should be raked out or cut back even with surface   Before applying the stucco the surface should be brushed free from all dust, dirt, and loose particles, and should be wetted to such a degree that water will not be rapidly absorbed from the plaster, but not to such a degree that water will remain standing on the surface when the plaster is applied

## Masonry Walls

Buildings of hollow terra cotta tile, brick, concrete, concrete block, and similar materials, are particularly well adapted for the application of stucco because of their rigidity  This however, depends upon good, solid footings or foundation, a requirement which should be met in all types of stucco structures.  Masonry walls should also provide a good surface for the bond or adhesion of the stucco, and wherever possible this bond should be insured by some form of mechanical key  For this reason raking out the joints in a brick wall is recommended as an added precaution, and similarly walls of concrete or concrete block should not be too smooth, but preferably rough and of coarse texture

It is most important that masonry walls be clean before the stucco is applied, as otherwise the bond of the stucco cannot be relied upon to stand the strain set up by moisture and temperature changes  Many a failure of stucco on masonry foundations has been attributed to frost action, when the primary cause of the failure has been lack of care in thoroughly cleaning the walls from dirt  Without secure and positive anchorage under such conditions the stucco cannot endure

Special attention should be called to the importance of properly wetting the surface of masonry walls just before applying the stucco.  Too dry a surface will absorb the water from the fresh plaster coat before the latter has had time to harden properly  On the other hand, a surface completely saturated has lost all its absorptive power, or "suction," a slight degree of which is necessary for best results  A moderate amount of suction tends to draw the fine cement particles into the pores and interstices of the surface, upon this action the bond of the stucco depends  If this bond is to be as strong as possible, the surface should be neither dry nor completely saturated

Wood lintels over openings in masonry walls should not be used

When old masonry walls are overcoated special attention is called to the necessity for obtaining thorough cleanliness, a good mechanical bond, and proper suction  When any of these condition are in doubt the walls should be furred and lathed

### FRAME WALLS

8    *Framing* —Studs spaced not to exceed 16 inch centers should be run from foundation to rafters without any intervening horizontal members    The studs should be tied together just below the floor joists with 1 x 6 inch boards which should be let into the studs on their inner side, so as to be flush and securely nailed to them    These boards will also act as sills for the floor joists, which, in addition, should be securely spiked to the side of the studs

9    *Bracing* —The corners of each wall should be braced diagonally with 1 x 6 inch boards let into the studs on their inner side, and securely nailed to them

In back-plastered construction in which sheathing is omitted, at least once midway in each story height, the studs should be braced horizontally with 2 x 3 inch bridging set 1 inch back of the face of the studs    This assumes that the studs are 2 x 4 inches    Larger sizes would require correspondingly larger bridging

In sheathed construction no bridging is necessary

## Frame Walls

Good bracing of the frame is important to secure the necessary rigidity. Bridging between the studs at least once in each story height is recommended whether the frame is to be sheathed or not. In the former case the bridging should be of the same size as the studs (usually 2 x 4 inch). In the back plastered type of construction where sheathing is not used, bridging is required for stiffening the frame, and should be 1 inch less than the studs in depth. It should be placed horizontally, and 1 inch back of the face of the studs, in order that the back-plaster coat may be carried past the bridging without break at this point. Diagonal bracing at the corners of each wall is recommended, especially when sheathing is omitted. Such bracing may be of 1 x 6 inch boards 6 or 8 feet long, let into the studs on their inner side in order not to interfere with the back plastering or the interior plastering. The length of the corner bracing will of course, depend to some extent on the location of window or other openings.

The committee feels that fire protection is an important feature of this type of structure, and that some form of fire stop is necessary to develop its full fire resistive value. Probably the best method is to form a basket of metal lath to occupy the spaces between the studs at the juncture of the floor joists and wall. This should be filled with cement mortar or concrete from the ceiling level to 4 inches above the floor level.

A preliminary report from the Underwriters Laboratories on back-plastered metal lath and stucco construction with Portland cement indicates that "this finish can be expected to furnish a substantial barrier to the passage of flame into the hollow spaces back of it and to provide sufficient heat insulation to prevent the ignition of the wooden supports to which it is attached for about one hour when exposed to fire of the degree of severity to which stucco finished buildings are likely to be subjected under average exterior fire exposures."

The committee wishes to recognize the development of metal lumber for frame construction, and believes its merits are such that its use will undoubtedly largely increase. Detailed reference to this form of construction will be made in subsequent additions to this recommended practice.

10     *Sheathing*—In back plastered construction the lath should be fastened direct to the studding and back plastered, and no sheathing is used

In sheathed construction the sheathing boards should not be less than 6 inches nor more than 8 inches wide, dressed on one or both sides to a uniform thickness of 13/16 inch   They should be laid horizontally across the wall studs and fastened with not less than two 8d nails at each stud

11     *Inside Waterproofing*—In back plastered construction no waterproofing is necessary

In sheathed construction, over the sheathing boards should be laid in horizontal layers, beginning at the bottom, a substantial paper, well impregnated with tar or asphalt   The bottom strip should lap over the baseboard at the bottom of the wall, and each strip should lap the one below at least 2 inches   The paper should lap the flashings at all openings.

12     *Furring*—Metal Lath   When furring forms an integral part of the metal lath to be used, then separate furring as described in this paragraph is omitted

In back plastered construction galvanized or painted ⅜ inch crimped furring, not lighter than 22-gage or other shape giving equal results, should be fastened direct to the studding, using 1¼ inch x 14-gage staples spaced 12 inches apart

In sheathed construction galvanized or painted ⅜ inch crimped furring not lighter than 22-gage, or other shape giving equal results, should be fastened over the sheathing paper and directly along the line of the studs, using 1¼ inch x 14 gage staples spaced 12 inches apart   The same depth of furring should be adhered to around curved surfaces, and furring should be placed not less than 1½ inches nor more than 4 inches on each side of and above and below all openings

Wood Lath   Furring 1 x 2 inches should be laid vertically 12 inches on centers over the sheathing paper and nailed every 8 inches with 6d nails

13     *Lath*   Metal lath should be galvanized or painted expanded lath weighing not less than 3 4 lbs per square yard

Wire lath should be galvanized or painted woven wire lath, not lighter than 19 gage, 2½ meshes to the inch, with stiffeners at 8 inch centers.

Wood lath should be standard quality, narrow plaster lath 4 feet long and not less than ⅜ inch thick

When sheathing is used it should be laid horizontally and not diagonally across the studs  The stucco test panels erected at the Bureau of Standards in 1915 and 1916 have demonstrated conclusively that diagonal sheathing tends to crack the overlying stucco by setting up strains in the supporting frame  This result is undoubtedly due to the shrinkage of the sheathing, and whatever benefit might be anticipated from the more effective bracing provided by diagonal sheathing appears to be more than offset by the shrinkage effect  Diagonal sheathing is also less economical than horizontal sheathing, both in material and labor

Waterproofing of the faces of the studs in back-plastered construction seems to be ineffective and unnecessary, and its elimination is recommended

The proper type and depth of furring is a question on which information is desired.  If metal lath is applied over sheathing and the commonly recommended practice of filling with mortar the space between lath and sheathing is to be followed, there seems to be no good reason for using furring deeper than ⅜ inch  On the other hand, 1 x 2 inch wood furring is widely used for both metal and wood lath, and there are good arguments both for and against this type of furring  The question of the proper length and gage of staples for metal lath is involved with that of furring  The entire subject needs investigation.

Metal lath should be specified by weight rather than by gage, and should be always galvanized or painted  Galvanized lath is a good investment in most cases, and is to be recommended in preference to painted lath, unless the method of applying the stucco is such as to insure complete embedment of the metal, as, for example, in the back plastered type of construction

The use of wood lath as a base for stucco finds many advocates and many opponents, but the committee does not feel that it can recommend wood lath for cement stucco  More field and test data should be available before the evidence for and against wood lath can be carefully weighed.  Further information is desired in regard to the type of wood lath best suited for cement stucco  In some of the most satisfactory work reported by the committee the lath were of white pine 1 inch wide and ½ inch thick  Both materials and size were here unusual, but the committee is of the opinion that this type of narrow lath is worthy of consideration  For want of information as to the practicability of specifying any particular kind of wood and unusual dimensions, no change is suggested at the present time  It may be stated, however, that nearly all of the test panels of wood lath erected at the Bureau of Standards developed large cracks, in such manner as to suggest that narrower lath (those used were 1¾ inches wide) with wider keys and heavier nailing would have given better results  The tests also indicate that counter lathing in which the lath are applied lattice fashion produces no more satisfactory results than plain lathing  In view of the much greater cost of counter lathing the committee recommends that reference to this type of application be omitted from specifications

### PREPARATION OF MORTAR

25   *Mixing*—The ingredients of the mortar should be mixed until thoroughly distributed and the mass is uniform in color and homogeneous   The quantity of water necessary for the desired consistency should be determined by trial and thereafter measured in proper proportion

Machine Mixing   The mortar should preferably be mixed in a suitable mortar mixing machine of the rotating drum type   The period of machine mixing should be not less than 5 minutes after all the ingredients are introduced into the mixer

Hand Mixing   The mixing should be done in a water-tight mortar box and the ingredients should be mixed dry until the mass is uniform in color and homogeneous   The proper amount of water should then be added and the mixing continued until the consistency is uniform

26   *Measuring Proportions*—Methods of measurement of the proportions of water should be used which will secure separate uniform measurements at all times   All proportions stated should be by volume   A bag of cement (94 lbs net) may be assumed to contain 1 cubic foot, 40 lbs may be assumed as the weight of 1 cubic foot of hydrated lime   Hydrated lime should be measured dry, and should not be measured nor added to the mortar in the form of putty.

27   *Retempering*—Mortar which has begun to stiffen or take on its initial set should not be used

28   *Consistency*—Only sufficient water should be used to produce a good workable consistency   The less water the better the quality of the mortar, within working limits

### Preparation of Mortar

The importance of proper and thorough mixing of the ingredients of the mortar cannot be too strongly emphasized  Machine mixing is in all cases to be recommended in preference to hand mixing  The use of hair or fiber is considered optional  and when used the method of incorporation should be such as to insure good distribution and freedom from clots  The maintenance of proper and uniform consistency should be insured by measurement of the water as well as of the other ingredients of the mortar  The question of retempering mortar is one which will bear further investigation  At the present time sufficient information is not available to warrant a change in the paragraph on retempering

14    *Application of Lath.*—Metal Lath. Lath should be placed horizontally, driving galvanized staples 1¼ inch by 14-gage not more than 8 inches apart over the furring or stiffeners   Vertical laps should occur at supports and should be fastened with staples not more than 4 inches apart   Horizontal joints should be locked or butted and tightly laced with 18 gage galvanized wire

Wood Lath   Lath should be placed horizontally on the furring with ½ inch openings between them   Joints should be broken every twelfth lath   Each lath should be nailed at each furring with 4d nails

15.   *Corners*—Metal Lath   The sheets of metal lath should be folded around the corners a distance of at least 3 inches and stapled down, as applied   The use of corner bead is not recommended

Wood Lath.   At all corners a 6-inch strip of galvanized or painted metal lath should be firmly stapled over the lath with 1¼ inch x 14 gage galvanized staples

16    *Spraying*—Before applying the first coat of plaster, wood lath should be thoroughly wetted, but water should not remain standing on the surface of the lath when the plaster is applied

17    *Insulation*—The air space in back plastered walls may be divided by applying building paper, quilting, felt, or other suitable insulating material between the studs, and fastening it to the studs and bridging by nailing wood strips over folded edges of the material   This insulation should be so fastened as to leave about 1 inch air space between it and the stucco   Care should be taken to keep the insulating material clear of the stucco, and to make tight joints against the wood framing at the top and bottom of the space and against the bridging

18    *Overcoating*—Old frame walls which are to be overcoated should be made structurally sound in every respect, and, as far as possible, the general conditions on pages 1 and 2 should be observed   otherwise the recommended practice for frame structures obtains

19    *Cement*—The cement should meet the requirements of the standard specifications for Portland cement of the American Society for Testing Materials, and adopted by this Institute   (Standard No 1 )

20    *Fine Aggregate*—Fine aggregate should consist of sand, or screenings from crushed stone or crushed pebbles graded from fine to coarse, passing when dry a No 8 screen   Fine aggregate should preferably be of silicious materials, clean, coarse, and free from loam, vegetable or other deleterious matter

21    *Hydrated Lime*—Hydrated lime should meet the requirements of the standard specifications for hydrated lime of the American Society for Testing Materials

22    *Hair or Fiber*—There should be used only first quality long hair, free from foreign matter, or a long fiber well combed out

23.   *Coloring Matter*—Only mineral colors should be used which are not affected by lime, Portland cement, or other ingredients of the mortar, or the weather.

24    *Water*—Water should be clean, free from oil, acid, strong alkali or vegetable matter

The results of tests and field observations indicate that more attention should be given to the application of lath to exterior surfaces  Cracks frequently develop in stucco over laps or at junctions of metal and wire lath, indicating a weakness at these points  This may be due in part to reduced thickness of the stucco where the lath is lapped, or to insufficient tying and fastening at the joints  The ideal job of lathing would obviously be that in which the lath forms a uniform fabric over the structure, without seams or lines of weakness, and with equal reinforcing value in all directions  This ideal condition cannot be realized  but evidence is at hand to indicate that butted and laced or well-tied horizontal joints are better than lapped joints, and in the case of ribbed lath that carefully locked joints are better than lapped joints  Vertical joints must almost of necessity be lapped, but the joints may be made secure if they occur over supports and are well stapled at frequent intervals

At the present time the warmth of the back-plastered stucco house in comparison with that of the sheathed house is questioned by some, but the available evidence seems to indicate that where insulation has been provided as specified, generally satisfactory results have been obtained

Ordinary building paper applied in a double layer is recommended as a satisfactory insulating medium

In this connection reference may be made to a series of tests conducted in 1919 at the Armour Institute of Technology, Chicago, to determine the relative heat conductivity of various types of walls  These tests indicated that by the use of building paper or quilting the loss of heat through a stucco wall of the back plastered type was less, under standardized conditions, than the loss through the ordinary wood frame wall covered with sheathing and drop siding  A complete report of these tests may be obtained on application to the Commissioner, Associated Metal Lath Manufacturers, Chicago, Ill

The paragraphs relating to materials are sufficiently specific as to the quality of the stucco ingredients  However, reference may be made to the recently developed colorimetric test for detecting the presence of organic matter in sands, a description of which is to be found in the report of Committee C 9, American Society for Testing Materials  1919

Hydrated lime should be specified to the exclusion of lump lime, chiefly for the reason that lime which is slaked on the job cannot as a rule be so thoroughly hydrated and so thoroughly mixed in the mortar as the mechanically hydrated product.

29    *Mortar*—All coats should contain not less than 3 cubic feet of fine aggregate to 1 sack of Portland cement. If hydrated lime is used it should not be in excess of one-fifth the volume of cement. Hair or fiber should be used in the scratch coat only on wood lath, on metal or wire lath that is to be back plastered, or on metal or wire lath which is applied over sheathing and is separated therefrom by furring deeper than ⅜ inch.

30    *Application.*—The plastering should be carried on continually in one general direction without allowing the plaster to dry at the edge. If it is impossible to work the full width of the wall at one time, the joining should be at some natural division of the surface, such as a window or door.

The first coat should thoroughly cover the base on which it is applied and be well troweled to insure the best obtainable bond. Before the coat has set it should be heavily cross scratched with a saw-toothed metal paddle or other suitable device to provide a strong mechanical key.

The second coat should be applied whenever possible on the day following the application of the scratch coat. The first coat should be dampened if necessary but not saturated, before the second coat is applied. The second coat should be brought to a true and even surface by screeding at intervals not exceeding 5 feet and by constant use of straightening rod. When the second coat has stiffened sufficiently it should be dry floated with a wood float and lightly and evenly cross scratched to form a good mechanical bond for the finish coat. The day following the application of the second coat, and for not less than three days thereafter the coat should be sprayed or wetted at frequent intervals and kept from drying out.

In back-plastered construction the backing coat should preferably be applied directly following the completion of the brown coat. The keys of the scratch coat should first be thoroughly dampened, and the backing coat then well troweled on to insure filling the spaces between the keys and thoroughly covering the back of the lath. The backing coat should provide a total thickness of plaster back of the lath of ⅝ inch or ¾ inch and should finish about ¼ inch back of the face of the studs.

The finish coat should be applied not less than a week after the application of the second coat. Methods of application will hereinafter be described under "finish."

31    *Two Coat Work.*—Whenever two coat work is required, the first coat should preferably be "doubled"—that is, as soon as the first coat is stiff enough it should be followed by a second application of mortar and this should then be treated as described for the second coat under paragraph 30. The finish should be applied not less than a week after the application of the first coat.          —

32    *Drying Out.*—The finish coat should not be permitted to dry out rapidly and adequate precaution should be taken, either by sprinkling frequently after the mortar is set hard enough to permit it, or by hanging wet burlap or similar material over the surface.

33    *Freezing.*—Stucco should not be applied when the temperature is below 32 degrees F., nor under any conditions such that ice or frost may form on the surface of the wall.

### Mortar Coats

Practice varies widely in the mixture and application of stuccos. The use of hair, lime and waterproofing materials, the variations in the mixtures for the different coats, the number and thickness of the coats, the intervals between the coats, the degree of wetting of the undercoats, and the precautions necessary in protecting the coats from too rapid drying, are details subject to question and all will stand further investigation. However, the study of the experimental panels at the Bureau of Standards has yielded considerable information on some of these points.

One of the most important indications from these panels is that lean mixtures containing well-graded aggregate give better results than those commonly specified. Mixtures as lean as one part of cement to six or seven parts of graded aggregate have given excellent results in these tests. The committee is of the opinion that the volume change of rich mortars is accountable for much of the unsightly cracking of stuccos, and that no mixture should be used in which the proportion of cement is greater than one part to three parts of fine aggregate.

The effect of hydrated lime in cement stucco has also been given considerable attention, and the conclusion which is forcing itself upon the committee is that hydrated lime does not improve the structure of the stucco, but by imparting better working quality to the mortar reduces the cost of application. On the other hand there is evidence that not more than 20% of hydrated lime, by volume of the cement, should be added to cement stucco if the best results are to be obtained.

There seems to be no good reason for varying the composition of the different coats, but if a variation is to be specified, the scratch coat should logically be the strongest mixture, followed by a leaner brown coat and a still leaner finish. No greater mistake has ever been made in stucco application than the use of a strong brown coat over a weak base or a weak scratch coat. The not uncommon practice of applying a strong brown coat over a lime mortar scratch coat has been responsible for many stucco failures.

The suggestion that the finish coat should logically be leaner than the undercoats immediately brings up the waterproofing question. There are two fundamental points to be considered in this connection, first, that the lean coat is not necessarily lacking in density, and second, that the waterproofing problem in good cement stucco is not one of overcoming permeability, but rather of reducing absorption. The entire question hinges on absorption, and the evidence at hand indicates that a moderate degree of absorption is a much more preferable condition than a surface covered with craze and map cracks, produced by the use of a too rich or wrongly manipulated finishing coat. Any waterproofing treatment that alters the natural texture and color of the stucco may be dismissed from considera-

tion, and the merit of any integral waterproofing in stucco is exceedingly difficult to determine.

The question as to number and thickness of coats may be best answered by assuming that each coat of stucco has its own particular function. The scratch coat is the first applied, and its purpose is to form an intimate bond and a secure support for the body of the stucco. On metal lath it also serves as a protective coat, and it should therefore be strong and not too lean. The use of hair or fiber is of questionable value. Hair or fiber should not be used when the space back of the lath is to be filled, and is probably not a necessary ingredient in any case. The committee at the present time would sanction its use only in scratch coats on wood lath, or on metal or wire lath that is to be back-plastered, or on metal or wire lath that is applied over furring deeper than $\frac{3}{8}$ inch. The thickness of the scratch coat should average about $\frac{1}{4}$ inch over the face of the lath.

The function of the second coat (commonly called the brown or straightening coat) is to establish a true and even surface upon which to apply the finish. It forms the body of the stucco and must fill the hollows and cover the humps of the scratch coat. For this reason an average thickness of $\frac{3}{8}$ inch to $\frac{1}{2}$ inch will usually be required. The brown and finish coats, or the scratch and brown coats, are sometimes combined in two coat work, which is permissible when the base upon which the stucco is applied is fairly true and even, or when, on account of cost considerations, the best obtainable finish is not required. It is difficult, however, to obtain a satisfactory finish on a coat which runs $\frac{1}{2}$ inch or more in thickness, since the tendency of a heavy coat to bag and slip is likely to produce an uneven surface.

The finish coat serves only a decorative purpose and has no structural value. Its function is solely to provide an attractive appearance, and any mixture or any method of application that may detract from the appearance, or in any way injure its permanency, should be avoided. Herein lies the argument for lean mixtures, which are more likely to be free from unsightly defects than rich mixtures, and are also more likely to improve in appearance under the action of the weather. The finish coat should be as thin as possible consistent with covering capacity, and may vary from $\frac{1}{8}$ to $\frac{3}{8}$ inch in thickness, depending upon the type employed.

It is obvious from the foregoing that first class stucco should be three-coat work, each coat serving its own particular purpose. The bond between the brown coat and the scratch coat needs to be strong in order to carry the weight of the body of the stucco, and for this reason it is now considered preferable to apply the brown coat the day following the application of the scratch coat. Except in dry or windy weather little wetting of the scratch coat should be necessary when the brown coat is to follow within 24 hours. A slight degree of absorption or "suction" in the scratch coat is probably better than complete saturation, for the brown coat, as well as the others, is necessarily mixed with a larger quantity of water than it requires for maximum strength. The removal of a portion of this excess water by

the suction of the undercoat not only improves the quality of the coat but also insures a better bond by tending to draw the fine particles of the cement into the pores and interstices of the undercoat

Whereas the interval between the brown coat and scratch coat as recommended above is relatively short, the interval before applying the finish coat should be as long as permissible under the conditions of the work. The reason for thus delaying the application of the finish is to enable the body of the stucco to obtain its initial shrinkage and a nearer approach to its final condition of strength and hardness before being covered with the surface coat. The bond of the latter needs to be intimate rather than of maximum strength, and if the body of the stucco has been allowed to thoroughly set and harden, it may be assumed that there is less liability of volume changes in the undercoats to disturb the finish coat. A week or more should elapse between the application of the brown and finish coats

The finish coat should be applied over a damp but not saturated undercoat, for excess water is likely to injure the bond seriously. Certain types of finish, such as the wet mixtures used for sand spraying or for the "spatter dash" finish, may preferably be applied to a fairly dry undercoat, since suction must be depended upon to prevent streakiness and muddy appearance. The fact that finishes of this type applied in this manner may set and dry out with little strength is not serious, they gradually attain sufficient hardness with exposure to the weather

Curing of the undercoats by sprinkling and protection of finish coats against the sun, wind, rain and frost by means of tarpaulins are always to be recommended. This is not always feasible however and the architect should be content to specify and insist upon reasonable precautions. The application of cement stucco in freezing weather should be avoided, and, in fact, temperatures slightly above the freezing point may allow frost to form on a damp wall. The application of stucco under such conditions is likely to result in failure

## FINISH.

34    *Stippled*—The finishing coat should be troweled smooth with a metal trowel with as little rubbing as possible, and then should be lightly patted with a brush of broom straw to give an even, stippled surface

35    *Sand Floated*—The finishing coat, after being brought to a smooth, even surface, should be rubbed with a circular motion of a wood float with the addition of a little sand to slightly roughen the surface   This floating should be done when the mortar has partly hardened

36    *Sand Sprayed*—After the finishing coat has been brought to an even surface, it should be sprayed by means of a wide, long fiber brush—a whisk broom does very well—dipped into a creamy mixture of one part of cement to two or three parts sand, mixed fresh at least every 30 minutes, and kept well stirred   This coating should be thrown forcibly against the surface to be finished   This treatment should be applied while the finishing coat is still moist and before it has attained its early hardening—that is, within 3 to 5 hours   To obtain lighter shades add hydrated lime not to exceed 10% of the weight of the cement

37    *Rough Cast or Spatter Dash*—After the finishing coat has been brought to a smooth, even surface with a wooden float and before finally hardened, it should be uniformly coated with a mixture of one sack of cement to 3 cubic feet of fine aggregate thrown forcibly against it to produce a rough surface of uniform texture when viewed from a distance of 20 feet   Special care should be taken to prevent the rapid drying out of this finish by thorough wetting down at intervals after stucco has hardened sufficiently to prevent injury

38    *Applied Aggregate*—After the finishing coat has been brought to a smooth, even surface, and before it has begun to harden, clean round pebbles, or other material as selected, not smaller than ¼ inch or larger than ¾ inch and previously wetted, should be thrown forcibly against the wall so as to embed themselves in the fresh mortar   They should be distributed uniformly over the mortar with a clean wood trowel, but no rubbing of the surface should be done after the pebbles are embedded

39.    *Exposed Aggregate*—The finishing coat should be composed of an approved, selected coarse sand, crushed marble, or granite or other special material, in the proportion given for finishing coats, and within 24 hours after being applied and troweled to an even surface should be scrubbed with a stiff brush and water   In case the stucco is too hard, a solution of one part hydrochloric acid in four parts of water by volume can be used in place of water   After the aggregate particles have been uniformly exposed by scrubbing, particular care should be taken to remove all traces of the acid by thorough spraying with water from a hose.

40    *Mortar Colors*—When it is required that any of the above finishes should be made with colored mortar not more than 10% of the weight of Portland cement should be added to the mortar in the form of finely ground mineral coloring matter

A predetermined weight of color should be added dry to each batch of dry fine aggregate before the cement is added   The color and fine

It is practically impossible to specify in written paragraphs the methods by which successful finishes are obtained  The quality of these depends upon the knowledge and skill of the plasterer, and the specification writer must content himself with a brief description of the several types  In the finishing of stuccos, however, there are certain causes and effects which should be more generally recognized, a brief discussion of which will help to explain the limitation of the commonly used finishes and indicate the methods to be pursued in the attempt to develop better finishes

In an earlier paragraph the defects resulting from the expansion and contraction of rich mortars have been referred to.  The chance of such defects occurring must be greatest in the finish coat, which is directly exposed to the extremes of moisture and temperature variations  The hope of overcoming these defects lies mainly in the use of leaner mixtures, in which the tendency to movement is cut down as the proportion of cement is reduced  The problem therefore is to use less cement and at the same time retain the necessary density by improved gradation of the aggregates  Considerable success has already attended experiments along this line, and even better results are anticipated in the future

All that may be accomplished in this direction, however, will hardly permit a smooth troweled finish to be used  This treatment produces a concentration of fine material at the surface, which will almost inevitably develop fine cracks  In the course of time these cracks will collect soot and dirt and become conspicuous and unsightly  At best the smooth troweled finish is not to be recommended, and specifications should eliminate all reference to it

The dash finishes—such as the sand spray, which is obtained by applying a mixture of sand, cement and water with a whisk broom or long fiber brush, or the spatter dash, which is usually a thin mortar containing coarse sand or stone screenings thrown from a paddle, or the rough cast, which is a mixture of pebbles and cement grout thrown from a paddle or the back of a trowel—are all relatively rich in cement and all develop fine cracks to a very marked degree, but the rough texture of the surfaces masks these defects, and the type is therefore generally satisfactory and very widely used  The use of these finishes is in general to be recommended, unless the work is done by a stucco specialist, whose skill and experience qualify him to execute the more difficult finishes to be discussed in the following paragraphs

The chief objection to the dash finishes as above described is their rather cold, unbroken cement color, which may be relieved and improved to a considerable extent by the judicious use of mineral pigments  Another means of varying the monotony of the natural grays and whites of the cement is by the use of the dry dash finishes, in which clean pebbles or stone chips are thrown against the fresh mortar of the finishing coat while it is still soft  When the dry dash is well selected, and the particles thickly and uniformly distributed over the surface, the finish thus obtained is pleasing and possesses decidedly more life and character than the wet dashes.

aggregate should be mixed together and then the cement mixed in
The whole should be then thoroughly mixed dry by shoveling from one
pile to another through a ¼ inch mesh wire screen until the entire
batch is of uniform color   Water should then be added to bring the
mortar to a proper plastering consistency

The sand-float finish deserves special consideration because it promises to be one of the most satisfactory finishes of the future. Due to the use of rich mixtures the sand-float finish has usually developed defects similar to those experienced with the smooth troweled finishes, differing from the latter only in degree. Sand-floated stuccos which have been covered with paint are to be found in every community, and this alone is sufficient evidence of unskillful manipulation of this finish and of the unsatisfactory results that have been obtained. In the experiments carried out at the Bureau of Standards the sand-float finish was found to be most satisfactory on mixtures containing not more than 1 part of portland cement to 4 parts of fine aggregate and mixtures as rich as 1:3, with a small addition of hydrated lime, were satisfactory as a rule only when the final floating was delayed until the mortar had well stiffened. In this manner the concentration of fine material in the surface was prevented. This experience confirms the necessity for using leaner mixtures than have been specified heretofore and for removing the cement from the surface by mechanical or other means if the sand-float finish is to come into its own.

There is no hard and fast line between the sand-float finish and the exposed aggregate finish since in the final water floating process of the former the aggregate is left sufficiently exposed to modify and improve the tone of the finished wall. When the sand-floated surface is further improved by an acid wash the grains of the aggregate are cleanly exposed. It seems preferable in classification, however, to limit the exposed aggregate finishes to those in which coarser aggregates are employed than would be feasible for the sand float finish. Thus defined, the exposed aggregate finish is obtained by the application of a coarser mortar containing carefully selected and graded aggregates, so that when the latter are exposed by brushing and cleaning the resulting texture resembles that of cast concrete which has been subjected to similar surface treatment. One of the members of the committee has recently developed a stucco of this type which has been applied to the Field House in East Potomac Park, Washington, D. C., over terra cotta tile. The color and texture of this finish, produced entirely by the aggregate, is the same as that of the concrete trim of the building. At the present time only the wings of this structure are completed, but the work thus far marks a distinct step in advance, not only in the treatment of the stucco, but also in the general adaptation of surface-treated concrete to exacting architectural requirements.

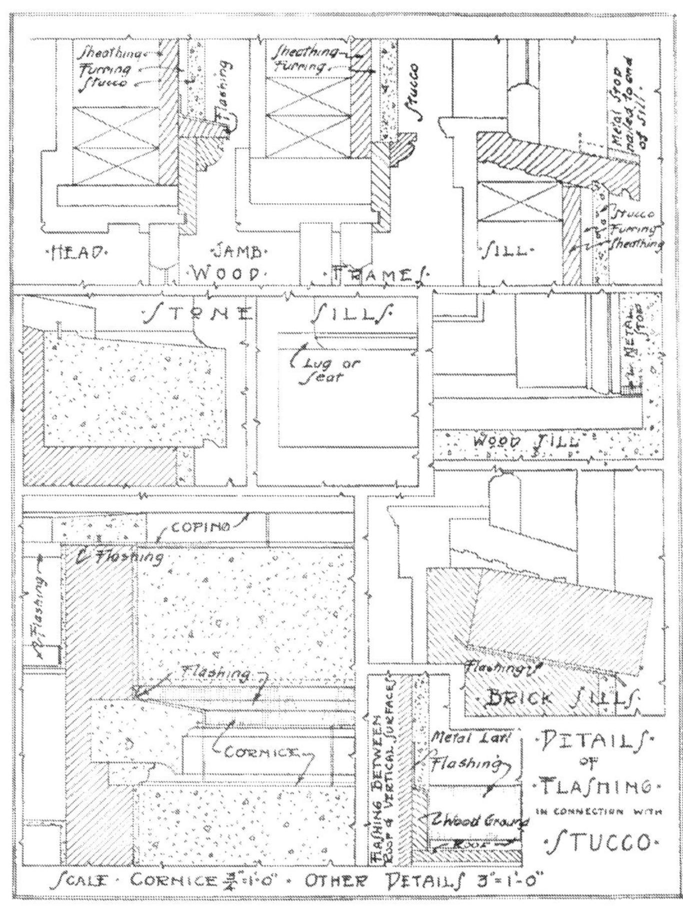


ARCHITECTURAL DETAILS STUCCO APPLICATION

In conclusion, the committee desires to state its conviction that while portland cement stucco may develop certain small defects which cannot always be guarded against the product may be depended upon, if applied in accordance with the accompanying recommended practice, to be structurally sound durable, and capable of giving satisfactory service, with little or no outlay for repairs or maintenance   The committee believes, however, that assurance of satisfactory results in stucco depends largely on the development of stucco specialists, experienced and skilled in this particular art, as distinguished from ordinary plastering   Intelligent and high-class workmanship is so essential to good stucco that only those contractors who have had sufficient experience to establish their own confidence in the product, and who are willing to guarantee their work, should be employed for its application

D  K  Boyd,<br>
E  D  Boyer<br>
C  M  Chapman,<br>
Wharton Clay,<br>
J  J  Earley,<br>
J  E  Freeman<br>
F  A  Hitchcock,<br>
J  B  Orr,<br>
J  C  Pearson, *Chairman*

DISCUSSION.

Mr WHARTON CLAY —The Associated Metal Lath Manufacturers have been very anxious to insure the proper attachment for metal lath on wood studs, and have made a canvass of the country to find out contractors' practice in this matter. In view of the impossibility, in some places, of securing staples at all, they recommend the following clause "Flat metal laths shall be attached to wood by means of 4d nails Where rib laths or furring is used, 6d nails shall be used All nails shall be driven solid, but shall be bent down over a juncture of strands a short distance before being driven home" This is offered as a part of the written discussion. It is the opinion of the committee that it would like to have an opportunity to study that before it is offered as an amendment to the report

Mr. A F ROBINSON —While this subject is up, I would like to recommend to the committee the consideration of heavier staples than those they have specified My experience has been that the staple now commonly used, No 14-gage, is very largely bent over and is likely to be insufficient when used with the ordinary metal lath I think in one case we have found on interior work as high as 51% of the staples bent over and insufficiently entering the wood, which had a decided influence on the strength of the stucco finish It would probably be sufficient to hold the stucco in ordinary service, but even there there may be some question If it can be brought about I think it would be to the advantage of the stucco to have a little heavier staple, just how heavy I am not prepared to say The different kinds of wood should also be discussed and considered in arriving at any conclusion covering the strength of the staples

Mr J. C PEARSON —There is no question about the necessity for getting a more secure attachment of the metal lath to the studs We had an interesting experience when we conducted the tests of several panels in 1915, we tried to procure some of these staples which have always been in the specifications, No 14-gage, and could not find any in the neighborhood of Washington and there was quite a bit of telegraphing around the country before we could locate them We decided it was a very unusual product I think the comments in that particular part of the report indicate the fact that we needed more information about that We felt that those staples were not satisfactory, but did not know what to put in and did not know what the common practice was Therefore I think these comments are very acceptable and the committee will give the matter attention in the next year's report

( 328 )

# AMERICAN CONCRETE INSTITUTE.

BUSINESS REPORTS

REPORT OF THE BOARD OF DIRECTION
to the American Concrete Institute
on Finances of the Organization
from the Treasurer's Report
to February 1, 1920

| | |
|---|---:|
| Bank balance May 31, 1919, as shown by Auditor's report | $2,288 54 |
| Receipts May 31, 1919, to January 31, 1920 | 4,812 11 |
| | $7,100 65 |
| Expenditures May 31, 1919, to January 31, 1920 | 5,698 91 |
| Balance January 31, 1920 | $1,401 74 |
| United States Victory Bonds | 3,000 00 |
| | $4,401 74 |
| Current unpaid bills February 1, 1920 | 2,117 41 |
| | $2,284 33 |

ABSTRACT OF MINUTES OF MEETING OF BOARD OF DIRECTION.

MEETING, NEW YORK CITY, Nov 5, 1919

Present  President Hatt, Messrs Turner, Wason, Humphrey, Boyer, Thompson and Secretary Alvord.

Six applications for membership were received and approved

Secretary presented financial report showing cash on hand October 1, $916 99 besides $3000 in Victory Bonds

Secretary reported adoption by letter ballot canvassed in September of the standard specifications for concrete sidewalks and floors as amended at the 1919 convention and the standard specifications for the manufacture of roofing tile

President announced the appointment as Institute's representatives on the Joint Committee on Concrete and Reinforced Concrete of W. K. Hatt, A. E. Lindau, E. J Moore and L. C Wason, with a fifth member to be appointed.*

A special committee consisting of H C Turner, chairman R W Lesley, W M Kinney, and L C Wason appointed by President Hatt to formulate a plan of organization for the future growth of the Institute, made its report  The outstanding items in the report, which was adopted are these  Recommendation that the activities of the Institute be centralized in a secretary's office, relieving the President of detail work  Establishing the secretary's office in the office of the Concrete Cement Age Publishing Co, Detroit, Mich, the Institute's individuality and independence to be maintained  Appointment of Harvey Whipple secretary  Funds for more aggressive work of the organization in participating in activities looking to the advancement of the industry to be provided through supporting memberships at fifty dollars a year.  Technical subjects to be investigated by special committees at once as follows  Standardization of specifications for concrete reinforcement bars, standardization of units of design, proper values for vertical shear, relative merits of different types of cement floor finish in building construction, the most economical design and construction for contractors plant in reinforced-concrete construction

Voted to ask Secretary Alvord to remain in office until his successor is duly qualified  The Board recorded its appreciation and thanks for the faithful services he had rendered

Voted to renew Institute's membership in the National Fire Protection Association.

President authorized to make arrangements for the convention at the Auditorium Hotel, Chicago, February 16 to 18, 1920

---

*The later appointment of Messrs Hatt and Lindau representing American Society of Civil Engineers on the Joint Committee resulted in change in Institute representation to stand as follows  S C Hollister, Chairman, R W Lesley, A R Lord E J Moore, L C Wason

( 331 )

Voted to continue the present Finance Committee consisting of Messrs Turner, Lesley and Kinney

The President was authorized to appoint a committee on the presentation of the Wason Medal

### MEETING, CHICAGO, FEB 17, 1920

Present.  President Hatt, Messrs Turner, Thompson, Humphrey, Ashton, Boyer and Secretary Whipple

Secretary presented a report outlining Institute's activities undertaken since establishing office in Detroit Nov 24 1919, getting in touch with each individual member, getting in touch with chairmen and members of committees, sending News Letters to members, issuing eleven preprints of reports and papers, a statement of membership as of Feb 1 — 383 active members at ten dollars a year, 232 of them in good standing 43 supporting members at thirty dollars a year, 28 of them in good standing subscribing libraries 70 *

Report of the Treasurer showing a bank balance February 1, $1401 74, Victory Bonds, $3000

It was voted to make the annual audit of the Institute accounts at the end of the fiscal year, the last audit having been made in May, 1919

Voted to advance for expenses of Institute's representation $100 to be paid to Duff A Abrams, Secretary and Treasurer of the Joint Committee

Committee consisting of Messrs Hatt, Wight and Humphrey was authorized to go over manuscript necessary for the completion of the Institute's Journal for 1915 and make recommendations as to its publication

Cost of 1920 Proceedings was discussed and decided to consider estimates from the former printer, The John C Winston Co Philadelphia, and from Detroit printers

All applications for membership in Secretary's hands to date (Feb 17) were approved, consisting of 13 contributing memberships at fifty dollars, and 47 active memberships at ten dollars

### MEETING, CHICAGO, FEB 18, 1920

Present  President Turner, Messrs Humphrey, Wason, Hatt, Ashton, Boyer and Secretary Whipple

Harvey Whipple was re elected Secretary for one year

Charles R Gow, Vice-President, was elected, and William M Kinney was re elected to membership on the Executive Committee to serve with the President, the Secretary and the Treasurer as provided in the by-laws (Sec 5)

It was voted as the sense of the Board that encouragement be given to the increase of contributing memberships in the Institute at $50 a year, and that each such annual $50 contribution entitle the donor to one representation in membership

Treasurer Robert W Lesley was instructed to take the necessary steps to put the Secretary under bond of $2000

---

*As a matter of information Secretary reports membership June 22, 1920, as follows Supporting Members 89, Active Members 486 (73 in questionable standing as to dues)

The Secretary was instructed to give certification of election of President Turner, and the re election of Treasurer Lesley and Secretary Whipple to the Guard Trust Company Philadelphia

It was voted that applicants for membership in the Institute in the latter half of the present fiscal year upon approval of their application be given a copy of Proceedings, Volume 15 in addition to Volume 16 of the 1920 Convention

Messrs Wason, Lesley and Gow were appointed to constitute the Finance Committee

It was voted that the appointment of a Publication Committee to advise with the editor of the Institute's Proceedings in the selection of material for publication be left to the President

It was voted to continue Frank C Wight as editor of Volume 16 or the Proceedings and a vote of thanks was extended to Mr Wight for his very efficient services as editor of the Proceedings previously issued under his direction

It was voted that all members of the Institute hereafter, beginning with Volume 16, be given one copy each of the Proceedings in a cloth binding, that paper bindings be supplied only on request and that half leather bindings be furnished to members at the additional cost of manufacture

It was voted to continue the *News Letters* to members inaugurated by the Secretary in January at intervals not greater than two months

It was voted to continue a policy of cooperation with technical and other periodicals interested in the more widespread knowledge of developments in concrete construction

Consideration was given to the desirability of publishing the Institute s standards in a single volume   This matter was laid on the table

It was voted as the sense of the Board that committee appointments be kept within the Institute membership so far as possible

The President was authorized to appoint a committee of three to make the award of the Wason Medal for the most meritorious paper presented at the 1920 Convention

It was voted as the sense of the Board that the next Convention concentrate attention upon a few major subjects, and that liberal time be given on the program for their consideration   that routine reports be received in full and presented in digested form

A tentative list of the major subjects to command the special attention of committees with the view to exhaustive reports for the 1921 convention is as follows   Floor Finish Contractors Plant Units of Design, Houses, Storage Tanks, Roads

It was voted to set aside an appropriation of $100 for the use of the Committee on Concrete Products as the nucleus of a fund to secure the tests of concrete building units, the appropriation to become available when the Committee submits a plan for raising further funds and an outline of the tests to be made, both to meet the approval of the Board of Direction

## MEMBERS AMERICAN CONCRETE INSTITUTE.

### JUNE, 1920.

*An Asterisk (*) indicates a Supporting Membership*

ABE MIKISHI, 24 Mita S Temple St , Shiba Tokyo, Japan

*ABERTHAW CONSTRUCTION Co , L C Wason, 27 School St , Boston, 9, Mass (3 supporting memberships)

ABRAMS, DUFF A , Lewis Institute, Madison and Rabey Sts , Chicago, Ill.

AFFLECK, B F , Universal Portland Cement Co , 210 S LaSalle St , Chicago, Ill

ALBRIGHT & MEBUS, Charles F Mebus, Land Title Bldg , Philadelphia, Pa

ALDRIDGE, E V , Universal Portland Cement Co , 208 S La Salle St , Chicago, Ill

ALLEN, O T , American Steel and Wire Co , 208 S La Salle St , Chicago, Ill

ALLIANCE HOLLOW CEMENT-BLOCK Co , J H. Van Middlesworth, Northampton, Pa

*ALPHA PORTLAND CEMENT Co , L Anderson, Jr , Easton, Pa

AMERICAN CAN Co , C G Piers, 120 Broadway, New York City

AMERICAN CEMENT TILE MFG Co , J de S Ficund, Oliver Bldg , Pittsburgh Pa

*AMERICAN SYSTEM OF REINFORCING, Arthur A Clement, 10 S La Salle St , Chicago, Ill.

AMHURSEN CONSTRUCTION Co . S W. Stewart, 61 Broadway, New York City

ANDREWS, TOWER & LAVALLE, 274 Main St , Springfield, Mass

ARBOUR, ERWIN F . Weyauvega Const Co , Fifth Ave and Oak St , Bayshore, Long Island, N Y.

ARCHIBALD & HOLMES, A R Holmes, Continental Life Bldg , Toronto, Ont , Can

ARMSBY, SIDNEY P , National Lime Assn 918 G St N W , Washington, D C

ASBESTOS SHINGLE, SLATE AND SHEATHING Co , Richard V Mattison, Ambler, Pa

ASHGROVE LIME AND PORTLAND CEMENT Co , A Lundteigan, Box 1132, Kansas City, Mo

ASHTON, ERNEST, Lehigh Portland Cement Assn , Allentown, Pa

ASSOCIATED METAL LATH MFRS , Wharton Clay, Edison Bldg , Chicago, Ill

ASSOCIATION OF PORTLAND CEMENT MFRS , LTD , H. R Cox, Park House, Gravesend, England

BAKER, HUGH J , Majestic Bldg , Indianapolis, Ind

BALLINGER, WALTER F , Ballinger & Perrot, 17th and Arch Sts . Philadelphia, Pa

Bangor Cast Stone Products Co , George Couzzo, 45 State St , Bangor, Me

Barbour, F A , 1120 Tremont Bldg , Boston, Mass

*Barney-Ahlers Construction Co , J G Ahlers, 110 W 40th St , New York City

Barrows, Frank G , National Eng Corp , 27 School St , Boston, Mass.

Bartlett, G S , Universal Portland Cement Co , 208 S. La Salle St , Chicago, Ill

*R H Beattie, 10 Purchase St , Fall River, Mass

Beattie & Cornell W H Beattie, 33 N Quarry St , Fall River, Mass

Bell, James C , Westinghouse, Church, Kerr & Co , 12 Twentieth St , Elmhurst, L I

Bent Bros , Arthur Bent, Central Bldg , Los Angeles, Calif

Bentley, A , & Sons Co , R B Daudt, Toledo, Ohio

Berger Mfg Co , A H Bromley Jr , Canton, Ohio

Best, Byron G , Oliver Iron Mining Co , 225 Lowell St , Ironwood, Mich

*Best, H D , Co , H D Best, Flatiron Bldg 5th Ave and 23d St , New York City

Billings, A W K , Ebro Irrigation and Power Co , Ltd , Apartado 570, Barcelona, Spain

Binswanger, S J , 5520 S Park Ave , Chicago, Ill

Birmingham Slag Co , Sidney G Reynolds 1607-16 Jeff Co Bank Bldg , Birmingham, Ala

*Blaw-Knox Co , C D McArthur, Box 915, Pittsburgh, Pa

Bodycomb, Walter C , 37 Wall St , New York City

Boyer, E D , Atlas Portland Cement Co , 30 Broad St , New York City

Brassert, Walter, Michigan Silo Co , 2006 Race St , Kalamazoo, Mich

Bromley, Albert H , Berger Mfg Co , 615 Cleveland Ave , S W , Canton, Ohio

Brooklyn Crozite Brick Corp , J L Miner, 110 Cedar St , New York City

Brooks, Gale M , Atlas Portland Cement Co , 1330 Corn Exchange Bank Bldg , Chicago, Ill

Brooks, R. E , Co , Frank I Ginsberg, 50 Church St , New York City

Brown, Harold P , 120 Liberty St , New York City

Brown, H Whittemore, care of Housing Co 248 Poylston St , Boston Mass

Bruer, James L , John W Couper Co , Inc , 319 Guerney Bldg , Syracuse, N Y

Bryant, Henry F , 334 Washington St , Brookline Mass

Bureau of Standards Library, Washington, D C

Burns, Homer S , Freeport Sulphur Co , Freeport, Tex

Burr, Henry A., Nashville, Chatt & St Louis Ry , 205 Fairfax Ave Nashville, Tenn

Burroughs, H Robins, 469 Fifth Ave , New York City.

*Burt Portland Cement Co , F P Monaghan, Bellevue, Mich

Bush, A L , 5313 Angora Terrace, Philadelphia, Pa

*CALUMET STEEL Co , A S Hook, 208 S La Salle St , Chicago, Ill
*CANADA CEMENT Co , LTD , H S. Van Scoyoc, Montreal, Que   Can
CAREY, PHILIP, Co   R H Kerster, Lockland, Cincinnati, Ohio
CASE SCHOOL OF APPLIED SCIENCE, F H Neff, Cleveland, Ohio
CEDLEBLAD, JOHN, Swedish Government, 927 Wilson Ave , Chicago, Ill
CLMENT GUN Co , INC , B C Callier, Allentown, Pa
*CHAIN BELT COMPANY, C. F Messinger  444 Wyoming P  Milwaukee, Wis
*CHAIN BELT COMPANY, B F Devine, 178 Twenty-fourth St , Milwaukee,
    Wis
CHAPMAN, CLOYD M , 171 Madison Ave , New York City
CHAPMAN, HOWARD, Timmis & Chapman, 315 Fifth Ave , New York City.
CHAPPELL, FRANK W , Henry Exal Elrod Co , Dallas, Tex
CHUBB, JOSEPH, Universal Portland Cement Co   836 Security Bank,
    Minneapolis, Minn
CISSEL, JAMES HARLAN, University of Michigan, 1213 S State St , Ann
    Arbor, Mich
CLARKE, T W , 179 Rawson Road, Brookline, Mass
CLEMENT, F H , & Co , F H Clement, Land Title Bldg , Philadelphia, Pa.
*CLINCHFIELD PORTLAND CEMENT CORPORATION, Kingsport, Tenn
*CLINTON WRIGHT WIRE Co , R D Bradbury, Worcester, Mass.
COBB, LOUIS R , Westinghouse, Church, Kerr & Co , 37 Wall St , New York
    City
COHEN, A B , 1 Madison Ave , New York City
"CONCRLIE," Harvey Whipple, 314 New Telegraph Bldg , Detroit, Mich.
CONCRETE PRODUCTS Co , E C Maiqua, Finance Bldg   Kansas City, Mo
CONCRETE PRODUCTS Co OF AMERICA, C F Buerte, 805 Diamond Bank
    Bldg , Pittsburgh, Pa
*CONCRETE MIXER ASSOCIATION, A A Mathews. 1206 Conway Bldg ,
    Chicago, Ill
*CONCRETE STEEL Co , John F. Havemeyer, 42 Broadway Ave , New York
    City
*CONCRETE STEEL Co , John F. Havemeyer, 42 Broadway Ave , New York
    City
*CONCRETE STEEL Co , Walter S Edge, 42 Broadway Ave , New York City
CONCRETE STEEL BRIDGE Co , F. D McEnteer, 606 E Pike St , Clarksburg
    W Va
CONCRETE STEEL FIREPROOFING Co , S V Taylor, 608 Lincoln Bldg , 73
    State St , Detroit Mich
CONDRON Co , T L Condron, 1433 Monadnock Bldg , Chicago, Ill
CONSOLIDATED EXPANDED METAL Co , Pittsburgh District. Braddock, Pa
CONZETI C D  Highway Engineer for Houston Co , Minn , Caledonia,
    Minn
COOLEY & MARVIN Co , J W Parker, Ford Bldg , 15 Ashburton Pl ,
    Boston, Mass
*COPLAY CEMENT MFG Co , W G Dutton, Widener Bldg  Philadelphia, Pa
CORBEN, HORACE J , City Hall, Darling St , Cape Town, Cape Province, S A
*CORRUGATED BAR Co , A L Johnson, 402 Mutual Life Bldg , Buffalo, N Y

*Corrugated Bar Co , W S Thomson, 402 Mutual Life Bldg , Buffalo, N Y
*Corrugated Bar Co , A P Clark, 402 Mutual Life Bldg , Buffalo, N Y
Cowell, Henry, Lime and Cement Co. W H George, 2 Market St , San
   Francisco Calif
*Cramp & Co , D L Kneedler, 801 Denckla Bldg , Philadelphia, Pa
Cranford Construction Co , John Stewart, 407 Gerke Bldg , Cincinnati,
   Ohio
Crary, Alfx , Thompson & Binger, Inc , 1956 Bogart Ave   Borough of
   Bronx, New York City
Crisp, Melbourne, San Francisco Ship Bldg  Co , 1201 Shrader St , San
   Francisco, Calif
Crowell-Lundoff-Little Co , C W Lundoff, 1951 S 57th St , Cleveland,
   Ohio
Cuban Portland Cement Corp , H M Rivers, Havana, Cuba
Dane, Nathan, Dwight Bldg  Co , 67 Church St , New Haven, Conn
Darling, E H , 47 Home Bank Bldg  Hamilton, Ont , Can
Davis, B H , 17 Battery Place, New York City
Davis, Watson, Bureau of Standards, 1418 Rhode Island Ave , N. W ,
   Washington, D C
Defiance Engineering and Construction Co , L E Binns, P O Box
   511, Orangeburg, S C
Deinboll, F K , 1263 Brookley Ave , Cleveland, Ohio
Densmore & LeClear, Henry C Robins, 88 Broad St , Boston, Mass
Denton & Co  P E Eisenmenger 7 E 42d St , New York City
Dewey Portland Cement Co , L Williamson  409 Scarritt Bldg , Kansas
   City, Mo
Dexter Portland Cement Co , J B Brobston Nazareth, Pa
Di Stasio, Joseph, Fougner Concrete Steel Co , 29 Broadway, New York
   City
Diver. M. L , San Antonio, Tex
*Dixie Portland Cement Co , Richard Hardy, 1010 James Bldg., Chat-
   tanooga, Tenn
Dixon, DeForrest H , Turner Construction Co  71 Gates Ave  Mont-
   clair, N J
Donohue, Jerry, 608 N 8th St , Sheboygan, Wis
Drehman Paving Co , C E Drehman, 2622 Parrish St , Philadelphia, Pa
Dupuy, Alberto, Apartado 893 Bogota, Columbia, S A
Duquesne Slag Products Co  C L McKenzie, Diamond Bank Bldg ,
   Pittsburgh, Pa
Eady, George M , Brook and Lee Sts , Louisville, Ky
Earlly, John J , 2131 G St , N W , Washington, D C
Ehm Concrete Steel Co  L L Ehm, 1206 W Liberty St , Cincinnati, Ohio
Eldridge, H W , Cement Gun Co , 30 Church St , New York City
Ellis, Theodore Irving, 17 Exchange St , Providence, R I
"Engineering News-Record," Frank C Wight, 10th Ave  at 36th St ,
   New York City
Erikson, Borge O , Canadian-Pacific Railroad, Montreal Que , Can

EVANS, FRANK M , C H & R C Peckworth, Inc , 1170 Broadway, New York City

FAIRLIE, J W , Co , J W Fairlie, 61 Steiner Bldg , Providence, R I

FAY, FREDERICK R , Fay, Spofford & Thorndike, 15 Beacon St , Boston, Mass

FELDRAPPE, M G , H K Ferguson Co , 1602 Bryn Mawr Road, Cleveland, Ohio

FELIX, R W , Lakewood Engr Co , 359 Union Arcade Bldg , Pittsburgh, Pa

FERGUSON, LEWIS R , Wig, Hollister & Ferguson, 320 Widener Bldg , Philadelphia, Pa

*FERGUSON, JOHN W , Co , J W Ferguson, 152 Market St , Paterson, N J

*FERRO CONCRETE CONSTRUCTION Co , W P Anderson, Richmond and Harriet Sts , Cincinnati, Ohio

*FISKE-CARTER CONSTRUCTION Co , Burton C Fiske, 11 Foster St , Worcester, Mass

FILMORE, HUGH H , Portland Cement Association, 926 Merchants Natl Bank Bldg , 548 S Spring St , Los Angeles, Calif

FIREPROOF PRODUCTS Co , P R Clark, 257 E 133d St , New York City

FISHER-DEVORE CONSTRUCTION Co , Frank W Fisher, 35-36 Blymyer Bldg , 514 Main St , Cincinnati, Ohio

FLEISCHMANN, LEON, Fleischmann Construction Co , 531 Seventh Ave , New York City

FLETCHER, AUSTIN B , Forum Bldg , Sacramento, Calif

FOGG, RALPH, Lehigh University, Bethlehem, Pa

FOLZ, FRANK W , & Co , G W Dickmeier, Cincinnati Ohio

*FOOTE Co , F L Dake, Nunda, N Y

*FOOTE Co , F C Wilcox, 1322 Michigan Ave , Chicago, Ill

FOSTER, ALEXANDER, JR , William Steele & Sons Co , 5828 Cedarhurst St , Philadelphia, Pa

*FOUGNER CONCRETE STEEL Co , H Fougner, 29 Broadway, New York City

FOUGNER, HERMAN, Fougner Concrete Steel Co , 29 Broadway, New York City

FRANCISCO, F LEROY, 50 Fifth Ave , New York City

*FRANKLIN STEEL WORKS, E E Hughes, Franklin, Pa.

FREEMAN, JOHN E , Portland Cement Association, 111 W Washington St , Chicago, Ill

FRENCH, A W , Polytechnic Institute, 202 Russell St , Worcester, Mass

FRENCH, S H , & Co , F T McBride, 4th and Callowhill Sts , Philadelphia, Pa.

FRIEBELE, J F , Karns, Smith Co , Broad St Bank Bldg , Philadelphia, Pa

FRIEL, FRANCIS S , Emergency Fleet Corp , 1739 Wallace St Philadelphia, Pa

FROEHLING & ROBERTSON, Henry C Froehling, 815 E Franklin St , Richmond, Va

FROST & CHAMBERLAIN, Slater Bldg , Worcester, Mass

FULLER, W J , University of Wisconsin, 1910 Adams St , Madison, Wis

FURBER, PIERCE P , Paul J Kalman Co , 131 E 14th St , Minneapolis, Minn

GABRIEL STEEL Co., W F Zabriskie, 1150 Penobscot Bldg , Detroit, Mich

Gale, L E, Truscon Steel Co, care of American Trading Co, Hankow, China

Gawthorp, Alfred H, American Car and Foundry Co, Wilmington, Del

General Fireproofing Co, W B Turner, Youngstown, Ohio

*Giant Portland Cement Co, Charles F Conn, Pennsylvania Bldg, Philadelphia, Pa

Gilman, Charles, Massey Concrete Products Corp, 50 Church St, New York City

Gjellerfald, O N, Forest City, Iowa

*Glens Falls Portland Cement Co, G F Boyle, 205 Lower Warren St, Glens Falls, N. Y.

Godfrey, Edward, Monongahela Bank Bldg, Pittsburgh, Pa

Gonnerman, H F, Univ of Illinois, Urbana, Ill.

Gow, Charles R, Charles R Gow Co, 166 Devonshire St, Boston, Mass

Gram, Lewis M, University of Michigan, 912 Oakland Ave, Ann Arbor, Mich

*Granette Products Co, J C Donaldson, 7th and Murphy Sts, Des Moines, Iowa

Granette Products Co, J C Donaldson, 7th and Murphy Sts, Des Moines, Iowa

Grant, Sydney, 189 Montague St, Brooklyn, N Y

Gray, J V, Construction Co, Ltd, Bank of Nova Scotia, Intersection of Queen, King and River Sts, Toronto, Ont, Can

Hamilton, Charles T, 510 Hastings St, W, Vancouver, B C

Hammer, Edmond Walter, Thompson-Starrett Co, Cass Ave and Grand Blvd, Detroit, Mich

Hammill, Harold B, John B Leonard Co, 2032 Parker St, Berkeley, Calif

Hardy, Richard, Dixie Portland Cement Co, 1011 James Bldg, Chattanooga, Tenn

Harris, Wallace R, International Trade Press, Inc, 5235 Cornell Ave, Chicago, Ill

Hart, Russell E, Watkins Institute Bldg, Nashville, Tenn

Hart, William Kendrick, Purdue University, Lafayette, Ind

Havlik, R F, Mooseheart, Ill

Hayes, J E, Engineering Corp, Tientsen, China

Hayward, Harrison W, Mass Inst of Technology, Cambridge, Mass

Healy, Clarence, Linde-Griffith Co, Newark, N J

Heine Chimney Co, Eric Plagwit, 123 W Madison Ave, Chicago, Ill

Hertzberg, Charles, S L, James, Landon & Hertzberg, 36 Toronto St, Toronto, Ont, Can

Hibbs, Manton E, 1423 N 15th St, Philadelphia, Pa

Hildreth & Co, Watson Vredenburgh, 15 Broad St, New York City

Hirschberg, W P, Federal Engr Co, 218 Stephenson Bldg, Milwaukee, Wis.

Hitchcock, Frank A, Bureau of Standards, Washington, D C

Hoagland, Ira G, 80 Maiden Lane, New York City

HOFF, OLAF, 149 Broadway, New York City.

HOFF, J HAAKON, Am Bridge Co, 208 S La Salle St, Chicago, Ill

HOOL, GEORGE A, University of Wisconsin, College Hills, Madison, Wis

HOOVER, A P, 33 Franklin Pl, Montclair, N J

HOPE ENGINEERING CO, HARRY M, S G Rosenblad, 185 Devonshire St, Boston, Mass

HORN, H M., Corrugated Bar Co, 17 Battery Place, New York City

HORNER, WESLEY W, 300 City Hall, St Louis, Mo

HOUGH, NORMAN G, Natl Lime Assn, 918 G St, N W, Washington, D C

HOWL, C D, C D Howe & Co, The Whelan Bldg, Port Arthur, Ont, Can

HOWE, H N, 76 Porter Bldg, Memphis, Tenn

HOYT, W A, Altoona, Pa

HUGHES, R G, John W Ferguson Co, 152 Market St., Paterson, N J

HULL, WALTER A, Bureau of Standards, Washington, D C

HUMPHREY, RICHARD L, 805 Harrison Bldg, Philadelphia, Pa

HURLBURT, R W, Canadian Inspection and Testing Co, 100 Jarvis St, Toronto Ont, Can

*HURON PORTLAND CEMENT CO, J W Boardman, Ford Bldg, Detroit, Mich

*HYDRAULIC STEELCRAFT CO, H O Davidson, 6001 Hydraulic Ave, Cleveland, Ohio.

HYDRO-ELECTRIC POWER CO, F A Gaby, 190 University Ave, Toronto, Ont, Can

ILLINOIS STEEL CO, T J Hyman, Chicago, Ill

INDEPENDENT GRAVEL CO, S A Fones, Frisco Bldg, Joplin, Mo

*INLAND STEEL CO, G H Jones, First Natl Bank Bldg, Chicago, Ill

INSLEY WM H, Insley Mfg Co, Indianapolis, Ind

*INSLEY MFG CO, Wm H Insley, Indianapolis, Ind

*INSLEY MFG CO, Alvin C Rasmussen, Indianapolis, Ind

INTERNATIONAL PORTLAND CEMENT CO, C R Smith, 1124 Old Natl Bank Bldg, Chicago, Ill

IRONTON PORTLAND CEMENT CO, A C Steece, Ironton, Ohio

IRWIN, ORLANDO W, Truscon Steel Co, 1128 Ford Ave, Youngstown, Ohio

JEWETT, JOHN Y, Administration Bldg, Balboa Park, San Diego, Calif

JOHNSON, A L, Corrugated Bar Co, Mutual Life Bldg, Buffalo, N Y

JOHNSON, A N, Portland Cement Association, 111 W Washington St, Chicago, Ill

JOHNSON, LEWIS J, Harvard University, Cambridge, Mass

JOHNSON, N C, Raymond Concrete Pile Co, 149 Broadway, New York City.

JOHNSON, T H, 319 Iowa Bldg, Sioux City, Iowa

JUNGCLAUS CO, W T, F W Jungclaus, 825 Moss Ave, Indianapolis, Ind

KAHN, GUSTAVE, Truscon Steel Co, Youngstown, Ohio

*KALMAN, PAUL J, CO, J A Scanlan, Merchants Natl Bank, St Paul, Minn.

*KALMAN, PAUL J, CO, G E Routh, Merchants Natl Bank, St Paul, Minn

KALMAN PAUL J, CO, J A Scanlon, 18th Floor, 22 Monroe St, N W, Chicago, Ill

*KEARNS CONSTRUCTION CO, W F Kearns, 153 Milk St, Boston, Mass

KEARNEY, E N , P O Box 206, New Orleans La

KELLEY, FREDERICK W , Hildenberg Cement Co , 126 State St , Albany, N Y

KERR, HORACE D , Atlas Portland Cement Co , 1320 Corn Exchange Bank Bldg , Chicago, Ill

KIKUCHI, AITATO, Onoday Cement Mfg Co , P O Box B24, Danen, Dalny, Manchuria, China

KIMBALL, C A , Atlas Portland Cement Co , 30 Broad St , New York City

KINNEY, WILLIAM M., Portland Cement Assn , 111 W Washington St , Chicago, Ill

KLINGER, W A , Warnock Bldg , Sioux City, Iowa

*KNICKERBOCKER PORTLAND CEMENT Co , A D Naylor, 30 E 42d St , New York City.

KNOWLES, MORRIS, INC , John M Rice, 1200 Jones Bldg , Pittsburgh, Pa

*KOEHRING MACHINE Co , G A Sherron, 31st St and Concordia Ave , Milwaukee, Wis

*KOEHRING MACHINE Co , P Koehring, 31st St. and Concordia Ave., Milwaukee, Wis

KRAFT, ADAM B , 511 S Water St , York, Pa

KRAUSE, MARK C , 120 W 4th St , Williamsport, Pa

LAKE, SIMON, 29 Broad St , Milford, Conn

*LAKEWOOD ENGR. Co , M L Bobeau, 11723 Detroit Ave , Cleveland, Ohio

*LAKEWOOD ENGR Co , 11723 Detroit Ave , Cleveland, Ohio

LAMBERT, WALTER E , 1128 Prudential Bldg , Buffalo, N Y

LANDOR, EDWARD J , 634 Renekert Bldg , Canton, Ohio

LANDER, R S , Burwell Bldg , Knoxville, Tenn

*LANQUIST & ILLSLEY Co , A Lanquist, 1100 N Clark St , Chicago, Ill

LARSON, R L , Anderson, Meyer & Co Ltd , Shanghai, China

LAUREL BRICK AND SAND Co , Austin E Potter, Cannel Station, Middletown, Conn

*LAWRENCE PORTLAND CEMENT Co , J S Van Middlesworth, Northampton, Pa

LEA, WILLIAM S , 809 New Birks Bldg , Phillips Sq , Montreal, Que , Can

LEFFLER, RALPH R , Hydraulic Steelcraft Co , 6001 Hydraulic Ave , Cleveland, Ohio

*LEHIGH PORTLAND CEMENT Co , Young Bldg , Allentown, Pa

*LEONARD CONSTRUCTION Co , Clifford M Leonard, 37 S Wabash Ave , Chicago, Ill

LEONARD, JOHN B , 57 Post St , San Francisco, Calif

LESLEY, ROBERT W , 611 Pennsylvania Bldg , Philadelphia, Pa

*LEVERING & GARRIGUE Co , C B Wigton, 532 W 23d St , New York City

*LEY, FRED T , INC , Raymond K Tunnel, 495 Main St , Springfield, Mass

LIBBERTON, J H , Universal Portland Cement Co , 210 S La Salle St , Chicago, Ill

LINDAU, A E , Corrugated Bar Co , Buffalo, N Y

LOBER, JOHN B , Vulcanite Portland Cement Co , Land Title Bldg , Philadelphia, Pa.

LOCK JOINT PIPE Co , A M. Hirsh, 165 Broadway, New York City

LOCKWOOD, GREENE & Co LIBRARY, Chester S. Allen 60 Federal St , Boston, Mass

LONEY, NEIL M , Thompson-Starrett Co , 151 Wall St , New York City

LORD, ARTHUR R , Lord Eng Co., 1004-5 Powers Bldg , 37 S Wabash Ave , Chicago, Ill

LOVE, HARRY J , Nat Slag Association, 933 Leader News Bldg Cleveland, Ohio

LOWELL, JOHN W , Universal Portland Cement Co , 208 S La Salle St , Chicago, Ill

LUTEN, DANIEL B , 1056 Lemcke Annex, Indianapolis, Ind

MACATEE, W L & SONS, Austin and Commerce Sts , Houston, Tex

McDANIEL, ALLEN B , care of Mr A J Klein, Service Bureau, Camp Grant, Ill

McFARLAND, DAVID H , 30 Broad St , New York City

McINTYRE, WILLIAM A , 1138 Widener Bldg , Philadelphia, Pa.

McKIBBEN, FRANK P , Union College, Schenectady N Y

McMAHON, JAMES J , Blaw-Knox Co , Westinghouse Bldg Pittsburgh, Pa

McMILLAN, FRANKLIN R , Turner Construction Co , 244 Madison Ave New York City

MAIN, CHARLES T , 201 Devonshire St , Boston ,Mass

MALMED, A. T , A T Malmed Co , 18 S 7th St , Philadelphia, Pa

MARQUETTE CEMENT MFG Co , T G Dickinson, Marquette Bldg , Chicago Ill

MARTIN, EVAN S , 59 Yonge St , Toronto, Canada

MARTIN, EDGAR D , 104 Michigan Ave , Chicago, Ill

MASSEY CONCRETE PRODUCTS CORP , J E Moody, Peoples Gas Bldg , Chicago, Ill

MAYNARD, ARTHUR J , Mass State Farm, State Farm, Mass

MEAD, C A , 165 Wildwood Ave , Upper Montclair, N J

MEADERS, ERNEST LAMAR, Emergency Fleet Corp , 1285 Government St , McComb, Miss

MERIWETHER, COLEMEN, 201 N West St , Indianapolis, Ind

METCALF & EDDY, Frank A Marston, 14 Beacon St , Boston, Mass

MEYER, C LOUIS, 608 Omaha Nat Bank Bldg , Omaha, Neb

MEYER, MORRISON & Co , B A Meyer, 299 Broadway, New York City

MICHIGAN PORTLAND CEMENT Co , G S Potter, Jr , Chelsea, Mich

MICHIGAN UNIVERSITY LIBRARY, Ann Arbor, Mich

MILLER, CHARLES R , Co , INC , 556 Susette St , Memphis, Tenn

MITCHELL, JAMES, 76 Montgomery St , Jersey City, N J

MONKS & JOHNSON, John R Nichols, 99 Chauncy St , Boston, Mass

MOORE, E J , Turner Construction Co , 244 Madison Ave , New York City

MORENO, MARIANO, MacClintic, Marshall Co , Hill Top of Y. M C A , Pittsburgh, Pa

MORRIS, CLYDE T , Ohio State University, Columbus, Ohio

MORRISON, R L , Pittsburgh Test Lab , 216 Clark Bldg , Birmingham, Ala

MORROW, DAVID W , 4500 Euclid Ave., Cleveland, Ohio

Morssen, C M , 37 Belmont St , Montreal, Que , Can
Moses, Frederick W , Firemens Ins Co , 10 Weybosset St , Providence,
R I
Moyer, Albert, Vulcanite Portland Cement Co , S W 10th St . New York
City
Mueller, J W , Palladium Bldg , Richmond, Ind.
Municipal Reference Library, Dorsey W Hyde, Jr., Municipal Bldg ,
New York City
Murphy, Gerald J , Messrs Harlan & Wolf, Ltd , Antrim Road, Fort
Williams Terrace, Belfast, Ireland
National Fireproofing Co , P. Bevier, Flatiron Bldg , New York City
*Nazareth Portland Cement Co  J. A Honer, Nazareth, Pa
Nelson, John A , Cut Stone Co , 1800 Eleventh St , Rock Island, Ill
New England Concrete Const Co , Wm T. Reed, 201 Devonshire St ,
Boston, Mass
New Jersey Zinc Co , 160 Front St  New York City
*Newaygo Portland Cement Co , J B John, Newaygo, Mich.
Newman, Ralph R , 3123 W 3d St , Los Angeles, Calif
Noonan, W H , Metropole Bldg , Halifax, Nova Scotia, Canada
Northwestern Expanded Metal Co , H W Fottee, 37 W Van Buren
St , Chicago Ill
Northwestern States Portland Cement Co , W Cowan, Mason City,
Iowa
Norton, Edgar W , 390 Main St , Worcester, Mass
Noyes, Proctor, Morris Knowles, Inc , Room 302, 4 S. Main St , Akron,
Ohio
Oesterbloom, 1 , American Trading Co , 53 Szechuen Road, Shanghai,
China
Older Clifford, State Highway Commission, Springfield, Ill
Oleson. Ole K., 822 Perdido St , New Orleans, La
Ord, William  Lakewood Eng Co , Cleveland, Ohio
Orr, John B , 11th St , Miami, Fla
*Ottawa Silica Co , C B Herring, Ottawa, Ill
Pagett, A Maxwell, Am Trading Co , 53 Szechuen Road, Shanghai, China.
Parker, Frank S , 41 Court St  Brooklyn, N Y
Paige, Fred , 1014 S Oak St , Casper, Wyo
Peabody, Dean, Jr , Mass Inst. of Tech , 120 Summer Ave , Reading, Mass
Pearse, Langdon, 910 S Michigan Ave , Chicago, Ill
Pearson, J C , Bureau of Standards, Washington, D C
Pease, B S , American Steel and Wire Co , 208 S La Salle St , Chicago, Ill
*Peerless Portland Cement Co , William M Hatch, Union City, Mich
Peiser, Fred, John W Ferguson Co , United Bank Bldg , Paterson, N J
*Penn-Allen Portland Cement Co , W E. Eidel, Widener Bldg , Allen-
town, Pa
*Pennsylvania Cement Co , William Beach, 30 E 42d St , New York City.
Pennsylvania State Highway Dept , Willis Whithed, Harrisburg, Pa

PERROT, EMIL G., 17th and Arch Sts., Philadelphia, Pa

PERRY, J P H , Turner Construction Co , 244 Madison Ave , New York City

PETROLEUM HEAT AND POWER Co , C W Stancliffe, 77 N Washington St , Boston, Mass

PETROLEUM HEAT AND POWER Co , G E. McCartney, 906 Turks Head Bldg , Providence, R I

PHILLIPS, JAMES City Hall, Richmond, Va

PITTSBURGH TESTING LABORATORY, J M Bailey, 7th St and Bedford Ave , Pittsburgh, Pa

PLUMBER, H E , 22 Ellicott Square, Buffalo, N Y

PORTER, F M , 53 N 3d St , Easton, Pa

*PORTLAND CEMENT ASSN , Wm M Kinney, 111 Washington St , Chicago, Ill

PRACK, BERNARD H , 50 Bay St , Toronto, Ont Can

PRE-CAST CONCRETE Co , Charles D Watson, 610 Bulletin Bldg , Philadelphia, Pa

PRINCETON UNIVERSITY, F H Constant, Princeton, N J

RANDALL, FRANK A , Berlin, Swern & Randall, 19 S La Salle St , Chicago, Ill

RANKIN, GEORGE A , Geophysical Laboratory, 2801 Capton St , Washington, D C

RANSOME, A W , Blaw-Knox Co , Monadnock Bldg , San Francisco Calif

*RANSOME CONCRETE MACHINERY Co , A P Robinson Dunellen, N. J

*RANSOME CONCRETE MACHINERY Co , A P Robinson, Dunellen, N J

*RAYMOND CONCRETE PILE Co , Paul D Case, 140 Cedar St , New York City

REYNVAAN, A J , care of Carnegie Steel Co , Duquesne, Pa

RHEINSTEIN & HAAS, INC , A Rheinstein 21 E 40th St , New York City

RHETT, ALBERT H , Toch Brothers, Room 709, 320 Fifth Ave , New York City

RICE, JAMES, Borough of Queens, Borough Hall, Hunters Point Ave , Long Island City, N Y

RICHARDSON, J R , Madero, Calif

RICHART, FRANK E , University of Illinois, Urbana, Ill

RICHMOND, KIGHT C 10 Weybossett St , Providence, R I

RIESCHE, ROBERT H , Reische, & Sanborn 306 Trimble Blk , Sioux City, Iowa

RITTER, LOUIS E , 1707 Marquette Bldg , 140 S Dearborn St , Chicago, Ill

ROBERTSON, H L , Robertson & Dewey, 502-3 Yorkshire Bldg , Vancouver, B C

ROBINSON, ALBERT FOWLER, A , T & S F. R R System, Room 1033, Railway Exchange Bldg , Chicago, Ill

ROBINSON, C C , Charles M Robinson, 1004-5 Times-Despatch Bldg , Richmond, Va

ROGERS, FLOYD, Newton, Iowa

ROGERS, J S , Co , C R Rogers, Moorestown, N J

ROLLINS, JAMES W , Holbrook, Cabot & Rollins, 6 Beacon St , Boston, Mass

RYAN, W R , Thompson-Starrett Co , 49 Wall St , New York City

RYLEY, E G , 506-7 P Burns Bldg , Calgary, Alberta, Can

SAFFORD, A T , 66 Broadway Ave , Lowell, Mass
SAMPSON, C A , Weston & Sampson 83 Pembroke St , Newton, Mass
*SANDUSKY CEMENT Co , William B Newberry, 626 Engineers' Bldg , Cleveland, Ohio
SAURBREY, ALEXIS, Mellon, Stuart Co , 2112 Oliver Bldg , Pittsburgh, Pa
SAVILL, CHRISTOPHER J , Commonwealth Portland Cement Co , Portland, New South Wales, Australia
SCHLYTER, RAGNAR, "Statens Provningsanstalt," Stockholm, Sweden
SCHOULER CEMENT CONSTRUCTION Co , W. W Schouler, 156 Frelinghuysen Ave , Newark, N J
SCHWALBE WILLIAM, University of Illinois, 709 W Nevada St , Urbana, Ill
SCHWAN, GEORGE H , Arch 1310, Peoples Bank Bldg , Pittsburgh, Pa
SCOFIELD ENGR CONSTRUCTION Co , E M Scofield, Wright-Callender Bldg , Los Angeles, Calif
SECURITY CEMENT AND LIME Co , John J Porter, Hagerstown, Md
SEELYE, ELWYN E , 101 Park Ave , New York City
SEWELL, JOHN S , Mason Furnace Engr Co , Muncie, Ind
SHAFER, IVAN O , Fleischman Construction Co , 531 Seventh Ave , New York City
*SHEARMAN, A N , Knoxville, Tenn
SHELDON, F P , & SONS, W S Brown Hospital Trust Bldg , Providence, R I
*SHENK Co , HENRY, E R Shenk, Erie, Pa.
SHERTZER, T. B , National Lime Assn , 100 Hamilton Pl , New York City
SIMPSON, GEORGE, Thompson-Starrett Co , 51 Wall St , New York City
SLATER, WILLIS, Bureau of Standards, Washington, D C
SMITH, BLAINE S , Universal Portland Cement Co , 210 S La Salle St , Chicago, Ill
SMITH, GEORGE A , Room 155 Industrial Bldg , Washington, D C
SMULSKI, EDWARD, 13 Park Row, New York City
SNODGRASS, R C , Truscon Steel Co , 110 W. 40th St , New York City
SOUTHWESTERN PORTLAND CEMENT Co , H C Swearingen, Herald Bldg , El Paso, Tex
SPACKMAN, HENRY S , ENGINEERING Co , H S Spackman, 2024 Arch St Philadelphia, Pa
SPAULDING, RALPH EDGAR, Suffield, Conn
SPEERS-JEVNE, G W Jevne, 836 Builders Exchange Bldg , Minneapolis Minn
SPIKER, WILLIAM C , 1121 Candler Bldg Atlanta, Ga
SPINOSA, ARTHUR V , Consolidated Exp Metal Co , Braddock, Pa
SPRINGER, G P , 2312 Woodridge St , Washington, D C
STANAGE, J L , 144 Oneida St , Milwaukee, Wis
STANCLIFFE, C W , Petroleum Heat and Power Co , 77 W Washington St , Boston, Mass
STANDARD OIL OF NEW JERSEY, Charles E Haupt, P O Box 16, Elizabeth, N J
STANDARD SLAG, F E Miller, Youngstown, Ohio.

STEELE, WILLIAM & SONS CO, Edward Steele, 1600 Arch St, Philadelphia, Pa

*STEELE, WILLIAM, & SONS CO, Alexander Foster, Jr, 1600 Arch St, Philadelphia, Pa

STEINHART, J H, P. O. Box 1070, Havana, Cuba.

STEPHENS, A. W., Turner Construction Co, 244 Madison Ave, New York City

*STEWART, JAMES, & CO, INC, Charles F Franson, 30 Church St, New York City

*STONE & WEBSTER, J H Manning, 147 Milk St, Boston, Mass

STRUCKMANN, HOLGER, Cuban Portland Cement Co, 347 Madison Ave, New York City.

STUBBS, ROBERT C, R. C. Stubbs Co, 1418 Pretorian Bldg, Dallas, Tex

STUHRMAN, EDWARD A, 762 Candler Annex, Atlanta, Ga

SUPERIOR PORTLAND CEMENT CO, C L Wagner, Seaboard Bldg, Seattle, Wash

SUTHERLAND, H C, Mass Institute of Technology, Cambridge, Mass.

SWAIN, GEORGE F, Harvard University, Cambridge, Mass

SWANSON, A G, Omaha Con Stone Co, 28th Ave and Sahler St, Omaha, Neb

TAIT, W. STUART, Hydraulic Steelcraft Co, Cleveland, Ohio

TALBOT, ARTHUR N, 1113 W California Ave, Urbana, Ill

TALBOT, KENNETH H, Koehring Machine Co, Milwaukee, Wis

TANNER, B M, Idaho Falls, Idaho

TEXAS PORTLAND CEMENT CO, H C Koch, Dallas, Tex.

THAYER, L V, 302 Broadway Ave, New York City

THOMAS, W E, Sanitary Engr Co, Law Bldg, Charlotte N C

THOMPSON & BINGER, W D Binger, 280 Madison Ave, New York City

THOMPSON-LICHTNER, S E Thompson, 136 Federal St, Boston, Mass.

*THOMPSON-STARRETT CO, N. M. Loney, 51 Wall St, New York City

TOCH BROS, Maximilian Toch, 320 Fifth Ave, New York City.

TOMPKINS, CHARLES H, 1883 Third St, N. W, Washington, D C

TORREY, JAMES E, John W. Ferguson Co, 652 E 26th St, Paterson, N J

TRAYLOR-DEWEY CONTRACTING CO, C L Dewey, Traylor Hotel, Allentown, Pa

TRUMBULL, MARK M, care of State Highway Commission, Raleigh, N C

*TRUSCON STEEL CO, S Techkemer, Owen Bldg, Detroit, Mich

*TRUSCON STEEL CO, H N Sturdy, Youngstown, Ohio

*TRUSCON STEEL CO, T H Kane, Youngstown, Ohio

TUBESING, WILLIAM F, Wauwatosa, Wis

TUCKER, E A, CO, Edward A Tucker, 101 Milk St, Boston, Mass

*TUCKER, EDWARD A, CO, Mitchell Allen, 101 Milk St, Boston, Mass.

*TUCKER, EDWARD A, CO, Walter Fox, 101 Milk St, Boston, Mass

TUFTS, ARTHUR, Candler Annex, Atlanta, Ga,

TURNER, C A P., 627 First Ave, N, Minneapolis, Minn

TURNER, JOHN J, & SONS, John J Turner, Amsterdam, N J

*Turner Construction Co , H  C  Turner, 244 Madison Ave , New York
 City
*Turner Construction Co , E  J  Moore, 244 Madison Ave , New York
 City.
*Turner Construction Co , A. W  Stephens, 244 Madison Ave , New
 York City
*Turner Construction Co , R  C  Wilson, 244 Madison Ave , New York
 City
*Turner Construction Co  H  C. Turner, 244 Madison Ave , New York
 City
 Twogood, L  Scott, Brighton, Colo
 Underwriters' Laboratories, W  C  Robinson, 207 E  Ohio St , Chicago,
 Ill
 United States Portland Cement Co , Fred S  Schmidt, 305 Ideal Bldg ,
 Denver, Colo
 Upson, Maxwell, M , Raymond Concrete Pile Co , 140 Cedar St , New York
 City
 Vandever, Jacob B , Nazareth Cement Co , 1270 Broadway, New York City
 Van Doorn, J  C , Universal Portland Cement Co , 836 Security Bank
 Bldg , Minneapolis, Minn
 Van Dyke, C  W , Atlas Portland Cement Co , 30 Broad St , New York City.
 Van Scoyoc, Harvey S , Canada Cement Co , Ltd , Montreal, Que , Can
 Villadsen, James M , 303 Dooly Bldg , Salt Lake City, Utah
 Villadsen, A  B , 303 Dooly Bldg , Salt Lake City, Utah
 Voshell, James T , P. O  Building, S. Chicago, Ill
 Voss Walter C , Wentworth Institute, Boston, Mass
*Vulcanite Portland Cement Co , A  Moyer, S W  40th St , New York
 City
 Wagner, E  C , 663 Kemper Bldg , Kansas City, Mo
 Walkwitz, Clarence A , 140 W  Hancock Ave , Detroit, Mich
 Wait, B. H , 347 Madison Ave , New York City
 Waldo Bros  & Bond Co , William F  Matthews, 181 Congress St , Boston,
 Mass
 Wallace, W  K , Midland Ry , York Rd , Belfast, Ireland
 Walter, Ernest Porlel Mfg  Co , 263 Midland Ave , Montclair, Mo
 Ward, Harry A , Turner Construction Co , 244 Madison Ave , New York
 City
 Warnecke, William H , 48 Clinton Pl , E  Rutherford, N  J
 Warner, Charles, Co , F  S  Lee, Finance Bldg , Philadelphia, Pa
 Warren  George E , 210 S  La Salle St , Chicago, Ill
 Waterloo Construction Machinery Corp , G  B  Arthur, Waterloo, Iowa
 Watson Engineering Co , J  Watson, 1011 Hippodrome Bldg , Cleve-
 land, Ohio
 Weatherford & Harris, J  H  Weatherford, 64 Porter Bldg , Memphis,
 Tenn
 Weber, A  G , 2311 Sacramento St , San Francisco, Calif
 Wells  A. E , Wells Bros  Const  Co , Monadnock Block, Chicago, Ill

WESTERGAARD, HAROLD M , University of Illinois, Urbana, Ill

WESTINGHOUSE, CHURCH, KERR & Co , L  R  Cobb, 37 Wall St , New York City.

WESTINGHOUSE ELECTRIC AND MFG  Co , East Pittsburgh, Pa

WHEAT CHARLES, Synstone Corporation, Peoria, Ill

*WHITE CONSTRUCTION Co , INC , G  Edward Escher, 95 Madison Ave , New York City

WHITNEY, CHARLES S , Hool & Johnson, 306 Colby & Abbott Bldg , Milwaukee, Wis

WICKERSHAM, JOHN H , 53 N  Duke St , Lancaster, Pa

WIDMER, ARTHUR, 941 Century Bldg , St  Louis, Mo

WIGHTMAN, S  H , Builders and Traders Exc  Penobscot Bldg , Detroit, Mich

WIGTON, C  B , Levering & Garrigues, 552 N  23d St , New York City

WILLIAMS, G  M., care of Bureau of Standards, Washington, D  C.

WILSON, FRANCIS F , 63 Hampstead Ave , Rockville Centre, L  I , N  Y

WILSON, HERBERT C , George W  Carr Co , 515 Main St , Worcester, Mass

WISCONSIN UNIVERSITY LIBRARY, W  M  Smith, Madison, Wis.

WOLF, ALBERT M , 347 William St , River Forest, Ill

WOLPERT, OTTO  Thompson-Starrett Co , 51 Wall St , New York City

WOOLSON, IRA H , National Board of Fire Underwriters, 76 William St , New York City

WOOTON, W  H , Gramtex Co , Inc , 171 Madison Ave , New York City

WORCESTER, J  R , J  R  Worcester & Co , 79 Milk St , Boston, Mass

WORCESTER  R  J  T , Concord, Mass

WRIGHT & KOWALSKI, Donald A  Wright, 1 Montgomery St , Jersey City, N  J

YEOMAN, R  C , Indiana National Sand and Gravel Producers Assn , 702 City Trust Bldg , Indianapolis  Ind

YOUNG, J  L , Trussed Con  Steel Co , 16 San Tiao Hutung, Peking, China

YOUNG, R  B , 8 Strachman Ave , Toronto, Ont , Can

YOUNG, R  W , Paulina, Iowa.

YOUNG, THOMAS F , 8 Great George St , Westminster, London, S  W  I

ZEIDLER, JOHN L , Zeidler Concrete Pipe Co , 101 Francis St  St  Joseph, Mo

ZIPPRODT, ROY R , 230-36 Grain Exch  Bldg , Sioux City, Iowa

# INDEX.

www.ingramcontent.com/pod-product-compliance
Lightning Source LLC
Chambersburg PA
CBHW051313060726
PP18533700001B/7